CW00644700

Name

Department

 RS Components Limited
PO Box 99, Corby,
Northants NN17 9RS
Tel: (0536) 201234 Telex: 342512

WIRING
AND
CABLE
DESIGNER'S
HANDBOOK

BERNARD S. MATISOFF

 TAB Professional and Reference Books

Division of TAB BOOKS Inc.
P.O. Box 40, Blue Ridge Summit, PA 17214

This book is dedicated to SHARON and KAREN.
Welcome to the family.

FIRST EDITION

SECOND PRINTING

Printed in the United States of America

Library of Congress Cataloging in Publication Data

Matisoff, Bernard S.
   Wiring and cable designer's handbook.

   Includes index.
   1. Electronic apparatus and appliances—Design
and construction.   2. Electric wiring.   I. Title.
TK7836.M38   1987   621.319'2   86-22977
ISBN 0-8306-2720-0

Questions regarding the content of this book
should be addressed to:

   Reader Inquiry Branch
   Editorial Department
   TAB BOOKS Inc.
   Blue Ridge Summit, PA 17294

Contents

Circuit Covercoat — Adhesives — Layout — Shielding — Producibility—Flexible Cable Connectors

Acknowledgments

I wish to sincerely thank all of those organizations and friends that responded so well to my request for information on wiring and cabling. Each of those listed provided me with data from standard catalogs and specification sheets to the educational papers they had generated as in-house training, promotional and marketing data. I hope that this handbook proves worthy of your trust and provides the assistance so sorely needed by those designers and engineers whose task it is to design and manufacture wiring and cable assemblies to the highest reliability standards.

Beldon Electronic Wire and Cable
Richmond, IN
Bendix Connector Division
Burndy Corp.
Norwalk, CT
Deutsch Electronic Components
Banning, CA
Flexible Circuits Inc.
Warrington, PA
W.L. Gore & Associates
Newark, DE
National Wire & Cable Corp.
Los Angeles, CA
Standard Wire & Cable Co.
El Segundo, CA

Introduction

Conductors play a vital role in reliable electronic equipment. With the rapid advances in equipment design over the past few years, the conductor variations have become as complex as the components and systems they serve. As the electronic system requirements become more severe, the wiring and cabling requirements must be extended to survive these environments.

Interconnecting conductors in military equipment are subject to extremely severe conditions of usage and the design and workmanship standards must be correspondingly high. Commercial equipment should be extremely reliable to remain competitive in the current marketplace, and therefore, the use of military methods and procedures provide a sound basis for the design and workmanship standards. Although they may be less cost effective in the front end of the commercial product program, the use of military requirements can be effectively used as a design and manufacturing guide.

Conductors are generally selected for their current carrying capacity, mechanical strength, and the properties of their insulation. But many unique conditions may require the use of wires and cables with special characteristics, and several types of special conductors may be required in a single unit or system. Although it is extremely rare to find a cable design engineering specialist, cable/wiring design and workmanship is one of the most critical areas in producing reliable electronic assemblies.

Any engineer responsible for the design and manufacture of wiring and cabling must consider the environmental applications, both natural and induced, the reliability, and the producibility of the systems and assemblies being developed. Test and inspection procedures must be generated to determine the adequacy of the wiring and cabling for its potential service use.

The mechanical design problems to be considered include resistance to shock and vibration, the positioning and routing of the wires, types of connections, serviceability, marking and identification, and materials compatibility with the intended service environment.

The environmental factors will include climatic protection, temperature, humidity, abrasion, fungus, exposure to sunlight, and such other environments as may be defined in the specifications.

The electrical problems will include current-carrying capacity, voltage breakdown, EMI/RFI interference (shielding), personnel protection, and the positioning of sensitive components.

The design of wiring and cabling is critical to the performance and reliability of all electronic systems and equipment and is best approached by a cooperative effort between the electrical and mechanical design engineers.

Chapter 1

Material Selection

The selection of the conductors and materials used is one of the most vital areas in the design and manufacture of highly reliable electronic equipment. With the advances in electronics over the past few years, wiring and cabling has become just as critical and complex as system design, and extreme judgement must be exercised in each step of the design process. The particular requirements for design and materials selection for wires and cables are usually governed by the detail specification. The design engineer must be familiar with the contract requirements and all of the service requirements.

CONDUCTOR TYPES AND USES

Electrical conductors are commercially available as solid or stranded, bare or insulated, and single or multiwire. Soft annealed copper is the most commonly used conductor in the manufacture of wire because of its high conductivity, ductility, resistance to corrosion and mechanical fatigue, and the ease of soldering. Aluminum wire is occasionally used when weight is the primary consideration, and other materials have been used for specific purposes.

Solid Wire is commercially available for various applications in round, square, and rectangular cross sections. The advantages of solid wire are its rigidity and efficiency at higher frequencies. When permitted by the product specification, solid wire may be used for jumpers up to three inches long, and when properly secured, longer lengths may be used when they are not subject to vibration.

Untinned solid copper wire is the most efficient at high frequencies, tinned or stranded wire tend to exhibit greater losses. However, a major disadvantage to solid wire is its susceptibility to stress concentrations. A very slight nick in the insulation, which may occur during the wire stripping operation, can and will become a breaking point when subjected to flexing.

Stranded Wire is recommended in preference to solid wire since it displays a much higher flexibility. It can be easily bent and formed into wire and cable assemblies. In addition, stranded wire is less apt to fracture during unsoldering or unwrapping during servicing. The most common stranded wire in use consists of seven strands twisted together.

Multiconductor Cables are selected using the same factors governing the selection of single conductors, except that special attention must be given to the interwire insulation. Cables are made in countless forms, special wires and insulation are formed into cables for applications in low-, medium-, or high frequencies.

One variety of the multiconductor wire assembly is the coaxial cable, which is used when the distributed capacity must be held constant over the entire length of the line. In coaxial cable one conductor follows a very precise concentric path through another where the space between the conductors is filled with an insulating material. It is extremely important that the concentricity be closely maintained between the two conductors. If the space relation between the two conductors is permitted to vary, the circuit efficiency will be affected.

Whenever a coaxial cable is bent or formed, the minimum bend radius should never be less than ten times the outside cable diameter. A bend radius of less than ten times the cable diameter will result in a cold flow of the dielectric and creeping of the inner conductor at the bend. Selection of coaxial cables should be made with regards to the impedance and attenuation at the design frequencies.

WIRE SIZE

Wire size is commonly designated by American Wire Gauge (AWG), circular mils, or by wire diameter in mils.

The selection of wire size is dependent on current capacity, allowable temperature rise, power loss, and physical requirements

2

such as space limitations, environmental compatibility, and mechanical strength.

The minimum wire size for hook-up wires in military equipment should be AWG 26 to minimize the potential danger of wire breakage. AWG 22 through AWG 24 are commonly accepted for general chassis wiring. Filament wiring should be AWG 20 or larger, depending on the current consumption requirements, particularly where heaters were wired in parallel. Conductors intended for audio-frequencies and direct currents are selected by their voltage and current ratings, while conductors to be used in rf applications are chosen by their impedance. Figure 1-1, Table 1-1, and Table 1-2 provide the electrical and physical characteristics of many

Q. WHAT ARE THE BASIC DIFFERENCES BETWEEN THE MANY HOOKUP WIRES AVAILABLE?

A. THE INSULATION THICKNESS & MATERIAL.

There are 3 common wall thickness categories.

Thin Wall	Medium Wall	Heavy Wall
Nominal .010" wall rated 300-600 volt	Nominal .015" wall rated 300-1000 volt	Nominal .030" wall rated 600-3000 volt
MIL-W-16878 Type B, vinyl	MIL-W-16878 Type C, vinyl	MIL-W-16878 Type D, vinyl
MIL-W-16878 Type E, teflon	MIL-W-16878 Type EE, teflon	IPCEA 600 volt, vinyl
U.L. AWM Style 1061, vinyl	U.L. AWM Style 1007, vinyl	U.L. AWM Style 1015, vinyl

Various outer coverings over the insulation, such as nylon, improve durability at the expense of flexibility.

Q. WHAT ARE THE COMMON HOOKUP WIRE INSULATION MATERIALS?

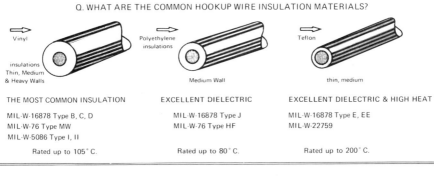

Vinyl insulations Thin, Medium & Heavy Walls

Polyethylene insulations Medium Wall

Teflon thin, medium

THE MOST COMMON INSULATION	EXCELLENT DIELECTRIC	EXCELLENT DIELECTRIC & HIGH HEAT
MIL-W-16878 Type B, C, D	MIL-W-16878 Type J	MIL-W-16878 Type E, EE
MIL-W-76 Type MW	MIL-W-76 Type HF	MIL-W-22759
MIL-W-5086 Type I, II		
Rated up to 105° C.	Rated up to 80° C.	Rated up to 200° C.

HOW DO THE CONDUCTORS DIFFER IN HOOKUP WIRES?

Solid, Bare Copper

Solid Tinned Copper

Stranded Bare Copper

Stranded Tinned or Silvered Copper

Lowest cost Commercial use, can corrode	Low cost Commercial use corrosion resistant	Low cost, flexible. Commercial use can corrode	Most military and top-quality commercial use. Flexible, corrosion resistant, easily soldered.

Fig. 1-1. Types of wires.

Table 1-1. Conductor Plating and Coating.

Type of Metal Coating	Characteristics	Advantages	Disadvantages	Service Temp.
Tin Plate (typical 40 Micro-inches per ASTM B-33)	Most widely used, least expensive when stranded. Each strand tinned then twisted.	Good shelf life. Ease of soldering. Low cost.	Solderability de-teriorates with heat-aging due to migration of tin and copper. Often requires solder dipping before termination.	150°C
Prefused Tin	Use of heavy tinned copper strands — bonded together by resistance heat.	Minimum pretinning required at termina-tion because strands are held together.	More expensive than tinned strands and some flexibility lost. Not generally accept-able under most MIL specs.	150°C
Heavy Tin (typically 100 Micro-inches nom. for AWG 31 & smaller) 150 Micro-in. nom. for AWG 30 & larger.	Flexibility maintained because all strands in-dividually tinned.	Bonding can be accom-plished with auto-matic high-frequency induction stripping equipment. Flexibil-ity maintained; only terminated part is bonded.	More expensive than prefused tin; heavier.	150°C

Topcoat	Copper strands are twisted then coated with tin.	Effectively bonds all strands the entire length of wire. Ease of termination.	Some flexibility lost. Not acceptable for MIL applications.	150°C
Overcoat	Tinned copper strands coated with additional tin to bond entire length.	Ease of termination; Strands held together.	Flexibility lost. More expensive than tinned or topcoat.	150°C
Silver Plate (typical 40 Micro-inches).	All strands coated with silver. Recommended for hi-temp usage 150-200°C.	Excellent solder-ability at higher temperature 200°C. No deterioration with heat. Excellent shelf life; stable contact resistance. Excellent for hi-frequency applications.	More expensive than tinned. May wick solder beyond termination.	200°C
Nickel Plate (typical 50 Micro-inches).	Nickel plate each strand. Recommended for Teflon, TFE for prolonged use at hi-temp. 260°C.	Higher temperature range. Conductivity stable with heat aging over temperature range. Does not wick solder.	Cost of termination is more expensive than tinned and silver plated. Some soldering technique required. Requires active flux.	260°C

Table 1-2. Copper Conductor AWG Standards.

Solid Bare Copper Wire

Gage (AWG) or (B&S)	Diameter Inches (Nom.)	Area Circular Mils	Weight Pounds per M'	Resistance at 68°F Ohms per M'
10	.1019	10380.0	31.43	.9989
11	.09074	8234.0	24.92	1.260
12	.08081	6530.0	19.77	1.588
13	.07196	5178.0	15.68	2.003
14	.06408	4107.0	12.43	2.525
15	.05707	3257.0	9.858	3.184
16	.05082	2583.0	7.818	4.016
17	.04526	2048.0	6.200	5.064
18	.04030	1624.0	4.917	6.385
19	.03589	1288.0	3.899	8.051
20	.03196	1022.0	3.092	10.15
21	.02846	810.1	2.452	12.80
22	.02535	642.4	1.945	16.14
23	.02257	509.5	1.542	20.36
24	.02010	404.0	1.223	25.67
25	.01790	320.4	.9699	32.37

Gage (AWG) or (B&S)	Diameter Inches (Nom.)	Area Circular Mils	Weight Pounds per M'	Resistance at 68°F Ohms per M'
26	.01594	254.1	.7692	40.81
27	.01420	201.5	.6100	51.47
28	.01264	159.8	.4837	64.90
29	.01126	126.7	.3836	81.83
30	.01003	100.5	.3042	103.2
31	.008928	79.7	.2413	130.1
32	.007950	63.21	.1913	164.1
33	.007080	50.13	.1517	206.9
34	.006305	39.75	.1203	260.9
35	.005615	31.52	.09542	329.0
36	.005000	25.00	.07568	414.8
37	.004453	19.83	.06001	523.1
38	.003965	15.72	.04759	659.6
39	.003531	12.47	.03774	831.8
40	.003145	9.888	.02993	1049.0

Stranded Tinned Copper Wire

AWG Size	Strand-ing	Nom. O.D. of Strand	Approx. O.D.	Circular Mil Area	Wgt. Per 1000'	Resistance Ohms Per 1000'
36	7/44	.002	.006	28.00	.085	371.0
34	7/42	.0025	.0075	43.75	.132	237.0
32	7/40	.0031	.008	67.27	.203	164.0
32	19/44	.002	.009	76.00	.230	136.4
30	7/38	.004	.012	112.00	.339	103.2
30	19/42	.0025	.012	118.75	.359	87.3
28	7/36	.005	.015	141.75	.529	64.9
28	19/40	.0031	.016	182.59	.553	56.7
27	7/35	.0056	.018	219.52	.664	51.47
26	7/34	.0063	.019	277.83	.841	37.3
26	10/36	.0050	.021	250.00	.757	41.48
26	19/38	.0040	.020	304.00	.920	34.43
24	7/32	.008	.024	448.00	1.356	23.3
24	10/34	.0063	.023	396.90	1.201	26.09
24	19/36	.0050	.024	475.00	1.430	21.08
24	41/40	.0031	.023	384.40	1.160	25.59
22	7/30	.0100	.030	700.00	2.120	14.74
22	19/34	.0063	.031	754.11	2.28	13.73
22	26/36	.0050	.030	650.00	1.97	15.94
20	10/30	.0100	.035	1,000.00	3.025	10.32
20	19/32	.0080	.037	1,216.00	3.68	8.63
20	26/34	.0063	.036	1,031.94	3.12	10.05

AWG Size	Strand-ing	Nom. O.D. of Strand	Approx. O.D.	Circular Mil Area	Wgt. Per 1000'	Resistance Ohms Per 1000'
20	41/36	.0050	.036	1,025.00	3.10	10.02
18	7/26	.0159	.048	1,769.60	5.36	5.86
18	16/30	.0100	.047	1,600.00	4.84	6.48
18	19/30	.0100	.049	1,900.00	5.75	5.46
18	41/34	.0063	.047	1,627.29	4.92	6.37
18	65/36	.0050	.047	1,625.00	4.91	6.39
16	7/24	.0201	.060	2,828.00	8.56	3.67
16	19/29	.0113	.058	2,426.30	7.35	4.27
16	26/30	.0100	.059	2,600.00	7.87	4.00
16	65/34	.0063	.059	2,579.85	7.81	4.02
16	105/36	.0050	.059	2,625.00	7.95	3.99
14	7/22	.0253	.073	4,480.00	13.56	2.31
14	19/27	.0142	.073	3,830.40	11.59	2.70
14	41/30	.0100	.073	4,100.00	12.40	2.53
14	105/34	.0063	.073	4,167.50	12.61	2.49
12	7/20	.0320	.096	7,168.00	21.69	1.45
12	19/25	.0179	.093	6,087.60	18.43	1.70
12	65/30	.0100	.095	6,500.00	19.66	1.75
12	165/34	.0063	.095	6,548.90	19.82	1.58
10	37/26	.0159	.115	9,353.60	28.31	1.11
10	49/27	.0142	.116	9,878.40	29.89	1.09
10	105/30	.0100	.116	10,530.00	31.76	.98

commonly used wire types and can be used in selecting the proper wires.

INSULATIONS

Insulation materials usually consist of a solid waterproof material which in some instances is covered with a braid. The primary solid insulation may be constructed from materials such as rubber, vinyl, polyethylene, or fluorocarbons. The braid provides additional protection against abrasion, and carries the identification and marking (color coding etc.). Polyethylene and similar materials are used extensively without the braided coverings.

A wide variety of insulating materials are commercially available and are selected by their electrical, environmental, and mechanical characteristics.

Electrically, all insulating materials are rated according to their dielectric strength, dielectric constant, resistance, and capacity-to-Q ratio. Each of these characteristics must be specified by the electronic design engineer and provided to the cable and wiring designer.

Physical characteristics include the permissible operating temperature, mechanical strength, ease of stripping and soldering, effects of aging, and the resistance to abrasion, vibration, moisture, flame, solvents and chemicals, and fungi.

Thermal properties are the primary factor in the selection of insulations. Many of the insulating materials will deteriorate rapidly at high temperatures, while others soften and lose their original shape. At lower temperatures insulation materials may become very brittle and are easily damaged by flexing.

Temperature limitations must be carefully considered early in the design phase, especially where the conductors are to be routed near heat generating components.

The wiring and cable designer must also consider non-operating temperature requirements. In general, military equipment must withstand non-operating temperatures of -62 °C to 85 °C, but these limits may vary based on the particular applications as defined in the governing specifications.

Voltage breakdown requirements are dependent on the specific applications, operating and non-operating temperatures, altitude and humidity. When the voltages are low the insulation resistance and the capacity-to-Q ratio are usually not important factors. However, capacity changes in high-frequency circuits can appreciably affect performance.

8

HIGH VOLTAGE WIRE AND CABLE

Corona is an ion and electron discharge set up in gases through which an electric field is impressed. All insulated wires have minute voids in the insulation material, and under the stress of high voltage gradients. ions are formed in these cavities and accelerated by the field. During periods of corona activity these ions bombard the walls of the cavity, breaking down the insulation and enlarging the voids. This process continues until an insulation failure occurs.

Corona, in air at atmospheric pressure, is initiated at voltage gradients between 80 and 200 volts-per-mil of insulation. However, once initiated, the corona will persist at much lower voltages. The extinction level may be as low as one half of the initiation level. High voltage transients are common in many circuits and once corona has started it may continue even after the transient has passed. Therefore, corona resistance is of importance in many applications where the working voltage is only moderately high and where insulations are thin.

Corona Resistant Teflon® has all of the advantages of the standard PTFE Teflon®, including chemical inertness, thermal stability, non-flammability, retention of its physical properties over a wide temperature range, and a high resistance to mechanical stress cracking (conventional HV cables, when bent sharply and subjected to corona stress develop cracks and fissures). Cables manufactured using this insulation can be effectively used from cryogenic temperatures through a high temperature of 300 °C for short periods of time.

The following factors have a direct influence on the duration of high voltage cables exposed to corona stress, and changes in any of these variables will alter the operating life of the cable.

Insulation Type. CR Teflon® demonstrates the best characteristics for high voltage applications.

Insulation Thickness. An increase in the insulation thickness increases the voltage rating of the cable. If the conductor size is not increased proportionally the voltage increase will not be proportional.

Frequency of Corona Bombardment. The "rule-of-thumb" is that corona life is inversely proportional to the frequency of the corona bombardment. However, the frequency of bombardment is not necessarily the frequency of the applied voltage. In dc applications, sporadic discharges occur even though the frequency of the applied voltage is zero.

Intensity of Corona Discharge. The intensity will increase

Table 1-3. Military Wire Specifications.

MILITARY Specification and Title	WIRE RANGE	Voltage Rating —V Max. R.M.S.	Amb. Temp. Rating —°C Max.	MATERIAL Conductor	MATERIAL Insulation	CONDUCTOR DIAMETER Wire Size	CONDUCTOR DIAMETER Nominal	INSULATION DIAMETER Wire Size	INSULATION DIAMETER Max.-Min.
MIL-W-16878D/1A **TYPE B** Wire Elec. Insul. Hi-Temp.	No. 32 to No. 14	600	105	Tin-Coated Copper	**PRIMARY:** Polyvinyl Chloride	26 / 24 / 22 / 20 / 18 / 16 / 14 / 12 / 10	.019 / .024 / .030 / .038 / .048 / .057 / .071 / — / —	26 / 24 / 22 / 20 / 18 / 16 / 14 / 12 / 10	.041-.035 / .047-.040 / .053-.046 / .061-.054 / .071-.064 / .081-.073 / .095-.087 / — / —
MIL-W-16878D/1A **TYPE C** Wire Elec. Insul. Hi-Temp.	No. 26 to No. 12	1000	105	Tin-Coated Copper	**PRIMARY:** Polyvinyl Chloride	26 / 24 / 22 / 20 / 18 / 16 / 14 / 12 / 10	.019 / .024 / .030 / .038 / .048 / .057 / .071 / .090 / —	26 / 24 / 22 / 20 / 18 / 16 / 14 / 12 / 10	.057-.049 / .062-.054 / .068-.060 / .076-.068 / .086-.078 / .095-.087 / .109-.101 / .128-.120 / —
MIL-W-16878D/1A **TYPE D** Wire Elec. Insul. Hi-Temp.	No. 24 to 1/0	3000	105	Tin-Coated Copper	**PRIMARY:** Polyvinyl Chloride	26 / 24 / 22 / 20 / 18 / 16 / 14 / 12 / 10	— / .024 / .030 / .038 / .048 / .057 / .071 / .090 / .111	26 / 24 / 22 / 20 / 18 / 16 / 14 / 12 / 10	— / .090-.075 / .096-.081 / .104-.099 / .114-.099 / .123-.108 / .137-.122 / .169-.154 / .189-.174
MIL-W-16878D/1A **TYPE E** Wire Elec. Insul. Hi-Temp.	No. 32 to No. 10	600	260 (Nickel-Coated Copper) / 200 (Silver-Coated Copper)	Nickel-Coated Copper / Silver-Coated Copper	**PRIMARY:** Polytetra-fluoroethylene	26 / 24 / 22 / 20 / 18 / 16 / 14 / 12 / 10	.019 / .024 / .030 / .038 / .048 / .057 / .071 / .090 / .111	26 / 24 / 22 / 20 / 18 / 16 / 14 / 12 / 10	.043-.035 / .048-.040 / .054-.046 / .062-.054 / .074-.064 / .087-.073 / .101-.087 / .120-.106 / .141-.127

MIL-W-16878D/1A TYPE EE — Wire Elec. Insul. Hi-Temp.
Size: No. 32 to No. 8; 1000 V; 260 °C (Nickel-Coated Copper) / 200 °C (Silver-Coated Copper)
PRIMARY: Polytetrafluoroethylene

AWG	Cond. Diam.	AWG	O.D. Range
26	.019	26	.053–.045
24	.024	24	.058–.050
22	.030	22	.064–.056
20	.038	20	.072–.064
18	.048	18	.084–.074
16	.057	16	.095–.083
14	.071	14	.113–.097
12	.090	12	.132–.116
10	.111	10	.156–.137

MIL-W-16878D/1A TYPE ET — Wire Elec. Insul. Hi-Temp.
Size: No. 32 to No. 20; 250 V; 260 °C (Nickel-Coated Copper) / 200 °C (Silver-Coated Copper)
PRIMARY: Polytetrafluoroethylene

AWG	Cond. Diam.	AWG	O.D. Range
26	.019	26	.033–.029
24	.024	24	.038–.034
22	.030	22	.044–.040
20	.038	20	.052–.048
18	—	18	—
16	—	16	—
14	—	14	—
12	—	12	—
10	—	10	—

MIL-W-16878D/1A TYPE F — Wire Elec. Insul. Hi-Temp.
Size: No. 24 to No. 12; 600 V; 200 °C; Tin-Coated Copper
PRIMARY: Silicone Rubber

AWG	Cond. Diam.	AWG	O.D. Range
26	—	26	.058–.052
24	.024	24	.064–.058
22	.030	22	.072–.066
20	.038	20	.082–.076
18	.048	18	.091–.085
16	.057	16	.121–.115
14	.071	14	.140–.134
12	.090	12	—
10	—	10	—

MIL-W-16878D/1A TYPE FF — Wire Elec. Insul. Hi-Temp.
Size: No. 24 to 4/0; 1000 V; 200 °C; Tin-Coated Copper
PRIMARY: Silicone Rubber

AWG	Cond. Diam.	AWG	O.D. Range
26	—	26	—
24	.024	24	.091–.083
22	.030	22	.097–.089
20	.038	20	.105–.097
18	.048	18	.115–.107
16	.057	16	.124–.116
14	.071	14	.170–.160
12	.090	12	.189–.179
10	.111	10	.210–.200

MIL-W-16878D/1A TYPE FFW — Wire Elec. Insul. Hi-Temp.
Size: No. 24 to No. 8; 1000 V; 200 °C; Tin-Coated Copper
PRIMARY: Silicone Rubber

AWG	Cond. Diam.	AWG	O.D. Range
26	—	26	—
24	.024	24	.091–.083
22	.030	22	.097–.089
20	.038	20	.105–.097
18	.048	18	.115–.107
16	.057	16	.124–.116
14	.071	14	.170–.160
12	.090	12	.189–.179
10	.111	10	.210–.200

Table 1-3. Military Wire Specifications. (Cont.)

MILITARY Specification and Title	WIRE RANGE	Voltage Rating —V Max. R.M.S.	Amb. Temp. Rating —°C Max.	MATERIAL Conductor	MATERIAL Insulation	CONDUCTOR DIAMETER Wire Size	CONDUCTOR DIAMETER Nominal	INSULATION DIAMETER Wire Size	INSULATION DIAMETER Max.-Min.
MIL-W-16878D/1A TYPE J Wire Elec. Insul. Hi-Temp.	No. 24 to 4/0	600	75	Tin-Coated Copper	Polyethylene	26	—	26	—
						24	.024	24	.053-.045
						22	.030	22	.060-.052
						20	.038	20	.068-.060
						18	.048	18	.080-.072
						16	.057	16	.091-.083
						14	.071	14	.109-.101
						12	.090	12	.128-.120
						10	.111	10	.156-.146
MIL-W-16878D/1A TYPE K Wire Elec. Insul. Hi-Temp.	No. 32 to No. 10	600	200	Silver-Coated Copper	PRIMARY: Fluorinated Ethylene Propylene	26	.019	26	.043-.035
						24	.024	24	.048-.040
						22	.030	22	.054-.046
						20	.038	20	.062-.054
						18	.048	18	.074-.064
						16	.057	16	.087-.073
						14	.071	14	.101-.087
						12	.090	12	.120-.106
						10	.111	10	.141-.127
MIL-W-16878D/1A TYPE KK Wire Elec. Insul. Hi-Temp.	No. 32 to No. 8	1000	200	Silver Coated Copper	PRIMARY: Fluorinated Ethylene Propylene	26	.019	26	.053-.045
						24	.024	24	.058-.050
						22	.030	22	.064-.056
						20	.038	20	.072-.064
						18	.048	18	.084-.074
						16	.057	16	.095-.083
						14	.071	14	.113-.097
						12	.090	12	.132-.116
						10	.111	10	.153-.137
MIL-W-16878D/1A TYPE KT Wire Elec. Insul. Hi-Temp.	No. 32 to No. 20	250	200	Silver-Coated Copper	PRIMARY: Fluorinated Ethylene Propylene	26	.019	26	.033-.029
						24	.024	24	.038-.034
						22	.030	22	.044-.040
						20	.038	20	.052-.048
						18	—	18	—
						16	—	16	—
						14	—	14	—
						12	—	12	—
						10	—	10	—

Specification / Use	AWG Size	Volts	Temp. (°C)	Conductor	Insulation	Max. Insulation Thickness (by AWG)	O.D. Range (by AWG)
MIL-W-5086A/2 TYPE I Wire Elec. 600V Copper Aircraft	No. 22 to No. 12	600	105	Tin-Coated Copper	**PRIMARY:** Polyvinyl Chloride **SECONDARY:** Nylon	22: .033, 20: .041, 18: .052, 16: .061, 14: .076, 12: .096	22: .072–.064, 20: .082–.074, 18: .092–.084, 16: .102–.094, 14: .122–.112, 12: .142–.132
MIL-W-5086A/2 TYPE II Wire Elec. 600V Copper Aircraft	No. 22 to 4/0	600	105	Tin-Coated Copper	**PRIMARY:** Polyvinyl Chloride **SECONDARY:** Glass Fiber Braid **THIRD:** Nylon	22: .033, 20: .041, 18: .052, 16: .061, 14: .076, 12: .096, 10: .128	22: .080–.070, 20: .090–.080, 18: .100–.090, 16: .110–.100, 14: .132–.118, 12: .150–.136, 10: .196–.182
MIL-W-5086A/2 TYPE III Wire Elec. 600V Copper Aircraft	No. 22 to 4/0	600	105	Tin-Coated Copper	**PRIMARY:** Polyvinyl Chloride **SECONDARY:** Glass Fiber Braid **THIRD:** Polyvinyl Chloride **FOURTH:** Nylon	22: .033, 20: .041, 18: .052, 16: .061, 14: .076, 12: .096, 10: .128	22: .090–.080, 20: .100–.090, 18: .115–.105, 16: .130–.120, 14: .150–.136, 12: .170–.156, 10: .200–.186
MIL-W-25038A Wire Elec. Hi-Temp. & Fire Res.	No. 22 to 4/0	600	343	Nickel-Clad Copper	**PRIMARY:** Asbestos **SECONDARY:** Glass Fiber Tape **THIRD:** TFE Coated Glass Braid **FOURTH:** TFE Finisher	22: .033, 20: .041, 18: .052, 16: .061, 14: .074, 12: .093, 10: .128	22: .116–.100, 20: .125–.109, 18: .135–.119, 16: .147–.127, 14: .170–.150, 12: .185–.165, 10: .230–.210
MIL-W-27300A Wire Elec. Poly. Insul. Copper 600V	No. 26 to No. 12	600	260	Nickel-Coated Copper	**PRIMARY:** Polytetra-fluoroethylene	26: .021, 24: .025, 22: .033, 20: .041, 18: .052, 16: .061, 14: .076, 12: .090	26: .041–.037, 24: .045–.041, 22: .052–.048, 20: .060–.056, 18: .070–.066, 16: .082–.078, 14: .113–.107, 12: .132–.124

Table 1-3. Military Wire Specifications. (Cont.)

MILITARY Specification and Title	WIRE RANGE	Voltage Rating —V Max. R.M.S.	Amb. Temp. Rating —°C Max.	MATERIAL Conductor	MATERIAL Insulation	CONDUCTOR DIAMETER	INSULATION DIAMETER
MIL-W-7139B CLASS 1 — Wire Elec. Polytetrafluoro-ethylene Insul. Copper 600 Volt	No. 22 to 4/0	600	200	Silver-Coated Copper	Polytetra-fluoroethylene	See detail below	See detail below
MIL-W-7139B CLASS 2 — Wire Elec. Polytetrafluoro-ethylene Insul.	No. 22 to 4/0	600	260	Nickel-Coated Copper	Polytetra-fluoroethylene	See detail below	See detail below
MIL-W-76B/1 TYPE LW — Wire & Cable Hook-up & Elec. Insul.	No. 30 to No. 20	300	80	Tin-Coated Copper or Copper-Clad Steel	Polyvinyl Chloride	See detail below	See detail below
MIL-W-76B/1 TYPE MW — Wire & Cable Hook-up & Elec. Insul.	No. 24 to No. 6	1000	80	Tin-Coated Copper or Copper-Clad Steel	Polyvinyl Chloride	See detail below	See detail below

MIL-W-7139B CLASS 1 and CLASS 2

Wire Size	Conductor Dia. Maximum	Insulation Dia. Max.-Min.
26	—	—
24	—	—
22	.033	.090-.080
20	.041	.100-.090
18	.052	.105-.115
16	.061	.125-.135
14	.076	.150-.136
12	.096	.170-.156
10	.128	.200-.186

MIL-W-76B/1 TYPE LW

Wire Size	Conductor Dia. Stranded Max.	Conductor Dia. Solid Nom.	Insulation Dia. Maximum	
26	.020	.0159	.043	.040
24	.025	.0201	.049	.044
22	.033	.0254	.057	.049
20	.041	.0320	.065	.056
18	—	—	—	—
16	—	—	—	—
14	—	—	—	—
12	—	—	—	—
10	—	—	—	—

MIL-W-76B/1 TYPE MW

Wire Size	Conductor Dia. Stranded Max.	Conductor Dia. Solid Nom.	Insulation Dia. Maximum	
26	.025	.0201	.062	.057
24	.033	.0254	.070	.062
22	.041	.0320	.078	.069
20	.052	.0403	.089	.077
18	.065	.0508	.102	.088
16	.078	.0641	.115	.101
14	.098	—	.135	—
12	.122	—	.159	—
10	—	—	—	—

MIL-W-76B/1 TYPE HW — Wire & Cable Hook-up & Elec. Insul.

- Conductor Size: No. 20 to 2/0
- Max Voltage: No. 22-16: 2500; No. 14-2/0: 600
- Max Temp: 80
- Conductor: Tin-Coated Copper or Copper-Clad Steel
- Insulation: Polyvinyl Chloride

AWG	Stranded Max.	Solid Nom.	Maximum	Maximum
26	—	—	—	—
24	—	—	—	—
22	.033	.0254	.106	.098
20	.041	.0320	.114	.105
18	.052	.0403	.125	.113
16	.065	.0508	.138	.124
14	.078	.0641	.180	.166
12	.098	—	.200	—
10	.122	—	.224	—

MIL-W-76B/1 TYPE HF — Wire & Cable Hook-up & Elec. Insul.

- Conductor Size: No. 24 to No. 16
- Max Voltage: 1000
- Max Temp: 80
- Conductor: Tin-Coated Copper or Copper-Clad Steel
- Insulation: Polyethylene

AWG	Stranded Max.	Solid Nom.	Maximum	Maximum
26	—	—	—	—
24	.025	.0201	.062	.057
22	.033	.0254	.070	.062
20	.041	.0320	.078	.069
18	.052	.0403	.089	.077
16	.065	.0508	.102	.088
14	—	—	—	—
12	—	—	—	—
10	—	—	—	—

MIL-W-8777B — Wire Elec. Silicone Insul, Copper, 600V, 200°C

- Conductor Size: No. 22 to 2/0
- Max Voltage: 600
- Max Temp: 200
- Conductor: Silver-Coated Copper
- Insulation: PRIMARY: Silicone Rubber; SECONDARY: Glass Fiber; THIRD: Polyester Fiber

AWG	Maximum	Maximum
26	—	—
24	—	—
22	.033	.090-.080
20	.041	.100-.090
18	.052	.115-.105
16	.060	.130-.120
14	.074	.150-.136
12	.093	.170-.156
10	.128	.200-.186

MIL-W-22759/1 Type (per MS 18000) — Wire, Elec., Fluorocarbon Insulated, Copper

- Conductor Size: No. 24 to No. 4
- Max Voltage: 600
- Max Temp: 200
- Conductor: Silver-Coated Copper
- Insulation: Polytetrafluoroethylene

AWG	Maximum	Maximum
26	—	—
24	.026	.064-.060
22	.033	.075-.071
20	.041	.084-.080
18	.052	.094-.090
16	.060	.105-.099
14	.074	.118-.122
12	.093	.137-.131
10	.128	.172-.164

MIL-W-22759/9 Type (per MS 18001) — Wire, Elec., Fluorocarbon Insulated, Copper

- Conductor Size: No. 24 to No. 4
- Max Voltage: 600
- Max Temp: 260
- Conductor: Nickel-Coated Copper
- Insulation: Polytetrafluoroethylene

AWG	Maximum	Maximum
26	—	—
24	.026	.064-.060
22	.033	.075-.071
20	.041	.084-.080
18	.052	.094-.090
16	.060	.105-.099
14	.074	.118-.112
12	.093	.137-.131
10	.128	.172-.164

Table 1-4. U.L. Wire Specifications.

| UL Style No. | Temp. Rating | Volt. Rating | Insulation | | Outer Covering | Gauge | Solid or Stranded | Fin. O.D. Inches |
			Material	Wall Thick.				
1212	80°C	Not Specified	Extruded TFE	8 Mil Min. Avg.	None	30-20	Inquire	
USE:	In office appliances where exposed to oil at a temperature not exceeding 60°C and where not subjected to undue mechanical abuse.							
1213	105°C	Not Specified	Extruded TFE	8 Mil Min. Avg.	None	30-20	Inquire	
USE:	In office appliances where exposed to oil at a temperature not exceeding 60°C and where not subjected to undue mechanical abuse.							
1422	105°C	Not Specified	Kynar* Halar**	5 Mil	None 28	30 28 26 24	7x38 7x36 7x34 7x32	.022 .025 .029 .034
USE:	In back panel areas of electronic computers and business machines where not subjected to movement or							

mechanical damage.

Part	Temp	Voltage	Insulation	Thickness	Shield	AWG	Stranding	O.D.
						22	7x30	.040
						20	10x30	.050
1423	105°C	Not Specified	Kynar* Halar**	4 Mil	None	30	7x38	.020
						28	7x36	.023
						26	7x34	.027
						24	7x32	.032
						22	7x30	.038
						20	10x30	.048

USE: In back panel areas of electronic computers and business machines where not subjected to movement or mechanical damage.

| 1429 | 80°C | 150v. | Irradiated PVC | 10 Mils | None | 30-16 | Inquire | |

USE: Internal wiring of appliances. Tags may indicate the following: 300 volts peak — for electronic use only.

| 1430 | 105°C | 300v. | Irradiated PVC | 15 Mils | None | 30-16 | Inquire | |

USE: Internal wiring of appliances. Tags may indicate the following: 600 volts peak — for electronic use only.

Table 1-4. U.L. Wire Specifications. (Cont.)

| UL Style No. | Temp. Rating | Volt. Rating | Insulation | | Outer Covering | Gauge | Solid or Stranded | Fin. O.D. Inches |
			Material	Wall Thick.				
1007	80°C	300v.	PVC	1/64	None	30	7x38	.046
						28	7x36	.049
						26	7x34	.053
						24	7x32	.058
						22	7x30	.064
						20	10x30	.074
						18	16x30	.082
						16	26x30	.095
USE:	Internal wiring of appliances where exposed to temperatures not exceeding 80°C or where exposed to oil at a temperature not exceeding 60°C or 80°C, whichever is applicable. Tags may indicate the following: 600 volts peak — for electronic use only.							
1015	105°C	600v.	PVC	1/32	None	28	7x36	.079
						26	7x34	.083
						24	7x32	.088
USE:	Internal wiring of appliances or internal wiring of							

18

appliances where exposed to oil at a temperature not exceeding 60°C or 80°C, whichever is applicable. Tags may indicate the following: 2500 volts peak — for electronic use only. Sizes 22-10, C.S.A. Approved.

22	7x30	.094
20	10x30	.104
18	16x30	.112
16	26x30	.125
14	41x30	.140
12	65x30	.160
10	105x30	.183
9	7x19x30	.205

| 1061 | 80°C | 300v. | PVC (Special) | 9 Mil | None |

USE: Internal wiring in electric bookkeeping, accounting or time-recording machines where exposed to temperatures not exceeding 80°C. Also, electronic equipment if within a chassis or protected from mechanical injury where exposed to temperatures not exceeding 80°C.

30	7x38	.032
28	7x36	.035
26	7x34	.039
24	7x32	.044
22	7x30	.050
20	10x30	.056
18	16x30	.065
16	26x30	.077

Table 1-5. Conductor Data Chart.

WIRE SIZE AWG	CONDUCTOR STRANDING	NOM. CDR. AREA IN CIRC. MILS	NOM. STR. DIA. IN INCHES	CONDUCTOR DIA. IN INCHES NOM.	MAX.	MAX. RESISTANCE OF FINISHED WIRE (OHMS/M FT. 20°C) SOFT OR ANNEALED COPPER TIN	SILVER	NICKEL	HIGH STRENGTH CU ALLOY TIN	SILVER	NICKEL	MAX. CONDUCTOR WEIGHT (POUNDS/1000 FT.) TIN	SILVER	NICKEL
32	SOLID	63.2	0.008	0.0079	0.0083	176.1	168.1	182.0				0.19	0.18	0.19
	7 x 40	69.2	0.003	0.0093	0.0096	177.1	169.1					0.23	0.21	0.20
30	SOLID	100.5	0.010	0.0099	0.0103	110.8	107.0	110.2	129.5	120.5	133.9	0.30	0.28	0.26
	7 x 38	112	0.004	0.0120	0.0124	107.7	100.3					0.40	0.38	0.36
28	SOLID	160	0.013	0.0126	0.0130	68.9	67.0	67.6	82.0	76.4	83.0	0.48	0.46	0.44
	7 x 36	175	0.005	0.0150	0.0154	68.2	63.6					0.61	0.58	0.56
26	SOLID	254	0.016	0.0159	0.0164	43.3	41.8	41.0	47.7	44.4	49.3	0.78	0.75	0.73
	7 x 34	278	0.006	0.0188	0.0195	40.9	40.9					0.86	0.82	0.79
	19 x 38	304	0.004	0.0201	0.0205	40.1	37.3					1.08	1.00	0.99
24	SOLID	404	0.020	0.0201	0.0207	27.3	26.8	25.1	30.2	28.1	30.6	1.22	1.14	1.13
	7 x 32	441	0.008	0.0240	0.0247	25.1	24.8					1.37	1.29	1.28
	19 x 36	475	0.005	0.0248	0.0255	25.4	23.6					1.64	1.54	1.53
22	SOLID	643	0.025	0.0254	0.0261	16.8	17.1	15.7	18.9	17.6	18.8	1.95	1.85	1.83
	7 x 30	707	0.010	0.0300	0.0309	16.2	15.2					2.18	2.10	2.08
	19 x 34	754	0.006	0.0312	0.0320	15.9	14.8					2.55	2.42	2.40
20	SOLID	1022	0.032	0.0320	0.0329	10.6	10.5	9.67	11.6	10.8	11.3	3.09	2.96	2.94
	7 x 28	1120	0.013	0.0378	0.0389	10.1	9.46					3.45	3.32	3.30
	19 x 32	1216	0.008	0.0396	0.0405	9.76	9.09					4.03	3.87	3.85
18	SOLID	1624	0.040	0.0403	0.0415	6.64	6.68	6.03	7.40	6.89	7.18	4.92	4.76	4.74
	7 x 26	1778	0.016	0.0477	0.0491	6.32	6.26					5.49	5.33	5.31
	19 x 30	1900	0.010	0.0495	0.0505	6.22	5.80					6.22	6.01	5.99
16	19 x 29	2426	0.011	0.0559	0.0570	4.82	4.54	4.73	5.72	5.38	5.58	7.89	7.66	7.63
14	19 x 27	3831	0.014	0.0703	0.0715	3.05	2.87	2.99	3.61	3.40	3.50	12.5	12.0	12.0
12	19 x 25	6088	0.018	0.0886	0.0905	1.92	1.81	1.88	2.36	2.22	2.23	19.3	18.5	18.4
10	37 x 26	9354	0.016	0.1102	0.1124	1.26	1.19	1.24	1.50	1.41	1.44	32.4	29.7	29.6
8	133 x 29	16983	0.011	0.1644	0.1693	0.702	0.661	0.688	0.842	0.792	0.822	56.8	55.2	55.0
6	133 x 27	26818	0.014	0.2066	0.2128	0.444	0.418	0.436	0.531	0.500	0.515	90.1	86.8	86.5

Table 1-6. Silver Plated Copper Wire Specifications.

AWG	Stranding Number	Stranding AWG	Nominal Strand Diameter	Nominal Conductor Diameter	Nominal Weight Lbs./M Ft.
12	19	25	—	.090"	18.45
14	19	27	—	.071"	11.58
16	19	29	—	.057"	7.27
18	1	—	.0403"	—	4.93
	7	26	—	.048"	5.63
19	19	30	—	.050"	5.78
	1	—	.036"	—	3.90
20	1	—	.032"	—	3.10
	7	28	—	.038"	3.39
	19	32	—	.040"	3.63
21	1	—	.0285"	—	2.46
22	1	—	.0254"	—	1.95
	7	30	—	.030"	2.13
	19	34	—	.032"	2.29
23	1	—	.0226"	—	1.54
24	1	—	.0201"	—	1.22
	7	32	—	.024"	1.34
	19	36	—	.025"	1.44
25	1	—	.0179"	—	.97
26	1	—	.0159"	—	.77
27	7	34	—	.019"	.84
	19	38	—	.020"	.90
	1	—	.0142"	—	.61
28	1	—	.0126"	—	.48
	7	36	—	.015"	.53

Table 1-6. Silver Plated Copper Wire Specifications. (Cont.)

AWG	Stranding		Nominal Strand Diameter	Nominal Conductor Diameter	Nominal Weight Lbs./M Ft.
	Number	AWG			
29	19	40	—	.016"	.57
	1	—	.0113"	—	.384
30	1	—	.010"	—	.30
	7	38	—	.012"	.33
	19	42	—	.013"	.36
31	1	—	.0089"	—	.24
32	1	—	.008"	—	.19
	7	40	—	.009"	.21
	19	44	—	.010"	.22
33	1	—	.0071"	—	.15
34	1	—	.0063"	—	.121
	7	42	—	.0075"	.13
35	1	—	.0056"	—	.095
36	1	—	.005"	—	.076
	7	44	—	.006"	.08
37	1	—	.0045"	—	.06
38	1	—	.004"	—	.048
39	1	—	.0035"	—	.037
40	1	—	.0031"	—	.033
41	1	—	.0028"	—	.024
42	1	—	.0025"	—	.019
43	1	—	.022"	—	.015
44	1	—	.0020"	—	.012

Table 1-7. Flat Conductor Specifications.

CONDUCTOR SIZES	EQUIVALENT AWG
.002″ x .025″	32
.004″ x .025″	29
.003″ x .040″	28
.005″ x .040″	26
.003″ x .063″	26
.005″ x .063″	24
.005″ x .100″	22
Tolerances: Width ± .003″ Thickness ± .0005″	

as the applied voltage is increased. At high altitudes and in cases where the conductor size is decreased the corona is more intense.

Conductor Size. Increasing the conductor size will increase the voltage rating of the cable.

High voltage wire and cable has applications where there are extremely stringent environmental demands (high temperatures, chemical resistance) combined with high voltage stress. It has been used in radar communications, oil furnace ignition systems, rocket ignition systems, transmitter power supplies, aircraft photoreconnaisance equipment and numerous other severe environment equipments. Tables 1-3 through 1-8 contain specifications for wire and cable that may be useful to you.

Table 1-8. Shielding Specifications.

Type	Flexibility	% Coverage	Termination	Mech. Protection or Resistance to Mech. Abuse
Braided Shield	Good	85% — 97%	Pigtail or Comb. DW	Excellent
Served Wire Shield	Excellent	99%	Pigtail	Very Good
Served Flat Wire	Poor	Up to 100%	Solder Sleeve or Drain Wire	Fair
Alumi- nized Mylar Shield	Excellent	Up to 100%	Drain Wire	Good

Shielding Effectiveness High Frequency	Shielding Effectiveness Low Frequency	Shielding Materials	O.D. Increase	Relative Weight
Good	Good	Stainless Steel Tungsten Nichrome Iron Nickel Silver-Plated Copper Tinned Copper	.016" - .020"	Heaviest
Poor	Good	Stainless Steel Tungsten Iron Nickel	.008" - .010"	Heavy
Excellent	Excellent	Silver-Plated Copper Tinned Copper Silver-Plated Copper Tinned Copper Bare Copper Nickel	.004" - .008"	Light
Excellent	Excellent	Aluminized Mylar	.003" - .005"	Lightest

Chapter 2

Insulation Materials and Compounds

The following tables, Table 2-1 to 2-15, are provided to aid the cable and wiring designer in selecting the most appropriate insulation materials for any given application. Once the environmental requirements have been defined the designer may enter any table and extract the physical and thermal properties, the electrical properties, and the environmental properties most suitable for a specific design requirement.

These tables also provide the designer with a ready comparison of the available materials and assist in establishing potential alternates.

Table 2-1. Insulation Temperature Ranges-Nominal.

Temp., °C	-100	-75	-50	-25	0	25	50	75	100	125	150	175	200	225	250	275

-30° NEOPRENE 90°
-40° RUBBER 75°
-60° POLYETHYLENE 80°
-20° VINYL STANDARD 80°
-55° VINYL PREMIUM 105°
-40° POLYPROPYLENE 105°
-70° TEFLON FEP 200° TFE 260°

Table 2-2. Properties of Rubber Insulations.

	SBR (Styrene-butadiene)	Natural	Synthetic Natural	Polybutadiene	Neoprene	Hypalon (Chloro-sulfonated Polyethylene)	NBR (Nitrile of Butadiene Acryloritrile)	EDPM (Ethylene Propylene Diene Monomer)	Butyl	Silicone
Oxidation Resistance	F	F	G	G	G	E	F	G	E	E
Heat Resistance	F-G	F	F	F	G	E	G	E	G	O
Oil Resistance	P	P	P	P	G	G	G-E	F	P	F-G
Low Temperature Flexibility	F-G	G	E	E	F-G	F	F	G-E	G	O
Weather, Sun Resistance	F	F	F	F	G	E	F-G	E	E	O
Ozone Resistance	P	P	P	P	G	E	P	E	E	O
Abrasion Resistance	G-E	E	E	E	G-E	G	G-E	G	F-G	F
Electrical Properties	E	E	E	E	F	G	P	E	E	O
Flame Resistance	P	P	P	P	G	G	P	P	P	F-G
Nuclear Radiation Resistance	F-G	F-G	F-G	P	F-G	G	F-G	G	P	E
Water Resistance	G-E	G-E	E	E	G	G-E	G-E	G-E	G-E	G-E
Acid Resistance	F-G	F-G	F-G	F-G	G	E	G	G-E	E	F-G
Alkali Resistance	F-G	F-G	F-G	F-G	G	E	F-G	G-E	E	F-G
Gasoline, Kerosene, Etc. (Aliphatic Hydrocarbons) Resistance	P	P	P	P	G	F	E	P	P	P-F
Benzol, Toluol, Etc. (Aromatic Hydrocarbons) Resistance	P	P	P	P	P-F	F	G	F	F	P
Degreaser Solvents Halogenated Hydrocarbons) Resistance	P	P	P	P	P	P-F	P	P	P	P-G
Alcohol Resistance	F	G	G	F-G	F	G	E	P	E	G

P = poor   F = fair   G = good   O = outstanding

These ratings are based on average performance of general purpose compounds. Any given property can usually be improved by the use of selective compounding.

27

Table 2-3. Properties of Plastic Insulations.

	PVC	Low Density Polyethylene	Cellular Polyethylene	High Density Polyethylene	Polypropylene	Polyurethane	Nylon	Teflon
Oxidation Resistance	E	E	E	E	E	E	E	O
Heat Resistance	G-E	G	G-E	E	E	G	E	O
Oil Resistance	E	G-E	G-E	G-E	E	E	E	O
Low Temperature Flexibility	P-G	G-E	E	E	P	G	G	O
Weather, Sun Resistance	G-E	E	E	E	E	F-G	E	O
Ozone Resistance	E	E	E	E	E	E	E	E
Abrasion Resistance	F-G	F-G	G	E	F-G	O	E	G-E
Electrical Properties	F-G	E	E	E	F-G	P-F	F	E
Flame Resistance	E	P	P	P	P	P	P	O
Nuclear Radiation Resistance	P-F	G	G	G	F	G	F-G	P-F
Water Resistance	E	E	E	E	E	P	P-F	E
Acid Resistance	G-E	G-E	G-E	G-E	E	F	P-F	E
Alkali Resistance	G-E	G-E	G-E	G-E	E	F	E	E
Gasoline, Kerosene, Etc. (Aliphatic Hydrocarbons) Resistance	G-E	P-F	P-F	P-F	P-F	F	G	E
Benzol, Toluol, Etc. (Aromatic Hydrocarbons) Resistance	P-F	P	P	P	P-F	P	G	E
Degreaser Solvents Halogenated Hydrocarbons) Resistance	P-F	P	P	P	P	P	G	E
Alcohol Resistance	G-E	E	E	E	E	P	P	E

P = poor   F = fair   G = good   O = outstanding

These ratings are based on average performance of general purpose compounds. Any given property can usually be improved by the use of selective compounding.

Table 2-4. Temperature Ranges of Insulation Materials.

| | Temperature °C | |
Insulation	Min.	Max.
PVC	− 20	80
PVC (high temperature)	− 55	105
Polyethylene	− 60	80
Rubber	− 40	75
Nylon	− 55	115
Teflon TFE	− 70	260
Teflon FEP	− 70	200
Polypropylene	− 20	105
Neoprene	− 30	90
Silicone rubber		150
Kapton HF	− 70	200
Cross-linked polyethylene	− 60	135

Maximum values shown are combination of ambient and conductor temperatures.

Table 2-5. Characteristics of Various Insulation Materials.

INSULATION CHARACTERISTICS	PVC	LOW DENSITY PE	HI DENSITY PE	CELLULAR PE	NYLON	TEFLON	SILICONE RUBBER	CROSS LINKED PE	KAPTON HF		
RESISTANCE TO:											
HEAT AGING	G	G	G	G	F	E	G	G	E		
OZONE	G	G	G	G	G	E	G	G	E		
FLAME	G	P	P	P	G	E	F	P	E		
MOISTURE	E	E	E	E	F	E	G	E	E		
OIL	E	G	G	G	E	E	F	G	E		
SKYDROL D	F	G	G	G	F	E	P	G	E		
SOLVENTS	G	P	P	P	G	E	P	P	E		
GASOLINE, KEROSENE	G	F	F	F	G	E	P	F	E		
AROMATIC FUELS	F	P	P	P	G	E	P	P	E		
NUCLEAR RADIATION	P	G	G	G	F	P	G	G	G		
OUTGASSING	P	F	F	F	F	E	P	F	E		
ALCOHOLS	G	E	E	E	P	E	F	E	E		
SUNLIGHT (ULTRA VIOLET)	G	E	E	E	F	E	E	E	E		
FUNGUS	E	F	G	G	G	E	F	G	E		
CORROSION	E	E	E	E	E	E	G	E	E		
ELECTRICALS:											
DIELECTRIC CONSTANT	P	G	G	E	P	E	F	G	F		

Table 2-5. Characteristics of Various Insulation Materials. (Cont.)

INSULATION CHARACTERISTICS	PVC	LOW DENSITY PE	HI DENSITY PE	CELLULAR PE	NYLON	TEFLON	SILICONE RUBBER	CROSS LINKED PE	KAPTON HF		
RESISTANCE TO:											
INSULATION RESISTANCE	G	G	G	G	F	E	G	G	E		
CORONA RESISTANCE	F	E	E	G	F	F	G	E	P		
SURFACE RESISTANCE	G	G	G	G	G	E	G	G	E		
LOW CAPACITANCE	P	G	G	E	P	E	F	G	F		
PHYSICALS:											
WEIGHT	F	F	F	G	G	F	G	F	E	E-EXCELLENT	
LOW TEMP. FLEXIBILITY	F	F	F	F	P	G	F	F	E	G-GOOD	
ABRASION RESISTANCE	G	G	G	F	E	G	P	E	E	F-FAIR	
COLD FLOW	E	E	E	G	E	F	E	E	E	P-POOR	
CUT THROUGH	E	G	G	F	G	G	P	G	E		
NOTCH SENSITIVITY	G	G	G	G	F	G	G	F	G		
SOLDER IRON RESISTANCE	P	P	P	P	F	E	G	G	E		

Table 2-6. Properties of Teflon® TFE.

PHYSICAL AND THERMAL	
PROPERTIES	TYPICAL VALUES
Specific Gravity	2.15
Tensile Strength, (p.s.i.)	4000
Elongation, (%)	300
Modulus of Elasticity in Tension, (p.s.i.)	0.58×10^5
Thermal Conductivity (cal sec^{-1} cm^{-1} $°C^{-1}$)	6×10^{-4}
Specific Heat (cal gm^{-1} $°C^{-1}$)	0.25
Thermal Expansion, ($°C^{-1}$)	10×10^{-5}
Continuous Use Temperature (°C)	260
10 Minute Endurance Temperature (°C)	325
Melt Temperature (°C)	327
Low Temperature Limit (°C)	Near −273
Flammability	Non-Flammable

ELECTRICAL	
PROPERTIES	TYPICAL VALUES
Dielectric Constant	2.1
Dissipation Factor	.0002
Volume Resistivity (ohm-cm)	$>10^{18}$
Corona Resistance	Fair

ENVIRONMENTAL	
RESISTANCE TO:	RATING
Cold Flow or Cut Through	Fair
Ultraviolet Radiation	Excellent
Nuclear Radiation	Poor †
Electrical-Mechanical Stress Cracking	Excellent
Chemical-Mechanical Stress Cracking	Excellent

*Du Pont Trademark
†In the absence of oxygen, radiation resistance is improved by a factor of more than 100.

Table 2-7. Properties of Teflon® FEP Resin.

PHYSICAL AND THERMAL	
PROPERTIES	TYPICAL VALUES
Specific Gravity	2.15
Tensile Strength, (p.s.i.)	2900
Elongation, (%)	250-330
Modulus of Elasticity in Tension (p.s.i.)	0.50×10^5
Thermal Conductivity (cal sec^{-1} cm^{-1} $°C^{-1}$)	6×10^{-4}
Specific Heat (cal gm^{-1} $°C^{-1}$)	0.28
Thermal Expansion, ($°C^{-1}$)	10×10^{-5}
Continuous Use Temperature (°C)	200
10 Minute Endurance Temperature (°C)	280
Melt Temperature (°C)	285
Low Temperature Limit (°C)	Near −273
Flammability	Non-Flammable

ELECTRICAL	
PROPERTIES	TYPICAL VALVES
Dielectric Constant	2.1
Dissipation Factor	.0002
Volume Resistivity (ohm-cm)	$>10^{18}$
Corona Resistance	Fair

ENVIRONMENTAL	
RESISTANCE TO:	RATING
Cold Flow or Cut Through	Fair
Ultraviolet Radiation	Excellent
Nuclear Radiation	Poor †
Electrical-Mechanical Stress Cracking	Excellent
Chemical-Mechanical Stress Cracking	Excellent

*Du Pont Trademark
†In the absence of oxygen, radiation resistance is improved by a factor of more than 100.

Table 2-8. Properties of Teflon® CR.

PHYSICAL AND THERMAL	
PROPERTIES	TYPICAL VALUES
Specific Gravity	2.0
Tensile Strength, (p.s.i.)	4000
Elongation, (%)	300
Modulus of Elasticity in Tension (p.s.i.)	0.58×10^5
Thermal Conductivity (cal sec^{-1} cm^{-1} $°C^{-1}$)	6×10^{-4}
Specific Heat (cal gm^{-1} $°C^{-1}$)	0.25
Thermal Expansion, ($°C^{-1}$)	10×10^{-5}
Continuous Use Temperature (°C)	180
10 Minute Endurance Temperature (°C)	325
Melt Temperature (°C)	327
Low Temperature Limit (°C)	Near −273
Flammability	Non-Flammable

ELECTRICAL	
PROPERTIES	TYPICAL VALUES
Dielectric Constant	2.2
Dissipation Factor	<.001
Volume Resistivity (ohm-cm)	$>10^{18}$
Corona Resistance	Excellent

ENVIRONMENTAL	
RESISTANCE TO:	RATING
Cold Flow or Cut Through	Fair
Ultraviolet Radiation	Excellent
Nuclear Radiation	Poor
Electrical-Mechanical Stress Cracking	Excellent
Chemical-Mechanical Stress Cracking	Excellent

Table 2-9. Properties of Kapton Film Type H.

PHYSICAL AND THERMAL	
PROPERTIES	TYPICAL VALUES
Specific Gravity	1.42
Tensile Strength, (p.s.i.)	25,000
Elongation, (%)	70
Modulus of Elasticity in Tension, (p.s.i.)	4.3×10^5
Thermal Conductivity (cal sec^{-1} cm^{-1} $°C^{-1}$)	4.5×10^{-4}
Specific Heat (cal gm^{-1} $°C^{-1}$)	0.261
Thermal Expansion, ($°C^{-1}$)	2×10^{-5}
Continuous Use Temperature (°C)	200
10 Minute Endurance Temperature (°C)	500
Melt Temperature (°C)	None
Low Temperature Limit (°C)	Near −273
Flammability	Non-Flammable

ELECTRICAL	
PROPERTIES	TYPICAL VALUES
Dielectric Constant	3.5
Dissipation Factor	.003
Volume Resistivity (ohm-cm)	10^{18}
Corona Resistance	Fair

ENVIRONMENTAL	
RESISTANCE TO:	RATING
Cold Flow or Cut Through	Excellent
Ultraviolet Radiation	Excellent
Nuclear Radiation	Excellent
Electrical-Mechanical Stress Cracking	Good
Chemical-Mechanical Stress Cracking	Good

Table 2-10. Properties of MIL-E-ENE B.

PHYSICAL AND THERMAL	
PROPERTIES	TYPICAL VALUES
Specific Gravity	1.48
Tensile Strength, (p.s.i.)	12,000
Elongation, (%)	100
Modulus of Elasticity in Tension, (p.s.i.)	3.6×10^{5}
Thermal Conductivity (cal sec^{-1} cm^{-1} $°C^{-1}$)	8.9×10^{-4}
Specific Heat (cal gm^{-1} $°C^{-1}$)	0.32
Thermal Expansion ($°C^{-1}$)	1.7×10^{-5}
Temperature Rating ($°C$)	105
10 Minute Endurance Temperature ($°C$)	180
Melt Temperature ($°C$)	250
Low Temperature Limit ($°C$)	−60
Flammability	Self Extinguishing

ELECTRICAL	
PROPERTIES	TYPICAL VALUES
Dielectric Constant (1 kc)	<3.5
Dissipation Factor (1 kc)	$<.025$
Volume Resistivity (ohm-cm)	$>10^{16}$
Corona Resistance	Fair

ENVIRONMENTAL	
RESISTANCE TO:	RATING
Cold Flow or Cut Throught	Excellent
Ultraviolet Radiation	Good
Nuclear Radiation	Unknown
Electrical-Mechanical Stress Cracking	Good
Chemical-Mechanical Stress Cracking	Good

MIL-ENE is a registered trademark of W. L. Gore & Associates, Inc.

Table 2-11. Properties of Polyurethane Elastomer.

PHYSICAL AND THERMAL	
PROPERTIES	TYPICAL VALUES
Specific Gravity	1.23
Tensile Strength, (p.s.i.)	5800-7500
Elongation, (%)	350-700
Modulus of Elasticity in Tension, (p.s.i.)	0.01×10^5
Thermal Conductivity (cal sec^{-1} cm^{-1} $^\circ$C^{-1})	5×10^{-4}
Specific Heat	0.43
Thermal Expansion ($^\circ$C^{-1})	10×10^{-5}
Continuous Use Temperature ($^\circ$C)	85
10 Minute Endurance Temperature ($^\circ$C)	105
Melt Temperature ($^\circ$C)	140
Low Temperature Limit ($^\circ$C)	- 60
Flammability	Slow Burning

ELECTRICAL	
PROPERTIES	TYPICAL VALUES
Dielectric Constant	7.1
Dissipation Factor	.015 – 0.017
Volume Resistivity (ohm-cm)	2×10^{11}
Corona Resistance	Poor

ENVIRONMENTAL	
RESISTANCE TO:	RATING
Cold Flow or Cut Through	Fair
Ultraviolet Radiation	Good***
Nuclear Radiation	Poor
Electrical-Mechanical Stress Cracking	Poor
Chemical-Mechanical Stress Cracking	Poor

***For black pigmented samples only.

Table 2-12. Types of Sleeving.

POLYVINYLCHLORIDE (PVC) SLEEVING

MIL-I-631   TYPE F   FORM U

Grade A — General Purpose
Grade B — Low Temperature
Grade C — High Temperature

Class I & II — Fungus Resistant

MIL-I-7444

Type I — Clear
Type II — Colored

34

TEFLON* SLEEVING

Standard Wall conforms to MIL-I-22129 and AMS 3653
Thin Wall conforms to AMS 3655
Light Wall conforms to AMS 3654

HEAT SHRINKABLE IRRADIATED

ST 9100 Flexible Polyolefin shrinks 50% at temperatures above 121° C

ST 93 and ST 94 Semi Rigid Polyolefin shrinks 50% in seconds when heat (above 275° F) is applied.

ST 96 Flexible PVC — meets the performance requirements of MIL-I-631 general purpose tubing.

Table 2-13. Tolerances of Thin Wall Spaghetti Tubing.

Awg Size	Nominal O.D.	Nominal I.D.	I.D. Maximum	I.D. Minimum	Wall Thickness	Tol. $^-_+$
30	.030	.012	.015	.010		
28	.033	.015	.019	.013		
26	.036	.018	.022	.016	.009	.002
24	.042	.022	.027	.020		
22	.047	.027	.032	.025		
20	.058	.034	.039	.032		
19	.062	.038	.043	.036		
18	.066	.042	.049	.040		
17	.071	.047	.054	.045		
16	.077	.053	.061	.051		
15	.083	.059	.067	.057	.012	.003
14	.090	.066	.072	.064		
13	.100	.076	.080	.072		
12	.109	.085	.089	.081		
11	.119	.095	.101	.091		
10	.130	.106	.112	.102		
9	.148	.118	.124	.114		
1/8	.155	.125	.130	.120		
8	.163	.133	.141	.129		
7	.178	.148	.158	.144		
6	.196	.166	.178	.162		
5	.216	.186	.198	.182	.015	.004
4	.238	.208	.224	.204		
3	.264	.234	.249	.229		
2	.293	.263	.278	.258		
1	.324	.294	.311	.289		
0	.360	.330	.347	.325		

Table 2-14. Tolerances of Light Weight Spaghetti Tubing.

Awg Size	Nominal O.D.	Nominal I.D.	I.D. Maximum	I.D. Minimum	Wall Thickness	Tol. $\bar{+}$
28	.027	.015	.017	.012		
26	.030	.018	.021	.016		
24	.034	.022	.025	.020		
22	.039	.027	.031	.025		
20	.046	.034	.038	.032	.006	.002
19	.050	.038	.043	.036		
18	.054	.042	.046	.040		
17	.059	.047	.054	.045		
16	.065	.053	.057	.051		
15	.071	.059	.063	.057		
14	.082	.066	.072	.064		
13	.092	.076	.080	.072		
12	.101	.085	.089	.081		
11	.111	.095	.099	.091	.008	.002
10	.122	.106	.110	.102		
9	.134	.118	.122	.114		
8	.149	.133	.139	.129		
7	.164	.148	.154	.144		
6	.186	.166	.172	.162		
5	.206	.186	.192	.182		
4	.228	.208	.214	.204	.010	.003
3	.254	.234	.241	.229		
2	.283	.263	.270	.258		
1	.314	.294	.301	.289		
0	.354	.330	.337	.325	.012	.003

Table 2-15. Tolerances of Standard Spaghetti Tubing.

Awg Size	Nominal O.D.	Nominal I.D.	I.D. Maximum	I.D. Minimum	Wall Thickness	Tol. $\bar{+}$
24	.046	.022	.027	.020	.012	.003
22	.051	.027	.032	.025		
20	.066	.034	.040	.032		
19	.070	.038	.044	.036		
18	.074	.042	.049	.040		
17	.079	.047	.054	.045		
16	.085	.053	.061	.051	.016	.003
15	.091	.059	.067	.057		
14	.098	.066	.074	.064		
13	.108	.076	.082	.072		
12	.117	.085	.091	.081		

Awg Size	Nominal O.D.	Nominal I.D.	I.D. Maximum	I.D. Minimum	Wall Thickness	Tol. +
11	.127	.095	.101	.091		
10	.138	.106	.112	.102		
9	.158	.118	.124	.114		
1'8	.165	.125	.130	.120		
8	.173	.133	.141	.129		
7	.188	.148	.158	.144		
6	.206	.166	.178	.162		
5	.226	.186	.198	.182	.020	.004
4	.248	.208	.224	.204		
3	.274	.234	.249	.229		
2	.303	.263	.278	.258		
1	.334	.294	.311	.289		
0	.370	.330	.347	.325		

Chapter 3

Cable and Wiring Design

The intent of this chapter is to provide the wiring and cable designer with the basic formulas and data he or she will require to generate a design of sufficient integrity to survive the intended service environments and applications.

The following information covers the specific requirements and applications data for reference use in wiring and cabling design. This data when applied together with the specific characteristics for the various types of wire and insulation materials provided in other chapters should be sufficient for generating designs of the highest quality.

SIMPLE WIRE BUNDLING CALCULATIONS

Wire harnesses and cables are often left to the Manufacturing Engineer. For the initial planning phase in production the wire bundle diameter is required to establish the harness or cable routing. The following method is a simple analytical method for determining the wire bundle diameters.

For wires of the same diameter the outside diameter of the wire bundle which will pass through a circular hole of a specified size the formula outlined in Fig. 3-1 can be used.

Where:

D = Diameter of wire bundle
d = Diameter of a single wire
N = Total number of wires

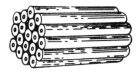

a. The expression for the outside diameter of a bundle of wires of the same diameter is:
$$D = 1.155d \ \sqrt{N}$$

b. The formula for the total number of wires of the same diameter which will pass through a a given circular opening is:
$$N = \pi/4 \ \frac{D^2}{d^2} - 1$$

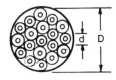

When a wire bundle consists of wires of different sizes (gauges) the outside diameter of the total wire bundle can be calculated by the following equations:

Let:

D = Outside diameter of wire bundle in inches
d_1 = Diameter of wire of first size
d_2 = Diameter of wire of second size
d_3 = Diameter of third size, etc., etc.
N_1 = Number of wires of first size
N_2 = Number of wires of second size
N_3 = Number of wires of third size, etc., etc.

$$D = \sqrt{21.3N_1 (d_1)^2 + 21.3N_2(d_2)^2 + 21.3N_3(d_3)^2 \ldots \ldots 0.0625}$$

Fig. 3-1. Simple wire bundle calculations.

ALLOWABLE BEND RADIUS
FOR CABLES AND HARNESSES

The bend radius for cables and harnesses should be calculated and allowed for during the design phase to ensure that there are proper clearances and access for the wiring operations, and all cables and harnesses should not interfere with other parts.

The three controlling factors in cables and harnesses are:

- Unsheathed harnesses without coaxial cables: the minimum bend radius should be 10 times the outside diameter of the trunk (or branch), except that termination points may be 3 times the outside diameter when they are properly supported.
- When coaxial cables are used: the bend radius may be 5 times the outside diameter of the harness or cable.
- Harnesses and cables that cannot meet the minimum bend radius defined above should be sheathed in their entirety in an insulation tubing without lacing, cord, or tape.

Figure 3-2 shows a typical harness installation.

EMC AND THE FCC

Electromagnetic compatibility or EMC is the acceptable state in which two or more components can co-exist without electrically interfering with each other. Twenty years ago this interference was termed RFI or radio frequency interference since most of the unwanted noise or energy originated from electrical components that generated radio frequencies. Today, with the advent of computers, switching power supplies, video games, etc., the interference is now termed EMI or electromagnetic interference.

When a television set displays static and distortion because a neighbor is playing his video game, a form of noise pollution or EMI exists and the FCC or Federal Communications Commission has taken steps to control this noise pollution by adopting rules that would limit the EMI levels emitted by all computing devices.

The following covers the FCC's definition of computing devices, a list of products covered and exempted by the ruling, limits on the two types of emission and the compliance dates for the FCC's EMI ruling. Figure 3-3 shows the allowed limits on emissions of both radiated and conducted types.

Definitions

Computing Device. Any electronic device that generates rf energy in excess of 10,000 cycles (pulses per second) and uses digital techniques. Rules apply to the complete device, not just to a microprocessor or other subassembly or component of the device.

Class A Computing Device. A computing device that is

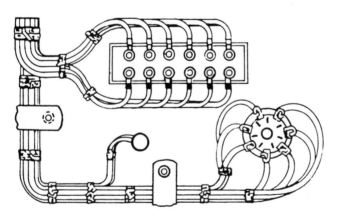

Fig. 3-2. Typical harness installation.

Limits on Radiated Emission

Frequency (MHz)	Class A (μV/m at 30m)	Class B (μV/m at 3m)
30–88	30	100
88–216	50	150
216–1000	70	200

Limits on Conducted Emission

Frequency (MHz)	Class A (μV)	Class B (μV)
0.45–1.6	1000	250
1.5–30	3000	250

Fig. 3-3. FCC emissions limitations.

marketed for use in a commercial, industrial, or business environment, exclusive of a device which is marketed for use by the general public, or which is intended to be used in the home.

Class B Computing Device. A computing device that is marketed for use in a residential environment notwithstanding use in a commercial, business, and industrial environment.

Products Covered

Computers
Computer peripherals
Computer terminals
Calculators
Data Terminals
Telephone and Data
Processing Equipment
Medical Diagnostic
Equipment

Products Exempted

Automobile Electronics
Industrial Control Systems
Appliances with microprocessors
Industrial, Scientific, Medical Test Equipment

Compliance Dates for the FCC's EMI Ruling

Jan. 1, 1981. Personal Computers and Electronic Games.

Oct. 1, 1981. All other computing devices first placed into production after Oct. 1, 1981.

Oct. 1, 1983. All computing devices regardless of date of first production.

Electromagnetic Spectrum

Table 3-1 shows part of the electromagnetic spectrum. A more complete table would show higher frequencies such as visible light

Table 3-1. Frequency Bands.

Band Number	Frequency Range	Frequency Subdivision	Example
2	30–300 Hz	ELF EXTREMELY LOW FREQUENCY	MUSICAL INSTRUMENTS
3	300–3K Hz	VF VOICE FREQUENCY	HUMAN SPEECH
4	3–30K Hz	VLF VERY LOW FREQUENCY	EARLY RADIO
5	30–300K Hz	LF LOW FREQUENCY	EARLY RADIO
6	.3–3M Hz	MF MEDIUM FREQUENCY	AM BROADCASTING
7	3–30M Hz	HF HIGH FREQUENCY	AM BROADCASTING
8	30–300M Hz	VHF VERY HIGH FREQUENCY	FM AND TV
9	.3–3G Hz	UHF ULTRA HIGH FREQUENCY	TV
10	30–300G Hz	SHF SUPER HIGH FREQUENCY	RADAR (MICROWAVE)
11	30–300G Hz	EHF EXTREMELY HIGH FREQUENCY	MICROWAVE

at 10^{15} Hz, but that frequency will not interfere with electronic equipment. A computer that operates with digital pulses at 4 MHz may interfere with radio reception if the computer is not properly designed for EMI.

E-Fields and H-Fields

It is beyond the scope of this article to cover electromagnetic theory but it is important for the mechanical engineer to know that electromagnetic waves are composed of two oscillating fields at right angles to each other. One is the electric field or E-Field and the other is the magnetic field or H-Field. Figure 3-4 shows the E- and H-components of electromagnetic waves.

E-Fields are generated by and they are the most susceptible to high impedance voltage driven circuitry such as a straight wire or a dipole and as a rule of thumb, E-Fields are best shielded by good conductors (materials that conduct electricity well) such as copper and aluminum.

H-Fields are generated by and they are the most susceptible to low impedance current driven circuitry such as a wire loop, and as a rule of thumb they are best shielded by magnetic materials such as iron.

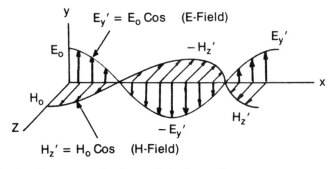

Fig. 3-4. Electromagnetic plane polarized wave form.

Conductive and Radiated EMI

Two types of interference levels must be controlled; conductive and radiated. Conductive EMI is the energy that is transferred from one circuit to another by wires or cables and the electrical engineer usually deals with the problem of conductive EMI by the application of circuit design, filters, and circuit grounding techniques.

Radiated EMI is energy that is radiated through the air and the electronic packaging engineer usually handles the problem of radiated EMI by the implementation of shielding materials and construction techniques in the design of enclosures and cabinets.

Grounding

Grounding in electronics does not mean earth ground, rather it is the term to describe a conductor that has a zero voltage potential (zero volts) in relation to the rest of the circuit. The three most common techniques of grounding are single (common) point grounding, multipoint grounding, and isolation point or floating point ground.

A single point occurs when all grounding points in a circuit are tied to one point. The advantage of that scheme is that all the grounding points in a circuit are tied to the same potential. The disadvantages are that the wire lengths needed to reach the single point may be too long and may create standing waves. There is also the mechanical disadvantage of trying to tie together a number of wires at one point. Figure 3-5 shows a single point ground.

The multipoint grounding system (See Fig. 3-6) uses a ground plane usually composed of a metal plate or a long conductive bar and every ground point on the circuit is connected directly to the ground plane at the closest available point on it, thus minimizing ground lead lengths. The advantages of this system is that the circuit construction is easier than for a single point and because the wires can be shorter, standing waves can be minimized. The disadvantage of multipoint grounding is that the ground plane may have different potential at different points on the plane because of

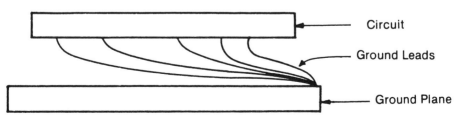

Fig. 3-5. Single point ground.

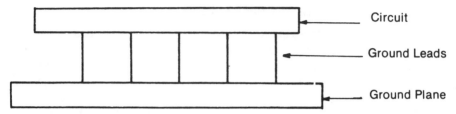

Fig. 3-6. Multipoint ground.

current flowing to and from the plane and that a potential exists for ground loops. In addition, care must be used in the mechanical design to insure protection of the ground plane from the environmental conditions such as corrosion, temperature expansion at junctions, etc.

The floating ground or isolation occurs when two circuits are electrically disconnected from one another and two or more physically separated grounds are used. The advantage of this type of grounding is to prevent ground loops composed of voltage spikes, conductive EMI, and other electrical noise from traveling from one circuit to another. The disadvantage of this grounding scheme is limited use. For example, the optoisolator circuit in Figure 3-7 is a circuit that uses isolation ground. It is actually two different circuits with the digital information transmitted light.

General Guidelines for Grounding

1. In dry areas it is recommended that the ground be tied to an area mostly likely to be kept damp, such as a lawn, or garden area that is constantly watered to improve the conductivity to earth.
2. Multipoint shield grounding reduces electrostatic coupling, however, if multipoint connections cannot be made, then at least the ends of the cable should be tied to ground, if a ground

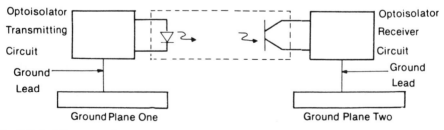

Fig. 3-7. Isolation ground.

loop or noise does occur when testing, then one end of the shield ground should be opened.

3. For short electrical leads or when the dimensions of the electronic assembly are less than 0.15, then a single point ground is acceptable.

$$\lambda = c/f$$

where λ = the wave length
f = the frequency
c = the speed of light or 3×10^8 meters per second

4. When the circuit dimensions exceed 0.15λ, then multiple point grounding at several locations spaced less than 0.15λ should be used.
5. Keep the ground leads as short and direct as possible.
6. To avoid ground loops, there should be separate ground systems for the signal shield returns, power system returns, and chassis or case ground.
7. Shields should not be used as signal return conductors.
8. Ground reference planes must be highly electrically conductive.
9. Provide multiple shields for low level transmission lines.
10. Whenever wires have to cross each other, they should cross at right angles to each other to minimize electrostatic coupling.

Shielding Material in the Perfect Shield

Shielding prevents electromagnetic energy from entering or leaving a specific region and its effectiveness depends on:

1. The shielding material and its thickness
2. The frequency of the radiated energy
3. The distance from the source to the shield
4. The quantity and the shape of any shield discontinuities.

A shield attenuates the electromagnetic energy by three methods: reflection, absorption, and internal reflection. The shield reflects part of the incident wave because the impedance of the metal is greater than the impedance of the air. The rest of the energy that is lost is either absorbed by the shield or internally reflected back into the shield when the energy reaches the other side of the shield's air-metal boundary. Referring to Fig. 3-8, it can be seen that:

$$SE_{dB} = R_{dB} + A_{dB} + B_{dB}$$

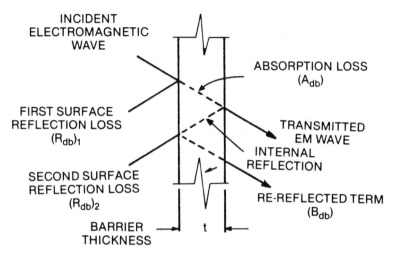

Fig. 3-8. Losses due to a solid conductive layer

Where: SE_{dB} = total shielding effectiveness
R_{dB} = sum of the reflection losses
A_{dB} = absorption losses
B_{dB} = re-reflection losses

The reflection loss R can be expressed by:

$$R_{dB} = 20 \log (Zw/4Z_b)$$

where: Zw = the electromagnetic wave impedance
Z_b = the barrier intrinsic impedance

The re-reflection loss, B_{dB}, is dependent upon the absorption loss and should be supplied by either the manufacturer or the electrical engineer.

Reflection is a function of the permeability of shield and the frequency of the electromagnetic energy, while the absorption losses can be calculated by:

$$A = 3.338 \times 10^{-3} \, T(f \, \mu_r \sigma_r)^{1/2}$$

Where A = absorption loss
f = frequency of the wave
σ_r = conductivity (relative to copper)
μ_r = material permeability relative to free space
T = shield thickness in mills

Tables 3-2 and 3-3 give the relative conductivity, relative

Table 3-2. Characteristics of Various Metals Used for Shields.

Metal	Relative Conductivity r	Relative Permeability at 150 kHz r	Absorption Loss A, db/mm at 150 kHz	Penetration Loss (db/mil) at 15 kHz
Silver	1.05	1	52	1.32
Copper-Annealed	1.00	1	51	1.29
Copper-Hard Drawn	.97	1	50	1.26
Gold	.70	1	42	1.08
Aluminum	.61	1	40	1.01
Magnesium	.38	1	31	0.79
Zinc	.29	1	28	0.70
Brass	.26	1	26	0.66
Cadmium	.23	1	24	0.62
Nickel	.20	1	23	0.58
Phosphor-Bronze	.18	1	22	0.55
Iron	.17	1,000	650	16.9
Tin	.15	1	20	0.50
Steel, SAE 1045	.10	1,000	500	12.9
Beryllium	.10	1	16	0.41
Lead	.08	1	14	0.36
Hypernick	.06	80,000	3500*	88.5
Monel	.04	1	10	0.26
Mu-Metal	.03	80,000	2500*	63.2
Permalloy	0.3	80,000	2500*	63.2
Steel, Stainless	.02	1,000	220*	5.7

Table 3-3. Comparative Data for Commonly Used RFI Shielding Materials.

Frequency	(Attenuation (db))				
	Galvanized Steel (22 gauge)	Aluminum Sheet (0.026 in.)	Copper Mesh (No. 22)	Electrosheet Copper (1 oz)	Electrosheet Copper (4 oz)
500 kc	75	71	66	75	65
1000 kc	80	80	71	70	71
0.15 Mc	100	100	100	100	100
0.50 Mc	100	100	100	100	100
1.5 Mc	100	100	100	100	100
5.0 Mc	100	100	100	100	100
10 Mc	100	100	100	100	100
60 Mc	87	76	70	87	77
100 Mc	77	69	48	74	64
400 Mc	42	61	64	59	57
750 Mc	55	54	64	73	61
1000 Mc	42	49	62	81	68
5000 Mc	30	23	32	29	39
10000 Mc	20	9	13	22	28

permeability, absorption loss, penetration loss, and frequency effects of various metals used for shields.

In the perfect shield, the thickness of the shield is more critical than just calculating the absorption loss. Any shields less than .25λ thick (called thin shielding) effectiveness is seriously degraded since there will be no internal reflection.

The Imperfect Shield, Discontinuities

The previous paragraphs dealt with the perfect shield: a shield with no discontinuities such as holes or seams. Discontinuities are more important than shield thickness since energy can travel through non-metallic sections of enclosures such as openings that behave as slot antennas.

The amount of electromagnetic leakage is a function of the longest dimension d, of the aperature and the wavelength λ. When λ < 2d, the electromagnetic energy will pass freely through the openings. For λ > 2d, the attenuation A:

$$A = 20 \log (\lambda/2d)$$

Different Methods to Shield Cables

Cables can be shielded by the use of braid, flexible conduit, or rigid conduit. Of these, braid is the easiest to handle and is relatively light in weight. However, no precise method is available to calculate woven materials shielding effectiveness and that information must be obtained from the manufacturer. In general, it's shielding effectiveness against the E-Field increases with the density of the weave, but decreases with frequency. Concerning the H-Field, the shielding effectiveness increases with:

1. Frequency
2. Density of the woven material
3. The permeability of the material

Braid shielding is made of non-permeable material. If magnetic shielding is required on a cable, annealed high permeability metal strips may be wrapped around the cable.

Solid or rigid conduit completely encloses the wire with metallic "pipes." It is extremely effective if designed correctly but could weigh too much or be hard to handle.

Flexible conduit has tiny holes which may make it ineffective if the frequency is high enough but in many cases it is effective and relatively easy to handle.

Filtering

A filter is basically a circuit that blocks energy at some frequencies and permits energy at other frequencies to pass through. It is well beyond the scope of this article to discuss filter design and chooosing the right filter should be left to the electrical engineer.

A filter should be used only as a last resort since a well-designed circuit should not need any filters.

BASIC CABLE DESIGN FORMULAS

Below is a collection of the standard equations used to establish the fundamental characteristics in the design of cable assemblies.

Conductor Weight

$$\text{Weight} = 340.0 \ D^2 \ GNK \ = \ \text{pounds/1000 feet}$$

Where:
- D = Diameter of conductor in inches
- G = Specific gravity of conductor material
    (Copper = 8.89, Aluminum = 2.71)
- K = Weight increase factor for stranded conductors
    (K = 1 for solid conductors)
- N = Number of strands

N	K
19	1.02
37	1.026
49	1.03
133 and more	1.04

Insulation Weight

$$\text{Weight} = 340.5 \ (D^2 - d^2)G \ = \ \text{pounds/1000 feet}$$

Where:
- D = diameter over the insulation, inches
- d = diameter over all conductors, inches
- G = specific gravity of the insulation

50

Jacket Weight

$$\text{Weight} = 340.5 \ (D^2 - d^2)G = \text{pounds/1000 feet}$$

Where:
- D = diameter over the jacket
- d = diameter under the jacket
- G = specific gravity of the jacket material

Wrapping Tape Weight

$$\text{Weight} = 1362Gt \ ((d+t) + (d+3t) \ f) = \text{pounds/1000 feet}$$

Where:
- t = tape thickness, inches
- f = multiplying factor from 0/0 lap
- d = diameter of cable under tape, inches
- G = specific gravity of tape

%Lap	f
17 1/2	0.35
25	0.5
33	0.67
50	1.0

Total Weight of Cable

$$\text{Weight} = N \times L \times W = \text{weight/1000 feet}$$

Where:
- N = number of conductors
- W = weight of one conductor
- L = twisting loss factor = 1.03

Cabling Factors

Number conductors	factors
2	2.0
3	2.154
4	2.414
5	2.7
6	3.0
7	3.0
10	4.0
12	4.155

Number conductors	factors
16	4.7
19	5.0
27	6.155
37	7.0
41	8.0
61	9.0

Note: the following equation is used for other combinations: O.D. = 1.155 × number of conductors × diameter of individual conductor. To approximate the over-all diameter of the finished cable, double the wall thickness of the wire and add to the O.D. of the selected stranded conductor. Multiply the result by the indicated factor above. Add 0.025 inches for bare tinned or silver plated shield of number 36 gauge wire. The resultant dimension does not include the jacket.

Shield Diameter

Shield O.D. = diameter under shield + Adder

AWG size (braid)	Adder, (inches)
#40	0.014
#38	0.018
#36	0.022
#34	0.028
#32	0.035
#30	0.044
#28	0.303

Shield Weight

$$\text{Weight} = \frac{N \times C \times W}{\cos a} \times 1.03 = \text{pounds/1000 feet}$$

Where:
- N = strands/carrier
- C = number of carriers
- W = weight of one shield strand, (lbs/1000 feet)
- a = braid angle

Twisting Loss

Twisting loss for all cables is approximately 3%.

Table 3-4. Current Capacities for Various Types of Wires and Insulation.

AWG SIZE SOLID STRAND	DIAM. IN INCHES	RESIST-ANCE OHMS PER 1000 FT	1 PVC 80°C (INSULATION)	1 PVC 105°C	1 POLYETHYLENE	1 TEFLON	2–3 PVC 80°C	2–3 PVC 105°C	2–3 POLYETHYLENE	2–3 TEFLON	4–5 PVC 80°C	4–5 PVC 105°C	4–5 POLYETHYLENE	4–5 TEFLON	6–15 PVC 80°C	6–15 PVC 105°C	6–15 POLYETHYLENE	6–15 TEFLON
24	.020	25.7	11.5	3.7	23.5	2.3	7.2	2.3	14.7	1.8	5.8	1.8	11.8	1.6	5.0	1.6	10.3	
22	.025	16.2	14.9	4.6	31.2	2.9	9.3	2.9	19.5	2.3	7.4	2.3	15.6	2.0	6.5	2.0	13.7	
20	.032	10.1	19.0	6.1	41.0	3.8	12.0	3.8	26.0	3.0	9.6	3.0	20.0	2.7	8.4	2.7	18.2	
18	.040	6.39	25.0	8.3	56.0	5.2	16.0	5.2	35.0	4.2	12.0	4.2	28.0	3.6	11.0	3.6	24.0	
16	.051	4.02	35.0	11.0	68.0	6.8	22.0	6.8	43.0	5.4	17.0	5.4	34.0	4.8	15.0	4.8	30.0	
14	.054	2.52	46.0	14.0	92.0	9.1	29.0	9.1	58.0	7.3	23.0	7.3	46.0	6.4	20.0	6.4	40.0	
12	.081	1.59	60.0	19.0	118.0	12.0	38.0	12.0	74.0	9.6	30.0	9.6	59.0	8.4	26.0	8.4	51.0	
10	.102	.99	83.0	25.0	160.0	16.0	52.0	16.0	100.0	12.0	41.0	12.0	80.0	11.0	36.0	11.0	70.0	
8	.129	.63	113.0	36.0	212.0	23.0	71.0	23.0	133.0	18.0	56.0	18.0	106.0	16.0	49.0	16.0	93.0	
6	.162	.39	152.0	49.0	283.0	31.0	95.0	31.0	177.0	24.0	76.0	24.0	141.0	21.0	66.0	21.0	123.0	

MAX. CURRENT IN AMPERES – AMBIENT TEMP. 25°C (78°F)

NUMBER OF CONDUCTORS

VALUES APPLY TO INDIVIDUAL WIRES

Table 3-5. Wire Data Chart.

Size	Diameter	Area	Area	Weight	SOFT OR ANNEALED			HARD DRAWN		
					Tensile Strength Maximum	Breaking Strength Minimum	Maximum DC Resistance at 68°F.	Tensile Strength Minimum	Breaking Strength Maximum	Maximum DC Resistance at 68°F
Awg	Inch	Cir. Mils	Sq. In.	Lbs. per 1,000 Ft.	Lbs. per Sq. In.	Lbs.	Ohms per 1,000 Ft.	Lbs. per Sq. In.	Lbs.	Ohms per 1,000 Ft.
4/0	.4600	211,600	.1662	640.5	36,000	5,983	.04901	49,000	8,143	.05045
3/0	.4096	167,800	.1318	507.9	36,000	4,745	.06180	51,000	6,722	.06361
2/0	.3648	133,100	.1045	402.8	36,000	3,763	.07793	52,800	5,519	.08021
1/0	.3249	105,600	.08291	319.5	36,000	2,984	.09827	54,500	4,517	.1011
1	.2893	83,690	.06573	253.3	37,000	2,432	.1239	56,100	3,688	.1289
2	.2576	66,360	.05212	200.9	37,000	1,929	.1563	57,600	3,003	.1625
3	.2294	52,620	.04133	159.3	37,000	1,530	.1970	59,000	2,439	.2049
4	.2043	41,740	.03278	126.4	37,000	1,213	.2485	60,100	1,970	.2584
5	.1819	33,090	.02599	100.2	37,000	961.9	.3133	61,200	1,591	.3258
6	.1620	26,240	.02061	79.46	37,000	762.9	.3951	62,100	1,280	.4108
7	.1443	20,820	.01635	63.02	37,000	605.0	.4982	63,000	1,030	.5181
8	.1285	16,510	.01297	49.97	37,000	479.8	.6282	63,700	826.0	.6533
9	.1144	13,090	.01028	39.63	37,000	380.5	.7921	64,300	661.2	.8238
10	.1019	10,380	.008155	31.43	38,500	314.0	.9989	64,900	529.2	1.039
11	.0907	8,230	.00646	24.92	38,500	249.0	1.260	65,400	422.9	1.310
12	.0808	6,530	.00513	19.77	38,500	197.5	1.588	65,700	336.9	1.652
13	.0720	5,180	.00407	15.68	38,500	156.6	2.003	65,900	268.0	2.083
14	.0641	4,110	.00323	12.43	38,500	124.2	2.525	66,200	213.5	2.626
15	.0571	3,260	.00256	9.858	38,500	98.48	3.184	66,400	169.8	3.312
16	.0508	2,580	.00203	7.818	38,500	78.10	4.016	66,600	135.1	4.176

54

17	.0453	2,050	.00161	6.200	38,500	61.93	5.064	66,800	107.5	5.266
18	.0403	1,620	.00128	4.917	38,500	49.12	6.385	67,000	85.47	6.640
19	.0359	1,290	.00101	3.899	38,500	38.95	8.051	67,200	67.99	8.373
20	.0320	1,020	.000804	3.092	38,500	30.89	10.15	67,400	54.08	10.56
21	.0285	812.0	.000638	2.452	38,500	24.50	12.80	67,700	43.07	13.31
22	.0253	640.0	.000503	1.945	38,500	19.43	16.14	67,900	34.26	16.79
23	.0226	511.0	.000401	1.542	38,500	15.41	20.36	68,100	27.25	21.17
24	.0201	404.0	.000317	1.223	40,000	12.69	25.67	68,300	21.67	26.69
25	.0179	320.0	.000252	.9699	40,000	10.07	32.37	68,600	17.26	33.66
26	.0159	253.0	.000199	.7692	40,000	7.983	40.81	68,800	13.73	42.44
27	.0142	202.0	.000158	.6100	40,000	6.331	51.47	69,000	10.92	53.52
28	.0126	159.0	.000125	.4837	40,000	5.020	64.90	69,300	8.698	67.49
29	.0113	128.0	.000100	.3836	40,000	3.981	81.84	69,400	6.908	85.10
30	.0100	100.0	.0000785	.3042	40,000	3.157	103.2	69,700	5.502	107.3
31	.0089	79.2	.0000622	.2413	40,000	2.504	130.1	69,900	4.376	135.3
32	.0080	64.0	.0000503	.1913	40,000	1.986	164.1	70,200	3.485	170.6
33	.0071	50.4	.0000396	.1517	40,000	1.575	206.9	70,400	2.772	215.2
34	.0063	39.7	.0000312	.1203	40,000	1.249	260.9	70,600	2.204	271.3
35	.0056	31.4	.0000246	.09542	40,000	.9904	329.0	70,900	1.755	342.1
36	.0050	25.0	.0000196	.07567	40,000	.7854	414.8	71,100	1.396	431.4
37	.0045	20.2	.0000159	.06001	40,000	.6228	523.1	71,300	1.110	544.0
38	.0040	16.0	.0000126	.04759	40,000	.4939	659.6	71,500	.8829	686.0
39	.0035	12.2	.00000962	.03774	40,000	.3917	831.8	71,800	.7031	865.0
40	.0031	9.61	.00000755	.02993	40,000	.3106	1,049	72,000	.5592	1,091
41	.0028	7.84	.00000616	.02374	40,000	.2464	1,323	72,000	.4434	1,375
42	.0025	6.25	.00000491	.01882	40,000	.1954	1,668	72,000	.3517	1,734
43	.0022	4.84	.00000380	.01493	40,000	.1549	2,103	72,000	.2789	2,187
44	.0020	4.00	.00000314	.01184	40,000	.1229	2,652	72,000	.2212	2,758

SAFE CURRENT RATINGS FOR WIRE AND CABLE

Prior to the selection of wire or cable for any application, the performance of the materials to the safety requirements must be established. Careful consideration to the following factors must be taken before a safe current rating can be applied to any wire or cable.

1. The temperature of an electrical conductor will increase as the square of the applied current.

Table 3-6. Raw Materials Specifications.

Property	Test Method	Unit of Measure	RMS-1 Nylon 6/6	RMS-2 Nylon Flame Retardant	RMS-3 Polycarbonate	RMS-4 PVC	RMS-5 Noryl*	RMS-6 Low Density Polyethylene	RMS-7 Flame Retardant Polyethylene
Tensile Strength at Yield	D638	psi	9.000	5.700	9.500	6.200	9.600	600-2.300	2.150
Elongation at Fail	D638	%	200	160	110	N.R.	60	400	
Flexural Modulus	D790	psi	190.000	135.000	340.000	350.000	360.000	80.000	118.000
Izod Impact	D756	ft-lb./in.	3.0	1.7	12-16	17.0	5	No Break	1.26
Deflection Temperature	D648	66 psi °F	430	421	280	N.R.	279	100	—
Deflection Temperature	D648	264 psi °F	160	212	265	163	265	90	
Dielectric Strength	D149	Volts/Mil	550	N.R.	380	690	500	450	
Volume Resistivity	D257	ohm/cm	2×10^{13}	2×10^{14}	8.2×10^{16}	5.1×10^{8}	10^{17}	$\cdot 10^{16}$	
Water Absorption	D570	24 hrs..%	1.1	1.2	15	04	007	01	
Flammability Rating Thickness	UL94	in.	V-2 .028	V-0 028	V-2 062	V-0 028	V-1 058	N.R.	V-2 062
Hardness			R105	R120	R118	R111	R119	D48	
U.L. Yellow Card File			E70062	E41938	E36063	E41877	E42239	N.R.	E51346
UL Continuous Use Temperature	w/impact w/o impact	°C	75/85 @ 058	65/65 @ 028	115/125 @ 058	50/50 @ 028	105/110 @ 030	N.R.	N.R.

N. R. — Not Rated

	Physical Properties		Adhesive Properties	
RMS-15 Double Coated Urethane Foam Tape This tape is a high density, flexible polyurethane foam, coated on both sides with pressure-sensitive acrylic adhesive.	Density 30 lbs./ft.[1] Water penetration rate (% volume): 2.00 max. Solvent resistance, after 24 hr. immersion		Polyethylene	Excellent
			Polypropylene	Excellent
			Acrylic	Excellent
			ABS	Excellent
	Toluene	Foam swelling, adhesive weakening	Polystyrene	Excellent
	JP-4	Slight foam swelling, adhesive softened	Other Plastics	Excellent
	Petrol	Some foam swelling, adhesive softened	Anodized Aluminum	Excellent
	Heptane	Slight foam swelling, adhesive softened	Stainless Steel	Excellent
	Lacquer Thinner	Considerable foam swelling, adhesive softened and partially dissolved	Other Metal Surfaces	Excellent
	Perchloreothylene	Some foam swelling, adhesive softened		
	Motor Oil	No effect	Note: Foam splits upon removal.	

2. Since conductor heat is normally dissipated from the insulation surface, the ambient temperature and the available dissipating surface will greatly affect the current carrying capacity.
3. Wire bundles and multi-conductor cables will have a greater temperature rise since the dissipating surface is reduced.
4. Because all wire insulations are ultimately affected by heat, careful consideration must be given to all of these factors.

Table 3-4 considers that there will be a temperature rise comen-

RMS-8 Polypropylene	RMS-9 ABS	RMS-10 Poly-allomer	RMS-11 CPVC	RMS-12 Propionate	RMS-13 Polyethylene	RMS-14 Acetal	RMS-16 High Impact Polystyrene	RMS-17 Nylon H.M.W.	RMS-18 Nylon Glass Filled	RMS-19 Nylon Flame Retardant	RMS-20 Rigid PVC	RMS-21 Nylon Co-polymer	RMS-22 Nylon 11	RMS-23 Polycarbonate Flame Retardant
5.000	6.300	4.100	8.250	3.000	1.200-3.500	9.900	4.400	11.200	12.000	5.700	6.500	10.900	3.500	9.000
>100		400	N.R.	50	50-600	20	30	>300	8	75		128	100	90
200.000	330.000	110.000	420.000	230.000	100.000	400.000	335.000	175.000	900.000	200.100	400.000	340.000	40.000	325.000
4	7.0	1.76	1.77	9.5	6-1.15	1.4	1.1	2.5	2.0	1.7	18			12
220	208	210	N.R.	157	120-165	335	N.R.	455	N.R.	397				280
130	192	124	221	127	105-120	250	170	194	480	158	162			270
N.R.	850	1.170	300	450/1.000	500	400		530	559	N.R.				380
N.R.	>10^{15}		10^{14}		10^{15}	10^{16}	10^{13}	10^{15}	1.1 × 10^{13}	N.R.				10^{16}
4	.01	.07	1.9	.01	32	.08	1.2	7	91			50	15	
N.R.	HB .058	N.R.	V-0 .045	N.R.	N.R.	HB .028	N.R.	V-2 .028	HB .028	V-0 .028	V-0 .065			V-0 .125
R90	R102	R76	R120	R51	D50	R120	M45	R108	M101	R120	D76		D63	M70
N.R.	E37943	N.R.	E41877	N.R.	N.R.	E66288	N.R.	E41938	E41938	E70062	E53006		N.R.	E36063
N.R.	60 @ .058	N.R.	N.R.	N.R.	N.R.	50/50 @ .028	N.R.	75/85 @ .058	65/105 @ .028	75/85 @ .058	N.R.		N.R.	N.R.

Characteristics	Proper Application
1. The adhesive's aggressiveness permits tape to be applied to rough surfaces with only enough pressure for maximum contact. 2. The long aging adhesive is suitable for permanent holding. 3. Best surface adhesion if attained when application temp. range is between 70°-120°F (20°-50°C). Application at slightly lower temperature range is possible if initial holding power is not critical. Once applied, adhesive is not effected by lower temperature. Tape will hold for extended periods of time at temperatures of 200°F (95°C) or slightly higher.	1. Max. recommended static loading at the adhesive surface is 1/4 pound per sq. in. of tape. 2. Remove dirt, wax, dust, soap, or oil from contact surface. 3. Apply to relatively flat surface on glass, metal, wood, tile, plastic, etc. 4. Do not use on fabric, coarse concrete, loose paint, or rough wallpaper. 5. Do not touch adhesive. 6. Remove liner. Place article in desired position and press firmly to insure good adhesive contact. 7. Do not attempt to reposition article. 8. If possible, allow overnight dwell before loading.

surate with the ambient temperature and the magnitude of the applied current. The current values that are listed at the indicated ambient temperatutre will not result in temperatures that will damage the conductor insulations. However, many military and commercial codes and specifications contain requirements for specific applications and these should be consulted in cases where they govern.

Current values in excess of the values shown in Table 3-4 can result in serious damage to the conductor insulations and will impose a safety hazard to the operators and service personnel during the performance of their normal duties.

Tables 3-5 and 3-6 provide you with vital information on materials used in wire and insulation.

Chapter 4

Wire Specifications

A number of specifications are available for both military and commercial applications. The following tables, 4-1 through 4-3 list the most commonly used design specifications for military and Underwriters Laboratory (UL) materials. The specifications should be used as a guide when designing commercial equipment. Table 4-4 is provided to allow the designer to make comparisons of the available military wires during the selection process. Figures 4-1 through 4-14 define the MIL-W-16878D wire types most frequently used in military and heavy industrial electronic equipment by type and application.

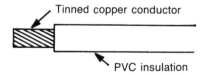

Fig. 4-1. Electronic hookup wire, MIL-W-16878D/1 TYPE BU.
Usage: For internal wiring of meters, panels, electrical and electronic equipment.

Table 4-1. Synopsis of Wire Specifications.

MIL-C-17C

This specification supersedes Jan-C-17A specification; however some types of cables listed in Jan-C-17A are not listed in the MIL-C-17C specification. The latter does cover flexible shielded cables, employing solid and semi-solid dielectrics, for use as radio-frequency transmission lines in radar and communications systems of the Armed Services. It covers coaxial, dual coaxial, twin conductor, and twin lead.

MIL-W-76B

This specification has been approved by the department of the Army, the Navy, and the Air Force. It covers synthetic-resin-insulated electrical hookup wire for use at temperatures up to approximately 80°C for internal wiring of electrical and electronic equipment. When a nylon jacket is used over the primary insulation, the temperature range for operation is increased to 90°C. However the wire covered by this specification is not intended for high-temperature applications. The voltage rating for this type wire ranges from 300 to 2500 volts.

NAS-702

This specification, issued by the National Aeronautical Standards Committee, covers insulated copper hook-up and general purpose wire suitable for use in temperatures ranging from −55°C to +105°C. Wire covered under this specification is divided into the following Types and Classes:

Type U	**Unshielded**	
	Class A	for 1000 volt general purpose service
	Class B	for 2500 volt general purpose service
	Class C	for 600 volt hook-up service
Type S	**Shielded**	
	Class A	for 1000 volt general purpose service
	Class B	for 2500 volt general purpose service
	Class C	for 600 volt general purpose service

NAS-703

This specification, issued by the National Aeronautical Standards Committee, covers Teflon* insulated, high temperature, copper hook-up wire. This wire is capable of operation at temperatures ranging from −65°C to +200°C, with operating voltages ranging from 600 to 1000 volts, in sizes from 32 gauge to 8 gauge.

MIL-C-3432A

This specification covers light-intermediate, medium, and heavy-duty flexible and extra-flexible, single-conductor and multiconductor cable, shielded and unshielded, for use in circuits of 300 and 600 volts (rms). It also covers heavy-duty, multiconductor, unshielded cable containing ground wires. The latter cable is limited to two, three, and four conductors, all of the conductors being of the same size, ranging from number 1 0 gauge to number 8 gauge inclusive. The operating temperature range for items covered by this specification is from −55°C to +75°C.

MIL-W-3795A

This specification covers uninsulated tinsel electrical wire used in the manufacture of tinsel electrical cord, where extreme flexibility is required.

MIL-W-3849

This specification covers tinsel cord of various constructions, suitable for use with telephones, switchboards, microphones, and associated equipment

under varying atmospheric conditions. The cord has a primary insulation of synthetic rubber, natural rubber, or thermoplastic, with an overall synthetic rubber, natural rubber, thermoplastic, or braided outer jacket. It is designed for an operating potential of 300 volts, over a temperature range of −40°C to +60°C.

MIL-W-3861

This specification covers solid, bunch-stranded, concentric-lay-stranded, and rope-lay-stranded round electrical wire fabricated from copper having a minimum purity of 99.900%, silver content being counted as copper.

MIL-W-5086A

This specification covers 600 volt, single-conductor, insulated copper wire for aircraft electrical use, that is capable of continuous operation at ambient temperatures ranging from −55°C (−67°F) to +105°C (+221°F). This general class of wire is further subdivided into three types:

Type I	Wire with stranded tinned-copper conductor, primary insulation, and extruded clear nylon outer covering.
Type II	Wire with stranded tinned-copper conductor, primary insulation, overall glass-fibre braid, with an extruded clear nylon outer jacket.
Type III	Wire with stranded tinned-copper conductor, primary insulation, overall glass-fibre braid, with an extruded secondary insulation, over which is extruded a clear nylon outer jacket.

MIL-T-5679A (ASG)

This specification covers thermocouple wires constructed of Iron and Constantan, Chromel and Alumel, Copper and Constantan. Also covered under this specification are the requirements outlining installation of these wires.

MIL-C-5756B

This specification covers single and multi-conductor portable power cords and cables for 600 volt heavy-duty, severe flexing service, having an outer jacket or cover of synthetic- or natural-rubber compounds. These cables are capable of operation over a temperature range of −55°C to +75°C, with 1 to 7 conductors ranging in size from number 18 gauge (AWG) to number 2 gauge (AWG).

MIL-W-5846B

This specification covers chromel and alumel thermocouple wire of the following Types and Classes:

Type I	**Solid and stranded conductor**	
	Class A	Bare solid conductor
	Class B	Insulated solid conductor
	Class C	Insulated duplex solid conductors
	Class D	Insulated stranded conductor
	Class E	Insulated duplex stranded conductors
Type II	**Insulated Duplex, stranded conductor, 7 ohms per 25 feet**	
	Class A	Standard insulation
Type III	**Insulated Duplex, stranded conductor, 7 ohms per 50 feet**	
	Class A	Standard insulation
Type IV	**Insulated Duplex, stranded conductor, 7 ohms per 100 feet**	
	Class A	Standard insulation

MIL-W-7072A

This specification covers low-tension, insulated, single-conductor, 600 volt, aluminum wire for aircraft electrical power distribution systems in sizes from 8 gauge to 4 0 gauge. It has a primary insulation of PVC thermoplastic and an outer jacket of glass or nylon braid that is nylon saturated, and will operate over a temperature range of −55 C to +80 C.

MIL-C-7078A

This specification covers shielded cable intended for installation on aircraft electrical systems where the potential does not exceed 600 volts (rms).
These electrical cables are divided into two types:

Type I   Consists of 1 to 7 color coded conductors in accordance with specification MIL-W-5086, with an overall shield.

Type II   Consists of 1 to 7 color coded conductors in accordance with MIL-W-5086, with an overall shield and from 4 to 6 thousandths of an inch nylon outer jacket.

MIL-W-7139A

This specification covers the requirements for 600 volt, single-conductor, insulated, copper wire to provide continuous operation at a total temperature up to +400°F, and to assure short-time emergency operation of electrical circuits in the event of fire. This wire comes in a size range of 22 gauge through 4/0 gauge, with a Teflon primary insulation and a saturated braid outer jacket, sufficient to sustain continuous operation from −55°C to +205°C.

MIL-W-8777A (ASG) (USAF)

Covered in this specification is aircraft wire with an operating temperature range from −55°C to +150°C at 600 volts. Primary insulation calls for silicon rubber and for an outer braid or protective cover. It is resistant to flame, fuels, abrasion, fungus, and solvents.

MIL-W-16878D

This specification covers wire designed for the internal wiring of meters, panels, electrical and electronic equipment to have a minimum size and weight consistant with maximum service requirements. The temperature rating of wire included under this specification ranges from −54 C (−67 F) to +200°C (+392 F) operational, with potential ratings from 75 to 3000 volts (rms). The wire is of the following types and ratings for continuous operation.

Type B	105°C maximum, 600 volts
Type C	105°C maximum, 1000 volts
Type D	105°C maximum, 3000 volts
Type E	200°C maximum, 600 volts
Type EE	200 C maximum, 1000 volts
Type ET	260°C maximum, 250 volts
Type F	200 C maximum, 600 volts
Type FF	200 C maximum, 1000 volts
Type FFW	200 C maximum, 1000 volts
Type J	75°C maximum, 600 volts
Type K	200 C maximum, 600 volts
Type KK	200 C maximum, 1000 volts
Type KT	200 C maximum, 250 volts

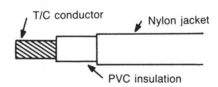

Fig. 4-2. Electronic hookup wire, MIL-W-16878D/1 TYPE BN.
Usage: For internal wiring of meters, panels, electrical and electronic equipment.

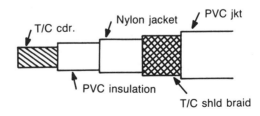

Fig. 4-3. Electronic hookup wire, MIL-W-16878D/1 TYPE BN. One conductor shielded and jacketed.
Usage: For internal wiring of meters, panels, electrical and electronic equipment.

Table 4-2. Synopsis of U.L and C.S.A. Electronic Hookup Wires and Control Cables.

UNDERWRITERS APPLIANCE WIRING MATERIAL (AWMI) HOOKUP WIRES

U.L. Style Number		UL Rating		Insulation Type	Size range (AWG)	Usage
		Voltage	Temp. °C.			
1004	✓	none	80.	.008" PVC + nylon	26 – 16	General purpose appliance wiring
1005	✓	none	90.	.008" PVC + nylon	26 – 16	
1006	✓	none	105.	.008" PVC + nylon	26 – 16	
1504	✓	none	105.	1/64" PVC	26 – 16	600 volt rating for electronic use. Rated 300. volts for appliance usage.
1007	✓	300	80.	1/64" PVC	32 – 16	
1569	✓	300	105.	1/64" PVC	30 – 16	
1008	✓	300	80.	1/64" PVC + nylon	28 – 16	Rated 600. volts for general appliance use, 2500. volts for electronic use.
1009	✓	300	90.	1/64" PVC + nylon	28 – 16	
1010	✓	300	105.	1/64" PVC + nylon	28 – 16	
1011	✓	600	80.	1/32" PVC	28 – 9	
1013	✓	600	90.	1/32" PVC	28 – 9	
1015	✓	600	105.	1/32" PVC	28 – 9	
1012	✓	600	80.	1/32" PVC + nylon	26 – 9	General purpose appliance wiring 2500. volt electronic use
1014	✓	600	90.	1/32" PVC + nylon	26 – 9	
1016	✓	600	105.	1/32" PVC + nylon	26 – 9	
1061	✓	300	80.	.009" PVC (semi-rigid)	30 – 16	Business machine & electronic equipment
1354	✓	30	60.	.007" – .100" P.E.	30 AWG Min.	Coaxial cable
1434	✓	30	60.	.009" – .012" F.R.P.E.	30 – 20	Flame retardant Coaxial cable

(✓) Indicates that National Wire & Cable Corp. is a UL listed manufacturer.

CANADIAN STANDARDS ASSOCIATION
APPROVED HOOKUP WIRES

CSA Type		CSA RATINGS		Insulation Type	Size Range (AWG)	Usage
		Voltage	Temp.			
TR-64 Radio wire	✓	300	90.	1/64" PVC	24 – 16	General Radio & electronic usage. Wires having both CSA and U.L. approval are available.
TR-32 Radio wire and AWM	✓	600	90.	1/32" PVC	24 – 10	

UNDERWRITERS-APPROVED MULTI-CONDUCTOR
BUSINESS MACHINE & COMPUTER CONTROL CABLES

U.L. Style Number		UL Rating		Wire Type	Size Range (AWG)	Construction
		Voltage	Temp.			
2343	✓	Same as Wire	80.C	Any AWM	26 ga. min.	Multiconductor jacketed cable shield optional, body O.D. up to .700'' - .060'' wall PVC.
2344	✓	Same as Wire	80.C	Any AWM	26 ga. min.	Multiconductor jacketed cable shield optional, body O.D. .701'' - 1.500'' wall PVC
2384	✓	30 Volt	60.C	Any AWM	30 ga. min.	Multiconductor low voltage cable, shield optional, body to .425'' jacket wall .035'' PVC.
2385	✓	30 Volt	60.C	Any AWM	30 ga. min.	Multiconductor low voltage cable, shield optional, body O.D. .425'' - .700'' - .060'' wall PVC
2386	✓	30 Volt	60.C	Any AWM	30 ga. min.	Multiconductor low voltage cable, shield optional, body O.D. .701'' - 1.500'' - .080'' wall PVC.
2387	✓	30 Volt	60.C	Any AWM	30 ga. min.	Multiconductor low voltage cable, shield optional, body O.D. 1.501'' - 2.500'' .110 wall PVC.
2388	✓	30 Volt	60.C	Any AWM	30 ga. min.	Multiconductor low voltage cable, shield optional, body O.D. 2.501'' and larger .140 wall PVC.
2464	✓	300 Volts	80.C	Any AWM 80.C or Better	30 – 16 ga.	Multiconductor jacketed cable, shield optional, cable bodies less than .700'' - .031'' wall PVC .701'' - 1.500'' - .080'' wall PVC.

Table 4-3. Military and Government Wire Specifications. (Continued on Page 65.)

J-C-90—Flexible cord and fixture wire.

J-C-95—Neoprene jacketed telephone wire.

J-C-580—Flexible cord and fixture wire.

J-C-741—Rubber and/or neoprene welding cable.

MIL-C-17—Coaxial cable—polyethylene and teflon dielectric.

MIL-C-442—Rubber jacketed two conductor parallel rip cord.

MIL-C-915, MIL-C-2194—Shipboard cable. Produce only types covered in supplementary specifications BuShips 660-L.

MIL-C-1486—10 conductor WM-46/U only.

MIL-C-3078—Cable, electric, insulated, low tension, single conductor.

MIL-C-3432—300 volt and 600 volt rubber insulated power and control cable.

MIL-C-3458—Cables, telephone.

MIL-C-3702—Cable, power electrical, ignition, high tension.

MIL-C-3849—Tinsel cord. Light duty low voltage flexible cord for switchboards, microphones, telephones, etc.

MIL-C-3883—Cord electrical (audio frequency),

MIL-C-3884—Conductor electrical (short lay).

MIL-C-4921A (ASG)—Single conductor 8-AWG 5,000 volt cable with butyl compound insulation and polychloroprene. For airport lighting.

MIL-C-5136—Cable, power, electrical, polychloropene sheathed, buna compound insulated.

MIL-C-5756—Low temperature rubber portable cords.

MIL-C-6166—Cord, headset-microphone CX1301/AR.

MIL-C-7078—600 volt aircraft wire using MIL-W-5086 components.

MIL-C-8554 (ASG)—Cable, ignition, high tension, aircraft quality.

MIL-C-8817 (ASG)—Cable, ignition, high tension, aircraft quality.

MIL-C-10065—Cables, special purpose electrical (multi-pair audio frequency).

MIL-C-10369—Cable, telephone field, for rapid payout.

MIL-C-10392—Cables, special purpose, electric (miniature).

MIL-C-10581—Cables, telephone, cable assemblies, telephone, coil assembly, telephone loading.

MIL-C-11060—Cables, twisted pair, internal hook-up, unshielded and shielded.

MIL-C-11097—Cable, telephone, (Wire W-50-A).

MIL-C-11440—Cable, power electrical.

MIL-C-12064—Low temperature power cable and cords for Arctic service.

MIL-C-12423—Cable, telephone WD-33U.

MIL-C-12881—Cables, telephone, switchboard (cables and cable assemblies).

MIL-C-12992—Cable assembly, power, electrical (Cord CX-227 TVQ-1).

MIL-C-13066—Cable, telephone (submarine No. 19 AWG and No. 22 AWG).

MIL-C-13077—Cable, special purpose, electrical.

MIL-C-13294—Cable, telephone, electrical (infantry field wire) twisted pair, Wire WD-1 TT and WD-14 TT.

MIL-C-13777—Multi-conductor missile ground support cable.

MIL-C-13892—Cable, telephone (flexible).

MIL-C-14189—Cable, power electrical, 3000 volt, for field use.

MIL-C-15325—Cable, tow, electric (three conductor).

MIL-C-15479—Cables, power, electrical, submarine, Navy Standard Harbor Defense.

MIL-C-18959—Cable, power, electrical, portable, neoprene jacketed 600 volt.

MIL-C-18961—Cable, special purpose, electrical and wire, electrical, shot firing.

MIL-C-18962—Cable, power, electrical, direct burial, neoprene jacketed 600 volt.

MIL-C-19381 (Ships)—Cables, special purpose. Electrical (nuclear plant).

MIL-C-19547—Cables, electrical, special purpose, shore use.

MIL-C-19638—Cables, power electric, submarine. Navy Harbor Defense.

MIL-C-19654—Cable, telephone, submarine.

MIL-C-19787—Cable, electric, torpedo, 65 conductor (torpedo control, electric setting).

MIL-C-19883—Cables, special purpose, electric, for remote control radar set AN/FPN-28.

MIL-C-21609—Cable, electrical, shield, 600 volt (non-flexing service).

MIL-C-22667—Cable, special purpose, buoyant, electrical (submarine use).

MIL-C-23020—Coxial cable for use inside submarines (water-blocked).

MIL-C-23206—Cable, special purpose electrical. Silicone rubber, water blocked.

MIL-C-23437—Cable, electrical, shielded pairs.

MIL-C-24145—(Ships) Cable, electrical special purpose for standard use (water blocked and and non-water blocked). Formerly BuShip 660-L.

MIL-C-25038—Nickel clad conductors, max. temp. 750°.

MIL-C-26468 (USAF)—Cables, guided missiles, ground installation, general requirements for.

MIL-C-27072—Multi-conductor ground support cable.

MIL-C-27212—Cable, power, electrical, airport lighting control.

MIL-C-27500—Shielded and unshielded aircraft and missile cables.

MIL-C-38359 (USAF)—Power cable of two voltage range for airport lighting 8AWG (3,000-5,000V) CCLP insulated.

MIL-C-55021—Cables, twisted pairs and triples, internal hook-up, shielded and unshielded.

MIL-C-55036—Cable, telephone, WM130##/6.

MIL-E-9085 (USAF)—Electrical cord—WM-85/u.

MIL-E-9088 (USAF)—Electrical cord—WF-14/u.

MIL-R-8333 (USAF)—RF cable—RG12/u.

MIL-STD-122—Color code for chassis wiring for electronic equipment.

MIL-STD-681—Identification coding and application of hook-up wire.

MIL-W-76—General purpose hook-up wire. Vinyl insulated types LW, MW and HW.

MIL-W-438—Wire, ignition, electric power.

MIL-C-442—Thermoplastic or rubber jacketed two conductor parallel rip cord.

MIL-W-538—Wire, magnet, electrical.

MIL-W-3093—Wire, insulated. W-121, W-122, W-123, WD15/u, WD-16, WF-9/u, WT-3/u, (distributing, frame wires).

MIL-W-3104—Wire, insulated (No. 20AWG—extra flexible).

MIL-W-3795—Wire, electrical (tinsel).

MIL-W-3861—Wire, electrical (bare copper).

MIL-W-5086—600 volt aircraft wire (copper conductors).

MIL-W-5274—Spec for aircraft wire. Type I 600V, Type II 600V, Type III 300 rating.

MIL-W-5845—Wire, electrical, iron and constantan thermocouple.

MIL-W-5846—Wire, electrical, chromel and or alumel, thermocouple.

MIL-W-5908—Wire, electrical, copper and constantan, thermocouple.

MIL-W-6370—Wire, electrical, insulated antenna.

MIL-W-7072—600 volt aircraft wire (aluminum conductors).

MIL-W-7139—TFE (Teflon) wire for aircraft.

MIL-W-7500—Wire, electrical, WS-31-U.

MIL-W-8777—600 volt silicone rubber insulated aircraft wire.

MIL-W-12995—Wire electrical (W-29 and W-120).

MIL-W-13074—Wire, electrical (W-27 and WS-19[u]).

MIL-W-13075—Wire, electrical.

MIL-W-13169—Wire, electrical (for instrument test leads).

MIL-W-13241—Wire, electrical.

MIL-W-16878—Electronic hook-up wire. Includes vinyl (Types B, C, and D). Teflon (Types ET, E, EE, KT, K and KK) and polyethylene (Type J).

MIL-W-17211 (Ships)—Wire, electrical, radio antenna 7/12, 7/14, 7/16, 7/18, 7/20, 7/22.

MIL-W-19150—Wire, insulated, hard drawn copper.

MIL-W-19583 (Navy)—Wire, electrical, magnet, high temperature, film insulated.

MIL-W-21306—Wire, electrical, twisted pair, color coded switchboard.

MIL-W-22759—Teflon* aircraft and hook-up wire to meet design sheets MS-21985, MS-21986, MS-18000, MS-18001, MS-17411, and MS-17412.

MIL-W-25038—Wire, electrical, high temperature and fire resistant aircraft.

MIL-W-—27300—Teflon insulated 600 volt aircraft wire.

MIL-W-81044—Irradiated wire for aircraft and hook-up. (Polyaprene and polyvinylidene fluoride, Kynar**.

MIL-W-81381—Wire, electrical polyimide insulated copper and copper alloy (Kapton*, H-film).

**Pennsalt Chemicals registered trademark
*Du Pont registered trademark

Table 4-4. Comparison of MIL Spec Wires.

Specification	Operating Temp.	Operating Voltage	AWG Size Range	Conductor Material	Primary Insulation	Secondary Insulation	Jacket	Dielectric Strength Min. kV.	
MIL-W 5086C I II III	−55°C +105°C	600	22-4/0	T.C.	P.V.C. P.V.C. P.V.C.	None Glass Glass-P.V.C.	Nylon Nylon Nylon	1.5	Supersedes ANJC-48A
MIL-W 7139B I II	−64°C+200°C −64°C+260°C	600	22-4/0	S.P.C. N.P.C.	TFE Film Glass Tape		Glass Braid TFE Enamel	1.5	
MIL-W 8777C MS 25471	−55°C +200°C	600	22-2/0	S.P.C.	Silicone Rubber	Lacquered Synth. Fiber	WHEN SPECIFIED FEP	1.5	
MIL-W 25038D M25038/1	−65°F +750°F (2000°F)✱	600	20-4/0	N.C.C.	TFE & Asbestos		Silicone or TFE Enameled Glass Braid	1.5	
MIL-W16878D Type B MIL-W16878/1	−54°C +105°C	600	32-14	T.C.	P.V.C.		AS SPECIFIED	2.0	
Type C MIL-W 16878/2	−54°C +105°C	1000	26-12	T.C.	P.V.C.		AS SPECIFIED	3.0	
Type D MIL-W 16878/3	−54°C +105°C	3000	24-1/0	T.C.	P.V.C.		AS SPECIFIED	6.0	
Type E MIL-W 16878/4	−65°C+200°C −65°C+260°C	600	32-10	S.P.C. N.P.C.	TFE		AS ■ SPECIFIED	2.2	
Type EE MIL-W 16878/5	−65°C+200°C −65°C+260°C	1000	32-8	S.P.C. N.P.C.	TFE		AS ■ SPECIFIED	3.0	
Type ET MIL-W 16878/6	−65°C+200°C −65°C+260°C	250	32-20	S.P.C. N.P.C.	TFE		AS ■ SPECIFIED	1.5	
Type F MIL-W 16878/7	−54°C +200°C	600	24-12	T.C. S.P.C. N.P.C.	Silicone Rubber		AS SPECIFIED Glass Braid ■ Recommended	2.2	
Type FF MIL-W 16878/8	−54°C +200°C	1000	24-4/0	T.C. S.P.C. N.P.C.	Silicone Rubber		AS SPECIFIED Glass Braid ■ Recommended	3.0	

Table 4-4. Comparison of MIL Spec Wires. (Cont.)

Specification	Operating Temp.	Operating Voltage	AWG Size Range	Conductor Material	Primary Insulation	Secondary Insulation	Jacket	Dielectric Strength Min. kV.	
MIL-W 22759A MS21986	−65°C +260°C	600	28-16	N.P.C.	TFE		None	2.2	
MIL-W 22759A MS90294	−65°C +200°C	600	22-2/0	S.P.C.	TFE Tape and/ or TFE Coated Glass Tape	TFE Coated Glass Braid	FEP	2.5	
MIL-W-22759 D M22759/1	−65°C +200°C	600	22-4/0	S.P.C.	TFE or TFE Tape	TFE Coated Glass Tape	TFE Coated Glass Braid	2.5	Supersedes Mil-W-7139B Class I
MIL-W-22759 D M22759/2	−65°C +260°C	600	22-4/0	N.P.C.	TFE or TFE Tape	TFE Coated Glass Tape	TFE Coated Glass Braid	2.5	Supersedes Mil-W-7139B Class II
MIL-W-22759 D M22759/3	−65°C +260°C	600	22-2/0	N.P.C.	TFE Tape and/ or TFE Coated Glass Tape	TFE Coated Glass Braid	TFE Tape	2.5	
MIL-W-22759 D M22759/4	−65°C +200°C	600	22-2/0	S.P.C.	TFE Tape and/ or TFE Coated Glass Tape	TFE Coated Glass Braid	FEP	2.5	Supersedes MS90294
MIL-W-22759 D M22759/5	−65°C +200°C	600	24-4	S.P.C.	TFE Mineral Filled		None	2.5	Supersedes MS17411
MIL-W-22759 D M22759/6	−65°C +260°C	600	24-4	N.P.C.	TFE Mineral Filled		None	2.5	Supersedes MS17412
MIL-W-22759 D M22759/7	−65°C +200°C	600	24-4	S.P.C.	TFE Mineral Filled		None	2.5	Supersedes MS18000
MIL-W-22759 D M22759/8	−65°C +260°C	600	24-4	N.P.C.	TFE Mineral Filled		None	2.5	Supersedes MS18001
MIL-W-22759 D M22759/9	−65°C +200°C	1000	28-8	S.P.C.	TFE		None	3.0	Supersedes MS18113
MIL-W-22759 D M22759/10	−65°C +260°C	1000	28-8	N.P.C.	TFE		None	3.0	Supersedes MS18114
MIL-W-22759 D M22759/11	−65°C +200°C	600	28-16	S.P.C.	TFE		None	2.2	Supersedes MS21985
MIL-W-22759 D M22759/12	−65°C +260°C	600	28-16	N.P.C.	TFE		None	2.2	Supersedes MS21986

Specification	Operating Temp.	Operating Voltage	AWG Size Range	Conductor Material	Primary Insulation	Secondary Insulation	Jacket	Dielectric Strength Min. kV.
MIL-W 22759A MS17331	−65°C +200°C	600	22-8	S.P.C.	TFE	TFE Impregnated Asbestos	None	2.5
MIL-W 22759A MS17332	−65°C +260°C	600	22-8	N.P.C.	TFE	TFE Impregnated Asbestos	None	2.5
MIL-W 22759A MS17410	−65°C +200°C	600	22-2/0	S.P.C.	TFE	TFE Coated Glass Braid	FEP	2.2
MIL-W 22759A MS17411	−65°C +200°C	600	24-4	S.P.C.	TFE Mineral Filled		None	2.5
MIL-W 22759A MS17412	−65°C +260°C	600	24-4	N.P.C.	TFE Mineral Filled		None	2.5
MIL-W 22759A MS18000	−65°C +200°C	600	24-4	S.P.C.	TFE Mineral Filled		None	2.5
MIL-W 22759A MS18001	−65°C +260°C	600	24-4	N.P.C.	TFE Mineral Filled		None	2.5
MIL-W 22759A MS18032	−65°C +200°C	600	30-2	S.P.C.	Laminated TFE		None	2.5
MIL-W 22759A MS18033	−65°C +260°C	600	30-2	N.P.C.	Laminated TFE		None	2.5
MIL-W 22759A MS18104	−65°C +200°C	600	28-12	S.P.C.	TFE		Polyimide	3.0
MIL-W 22759A MS18105	−65°C +260°C	600	28-12	N.P.C.	TFE		Polyimide	3.0
MIL-W 22759A MS18113	−65°C +200°C	1000	28-8	S.P.C.	TFE		None	3.0
MIL-W 22759A MS18114	−65°C +260°C	1000	28-8	N.P.C.	TFE		None	3.0
MIL-W 22759A MS21985	−65°C +200°C	600	28-16	S.P.C.	TFE		None	2.2

Table 4-4. Comparison of MIL Spec Wires. (Cont.)

Specification	Operating Temp.	Operating Voltage	AWG Size Range	Conductor Material	Primary Insulation	Secondary Insulation	Jacket	Dielectric Strength Min. kV.
MIL-W-22759D M22759/16	−65°C +150°C	600	24-2/0	T.C.	ETFE		None	2.2
MIL-W-22759D M22759/17	−65°C +150°C	600	26-20	S.P.C. Alloy	ETFE		None	2.2
MIL-W-22759D M22759/18	−65°C +150°C	600	26-10	T.C.	ETFE		None	2.0
MIL-W-22759D M22759/19	−65°C +150°C	600	26-20	S.P.C. Alloy	ETFE		None	2.0
MIL-W-22759D M22759/20	−65°C +200°C	1000	28-20	S.P.C. Alloy	TFE		None	3.0
MIL-W-22759D M22759/21	−65°C +200°C	1000	28-20	N.P.C. Alloy	TFE		None	3.0
MIL-W-22759D M22759/22	−65°C +200°C	600	28-20	S.P.C. Alloy	TFE		None	2.2
MIL-W-22759D M22759/23	−65°C +260°C	600	28-20	N.P.C. Alloy	TFE		None	2.2
MIL-W-22759D M22759/24	−65°C +150°C	600	24-2/0	T.C.	ECTFE		None	2.2
MIL-W-22759D M22759/25	−65°C +150°C	600	26-20	S.P.C. Alloy	ECTFE		None	2.2
MIL-W-22759D M22759/26	−65°C +150°C	600	26-10	T.C.	ECTFE		None	2.0
MIL-W-22759D M22759/27	−65°C +150°C	600	26-20	S.P.C. Alloy	ECTFE		None	2.0
MIL-W-22759D M22759/28	−65°C +200°C	600	28-8	S.P.C.	TFE	Polymide	None	2.2
MIL-W-22759D M22759/29	−65°C +260°C	600	28-8	N.P.C.	TFE	Polymide	None	2.2

70

Specification	Operating Temp.	Operating Voltage	AWG Size Range	Conductor Material	Primary Insulation	Secondary Insulation	Jacket	Dielectric Strength Min. kV.
MIL-W-22759D M22759/30	−65°C +200°C	600	28-20	S.P.C. Alloy	TFE	Polymide	None	2.2
MIL-W-22759D M22759/31	−65°C +260°C	600	28-20	N.P.C. Alloy	TFE	Polymide	None	2.2
MIL-W-22759D M22759/32	−65°C +150°C	600	30-12	T.C.	XETFE		None	2.5
MIL-W-22759D M22759/33	−65°C +150°C	600	30-20	S.P.C. Alloy	XETFE		None	2.5
MIL-W-22759 M22759/34	−65°C +150°C	600	24-2/0	T.C.	XETFE	XETFE	None	2.5
MIL-W-22759 M22759/35	−65°C +150°C	600	26-20	S.P.C. Alloy	XETFE	XETFE	None	2.5
MIL-W-22759 M22759/36	−65°C +135°C	600	26-12	T.C.	XLPA		ECTFE	2.5
MIL-W-22759 M22759/37	−65°C +150°C	600	24-12	T.C.	XLPA		ECTFE	2.5
MIL-W-22759 M22759/38	−65°C +135°C	600	26-20	S.P.C. Alloy	XLPA		ECTFE	2.5
MIL-W-22759D M22759/39	−65°C +135°C	600	26-10	T.C.	XLPA		ECTFE	2.5
MIL-W-22759 M22759/40	−65°C +135°C	600	26-20	S.P.C. Alloy	XLPA		ECTFE	2.5
MIL-W-22759 M22759/41	−65°C +200°C	600	26-10	N.P.C.	XETFE	XETFE	None	2.5
MIL-W-22759 M22759/42	−65°C +200°C	600	26-20	N.P.C. Alloy	XETFE	XETFE	None	2.5
MIL-W-27300A MS24284	−65°C +260°C	600	26-16 14-12	N.P.C.	TFE		None	2.5 2.0

Table 4-4. Comparison of MIL Spec Wires. (Cont.)

Specification	Operating Temp.	Operating Voltage	AWG Size Range	Conductor Material	Primary Insulation	Secondary Insulation	Jacket	Dielectric Strength Min. kV.
M81044/1	−65°C +135°C	600	24-4	S.P.C.	XLPA		XLPVF	2.5
M81044/2	−65°C +135°C	600	24-4	T.C.	XLPA		XLPVF	2.5
M81044/3	−65°C +135°C	600	30-12	S.P.C.	XLPA		XLPVF	2.5
M81044/4	−65°C +135°C	600	30-12	T.C.	XLPA		XLPVF	2.5
M81044/5	−65°C +150°C	600	24-1/0	S.P.C.	XLPA		XLPVF	2.5
M81044/6	−65°C +150°C	600	24-1/0	T.C.	XLPA		XLPVF	2.5
M81044/7	−65°C +150°C	600	26-20	S.P.C. Alloy	XLPA		XLPVF	2.5
M81044/8	−65°C +150°C	600	24-1/0	S.P.C.	XLPA		XLPVF	2.5
M81044/9	−65°C +150°C	600	24-1/0	T.C.	XLPA		XLPVF	2.5
M81044/10	−65°C +150°C	600	26-20	S.P.C. Alloy	XLPA		XLPVF	2.5
M81044/11	−65°C +150°C	600	30-12	S.P.C.	XLPA		XLPVF	2.5
M81044/12	−65°C +150°C	600	30-12	T.C.	XLPA		XLPVF	2.5
M81044/13	−65°C +150°C	600	30-20	S.P.C. Alloy	XLPA		XLPVF	2.5

Specification	Operating Temp.	Operating Voltage	AWG Size Range	Conductor Material	Primary Insulation	Secondary Insulation	Jacket	Dielectric Strength Min. kV.
M81044/14	−65°C +135°C	600	24-1/0	T.C.	XLPA		XLPVF	2.5
M81044/15	−65°C +135°C	600	26-20	S.P.C.	XLPA		XLPVF	2.5
M81044/16	−65°C +150°C	600	24-2/0	T.C.	XLAP	XLAP	MIP	2.5
M81044/17	−65°C +150°C	600	26-20	S.P.C. Alloy	XLAP	XLAP	MIP	2.5
M81044/18	−65°C +150°C	600	30-12	T.C.	XLAP	XLAP	MIP	2.5
M81044/19	−65°C +150°C	600	30-20	S.P.C. Alloy	XLAP		MIP	2.5
M81044/20	−65°C +150°C	600	26-8	T.C.	Polyarylene	Polyarylene	None	2.5
M18044/21	−65°C +200°C	600	26-8	S.P.C.	Polyarylene	Polyarylene	None	2.5
M81044/22	−65°C +200°C	600	30-20	S.P.C. Alloy	Polyarylene	Polyarylene	None	2.5
M81044/23	−65°C +260°C	600	26-8	N.P.C.	Polyarylene	Polyarylene	None	2.5
M81044/24	−65°C +260°C	600	30-20	N.P.C. Alloy	Polyarylene	Polyarylene	None	2.5
M81044/25	−65°C +150°C	600	30-12	T.C.	Polyarylene		None	2.5
M81044/26	−65°C +200°C	600	30-12	S.P.C.	Polyarylene		None	2.5

Table 4-4. Comparison of MIL Spec Wires. (Cont.)

Specification	Operating Temp.	Operating Voltage	AWG Size Range	Conductor Material	Primary Insulation	Secondary Insulation	Jacket	Dielectric Strength Min. KV.
MIL-W-81381/1	−65°C +200°C	600	26-10	S.P.C.	Fl Pol Tape		FEP Dispersion	2.5
MIL-W-81381/2	−65°C +200°C	600	26-10	N.P.C.	Fl Pol Tape		FEP Dispersion	2.5
MIL-W-81381/3	−65°C +200°C	600	26-2	S.P.C.	Fl Pol Tape		FEP Dispersion ■ or TFE Tape	2.5
MIL-W-81381/4	−65°C +200°C	600	26-2	N.P.C.	Fl Pol Tape		FEP Dispersion ■ or TFE Tape	2.5
MIL-W-81381/5	−65°C +200°C	600	26-20	S.P.C. Alloy	Fl Pol Tape		FEP Dispersion	2.5
MIL-W-81381/6	−65°C +200°C	600	26-20	N.P.C. Alloy	Fl Pol Tape		FEP Dispersion	2.5
MIL-W-81381/7	−65°C +200°C	600	26-10	S.P.C.	Fl Pol Tape		FEP Dispersion	2.5
MIL-W-81381/8	−65° +200°C	600	26-10	N.P.C.	Fl Pol Tape		FEP Dispersion	2.5
MIL-W-81381/9	−65°C +200°C	600	26-20	S.P.C. Alloy	Fl Pol Tape		FEP Dispersion	2.5
MIL-W-81381/10	−65°C +200°C	600	26-20	N.P.C. Alloy	Fl Pol Tape		FEP Dispersion	2.5
MIL-W-81381/11	−65°C +200°C	600	24-2	S.P.C.	Fl Pol Tape		AromPolyimide ■ or TFE Tape	2.5
MIL-W-81381/12	−65°C +200°C	600	24-2	N.P.C.	Fl Pol Tape		AromPolyimide ■ or TFE Tape	2.5
MIL-W-81381/13	−65°C +200°C	600	26-20	S.P.C. Alloy	Fl Pol Tape		Aromatic Polyimide	2.5

Specification	Operating Temp.	Operating Voltage	AWG Size Range	Conductor Material	Primary Insulation	Secondary Insulation	Jacket	Dielectric Strength Min. kV.
MIL-W-81381/14	−65°C +200°C	600	26-20	N.P.C. Alloy	FI Pol Tape		Aromatic Polyimide	2.5
MIL-W-81381/15		CANCELLED						
MIL-W-81381/16		CANCELLED						
MIL-W-81381/17	−65°C +200°C	600	26-12	S.P.C.	FI Pol Tape		Aromatic Polyimide	2.5
MIL-W-81381/18	−65°C +200°C	600	26-12	N.P.C.	FI Pol Tape		Aromatic Polyimide	2.5
MIL-W-81381/19	−65°C +200°C	600	30-20	S.P.C. Alloy	FI Pol Tape		Aromatic Polyimide	2.5
MIL-W-81381/20	−65°C +200°C	600	30-20	N.P.C. Alloy	FI Pol Tape		Aromatic Polyimide	2.5
MIL-W-81381/21	−65°C +150°C	600	26-10	T.C.	FI Pol Tape	FI Pol Tape	Aromatic Polyimide	2.5
MIL-W-81381/22	−65°C +150°C	600	24-2/0	T.C.	FI Pol Tape	FI Pol Tape	Aromatic Polyimide Resin or Braid	2.5

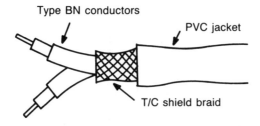

Fig. 4-4. Miniature electronic cable, MIL-W-16878D/1 TYPE BN. One conductor shielded and jacketed.
Usage: For internal wiring of meters, panels, electrical and electronic equipment.

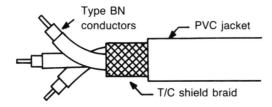

Fig. 4-5. Miniature electronic cable, MIL-W-16878D/1 TYPE BN. Three conductor shielded and jacketed.
Usage: For internal wiring of meters, panels, electrical and electronic equipment.

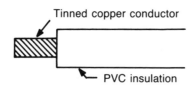

Fig. 4-6. Electronic hookup wire, MIL-W-16878D/2 Type CU.
Usage: For internal wiring of meters, panels, electrical and electronic equipment.

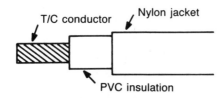

Fig. 4-7. Electronic hookup wire, MIL-W-16878D/2 Type CN.
Usage: For internal wiring of meters, panels, electrical and electronic equipment.

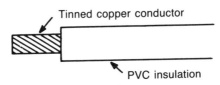

Fig. 4-8. Electronic hookup wire, MIL-W-16878D/3 Type DU.
Usage: For internal wiring of meters, panels, electrical and electronic equipment.

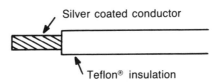

Fig. 4-9. Electronic hookup wire, high temperature, MIL-W-16878D/4 Type E.
Usage: For internal wiring of meters, panels, electrical and electronic equipment.

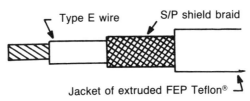

Fig. 4-10. Miniature electronic cables, high temperature, MIL-W-16878D/4 Type E. One conductor shielded and jacketed.
Usage: For internal wiring of meters, panels, electrical and electronic equipment.

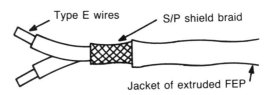

Fig. 4-11. Miniature electronic cables, high temperature, MIL-W-16878D/4 Type E. Two conductor shielded and jacketed.
Usage: For internal wiring of meters, panels, electrical and electronic equipment.

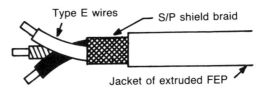

Fig. 4-12. Miniature electronic cables, high temperature, MIL-W-16878D/4 Type E. Three conductor shielded and jacketed.
Usage: For internal wiring of meters, panels, electrical and electronic equipment.

Silver coated conductor

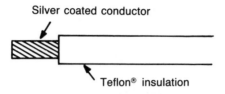

Teflon® insulation

Fig. 4-13. Electronic hookup wire, high temperature, MIL-W-16878D/5 Type EE.
Usage: For internal wiring of meters, panels, electrical and electronic equipment.

Silver coated conductor

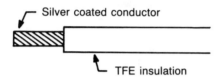

TFE insulation

Fig. 4-14. Electronic hookup wire, high temperature, MIL-W-16878D/6 Type ET.
Usage: For internal wiring of meters, panels, electrical and electronic equipment.

Chapter 5

Manufacturing Procedures

Manufacturing of wiring and cable assemblies that will withstand severe operating environments and facilitate producibility and servicibility requires that proper procedures be implemented and followed throughout the entire manufacturing cycle. The basic steps of wiring are the same for a single unit as for a composite of subassemblies. The manufacturing operations required include wire routing and dressing, harnessing and cabling, and the preparation of the wires for termination. Today many organizations require a training program for assembly personnel prior to assigning them to the manufacturing staff.

GENERAL

All insulated wiring should be supported and laced into a cable, except where the resulting cable would be excessively large and would interfere with the operation and maintenance of the equipment.

The primary purpose of lacing a cable is to keep the wires in position while the cable is being handled during installation, and during subsequent normal service. The use of individual spot ties or lockstitch in electronic equipment is mandatory. The running stitch is used only when it is specified by the user since the entire cable could become loose during servicing of the equipment.

Improper placing or dressing of cable or wires may result in serious operating difficulties such as spurious oscillation, restriction of mechanical operation, etc. Frayed, burned, or pinched insulation could cause shorting or current leakage that could seriously interfere with the performance of the equipment.

Improper terminations often result in loose connections due to metal fatigue. Good workmanship requires that all of the above defects be carefully avoided.

ROUTING AND DRESSING

Routing is the layout of the wiring to achieve the most efficient and direct order throughout the assembly. Dressing is the arrangement of wiring to secure a neat and orderly appearance, and to insure that proper access is provided for servicing at a later date.

Due to the competitive nature of the commercial market, the old methods of point-to-point wiring are no longer acceptable. Commercial products now employ military methods as a guideline for manufacturing. The wires are installed either parallel or at right-angles to each other so a neat and orderly appearance is achieved. This method also reduces cost in assembly and servicing since the assembly is more easily inspected and traced in any rework situations.

The manner of routing and dressing the wiring of an assembly is determined by the nature of each circuit, planned service life, and cost. The proper routing and dressing of an assembly should accomplish the following:

All wiring and cabling should be neat, sturdy, and should take the shortest practical route. It must permit easy inspection and testing of the completed unit, and should be arranged to prevent any damage to the assembled parts by any additional manufacturing operations. Wiring and cabling should not be installed where it may interfere with the normal operating and servicing of the unit. As an example, the wires or cables should never cross over an access hole provided for adjustments. Care should also be taken to insure that wiring or cabling does not cross over any openings required for cooling air. Clearance for moving mechanical parts must be provided.

All wiring and cabling must be positioned to prevent or minimize the inductive and capacitive effects, and should be firmly supported to prevent any strain on the conductor or terminals and to eliminate potential changes in performance due to shifting.

To prevent the deterioration of the wire insulation, care must be taken to provide sufficient clearance between the conductors and the heat generating components as shown in Fig. 5-1. The rout-

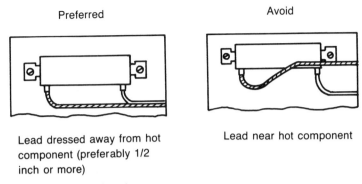

Preferred

Avoid

Lead dressed away from hot component (preferably 1/2 inch or more)

Lead near hot component

Fig. 5-1. Dressing of leads.

ing of all wires and cables should insure that they do not pass over any sharp edges, such as screws, nuts, lugs or terminals and they should not be routed or bent over sharp details that could cause abrasions under normal operating conditions. Grommets and cable shields should be installed at any sharp edges to prevent abraiding the insulation. When it is necessary to pass wires or cables through holes in a metal chassis, they should be protected by the installation of a grommet. See Figs. 5-2 & 5-3. Where the wires or cables are passing through a metal part that is at least 1/8 inch thick the sharp edges may be rounded to a radius of 1/2 the total metal thickness. Synthetic rubber tapes should not be used to protect wires. A fiberglass or high-temperature vinyl sleeving is recommended.

All wiring should be preformed in the proper sequence. Select

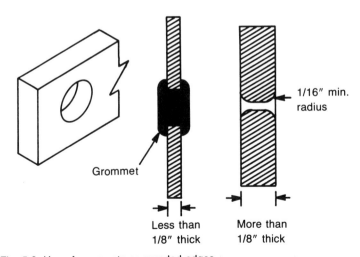

1/16″ min. radius

Grommet

Less than 1/8″ thick

More than 1/8″ thick

Fig. 5-2. Use of grommets or rounded edges.

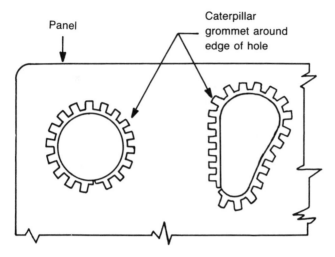

Fig. 5-3. Caterpillar grommet.

and cut the wires to the proper length, strip the insulation and tin the exposed conductor, position the wire and solder, crimp or wrap the ends as required. The terminals should be wired in a definite order. First, all adjacent terminals should be connected, then the non-adjacent terminals and finally the small components are connected. There should always be enough slack left in the wires for a minimum of 3 reconnections in the event that a repair or rework must be made. This slack also permits limited movement of parts without stressing the wires and connections. Each level of wiring must be inspected before adding another level that will cover it.

In the fabrication of electrical and electronic devices, five basic types of conductors are used.

Solid Wire, Uninsulated, (Buss Wire). A conductor consisting of one rod of metal. See Fig. 5-4.

Solid Wire, Insulated. A conductor consisting of one rod of metal with an insulation covering. See Fig. 5-5.

Stranded Wire Conductor. A conductor consisting of a group of wires or any combination of groups of wire. See Fig. 5-6.

Shielded Conductors. An insulated conductor or group of conductors enclosed in a conducting envelope. See Fig. 5-7.

Coaxial Cable. A cable consisting of an electrical conductor

Fig. 5-4. Solid wire conductor, uninsulated.

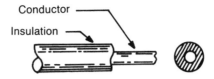

Fig. 5-5. Solid wire conductor, insulated.

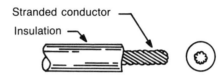

Fig. 5-6. Stranded conductor.

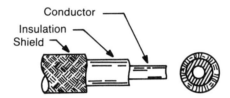

Fig. 5-7. Shielded conductor.

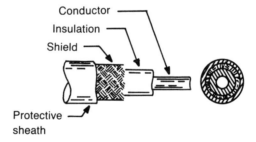

Fig. 5-8. Coaxial cable.

enclosed in a dielectric having an outer concentric conductor with or without a protective sheath; two or more such cables with an outer electrical shield and/or a common sheath. See Fig. 5-8.

WIRE PREPARATION

All of the wires should be cut to their proper length before they are moved to the assembly operation. The proper length of the wire will include the stripped ends and will provide sufficient length for any required service loops. Stripping the wire ends can be accomplished with several types of wire stripping tools, but care must be taken to insure that the tool is properly adjusted. For stripping coaxial cables see Chapter 7.

The stripping operation should provide for a clearance of 1/32 to 1/8 of an inch of exposed conductor between the end of the insulation and the soldered connection.

After the stripping operation, the unwound strands should be twisted back into position to follow the normal lay of the wire. When it is necessary to install an over size conductor it should be handled in this manner;

- After the stripping operation, fan out the strands and make a diagonal cut of the wire. See Fig. 5-9A & 5-10B.
- After the cut, twist the ends into a cone shape. See Fig. 5-10C.
- After the twisting, tin the wire.

This method provides a pointed tinned cone which is easily inserted into the terminal.

CLEANING

New plastic covered wire often has an oil bleed-through, and it should be wiped clean before use in wiring a chassis or cable. If this is not done, the lacing string will have a tendency to slip out of place. This oil bleed-through cannot be prevented, but it can be controlled by wiping the wire clean as it is removed from the spool.

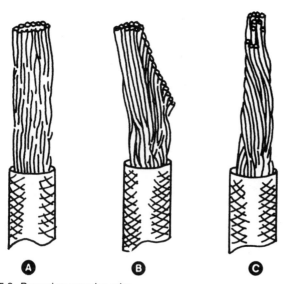

Fig. 5-9. Preparing oversize wire.

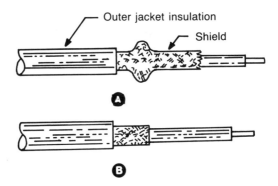

Fig. 5-10. Removing shielding.

Heavy buss wire should also be cleaned before use to prevent the possibility of contaminated solder joints.

The cleaning of wires may be accomplished with several different solvents, alcohol being the safest. Caution: The solvents selected throughout the manufacturing cycle should be carefully evaluated, since many common solvents used in the past have been found to be carcinogenic.

Straightening

When using #22, #20 or #18 AWG wire for bussing, it should be straightened before it is installed. Short lengths may be straightened by rolling them between two wooden blocks. Longer lengths are straightened by stretching them. After the straightening operation the wires must be cleaned again. (Shielded wire should never be pulled through a wire straightener.)

SHIELDED WIRE

Wires enclosed by a metal shield have an additional layer of material beneath the shield and may have an additional layer of material over the shield. In most cases these additional layers of material will not affect the following procedures. The additional materials usually are of two distinct types, textile braid or an extruded material.

Very often the textile braid has not been treated to prevent fraying. When this is the case, the end of the outer braid should be dipped in an approved varnish before any cutting is done. In cases where the braid under the shield is exposed, the exposed portion of the braid should be treated in the same manner.

There are several methods of preparing shielded wire. In this operation the following precautions should be taken.

- The conductor must not be nicked or damaged.
- The insulation must not be burned, nicked, deformed, or be exposed to excessive heat for long periods of time (more than 3 seconds).
- The shield must not be twisted to a point where it will damage the insulation.

Removing Shielding

Shields are always removed by hand. The standard method of removing shielding from a wire is:

- Remove the outer insulation jacket by hand taking care to avoid damaging the individual strands.
- Loosen the shield and push it back to the desired location forming a lump. See Fig. 5-10.
- Cut the shield at the lump and remove the unwanted portion. See Fig. 5-10.
- Trim the shield being careful not to damage the jacket or insulation.

Serving Shield Ends

When a shield is to be served and no pigtail is required, remove the proper length of the outer jacket and splay the braid as shown in Fig. 5-11A. Trim the shield strands long enough to be folded back over the outer jacket, as shown in Fig. 5-11B, so it forms an even and smooth surface on the insulation. Place a short length of shrink sleeving over the folded braid and apply heat. See Fig. 5-11C.

TINNING

The tinning on a wire or lead should only extend far enough to take full advantage of the depth or wrap of the terminal. Tinning or solder on wires outside of the solder joint will cause stiffness of the wire and result in fracturing (breaking). Wires that have been pre-tinned by the supplier do not require retinning before the soldering operation.

Stranded wires of size #16 AWG and smaller must always be tinned before soldering. This is normally done with a hand soldering iron or by dipping them in a solder pot after the strands have been twisted back to their normal lay.

Hand tinning is done after the wire has been properly cleaned by placing the soldering iron tip under the wire and the solder on top and drawing both the soldering iron and solder along the wire.

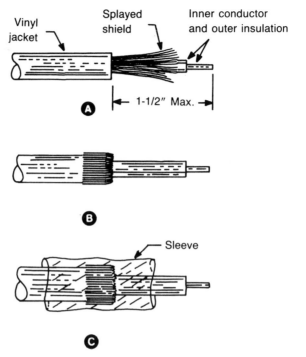

Fig. 5-11. Serving shield end.

See Fig. 5-12. Care must be taken so that the insulation is not burned and the conductor is not damaged.

CABLE MAKING

Where it is impractical to preform wires into a harness before assembly, the wires may be grouped and laced as they are connected to the terminals. Wires that run in the same direction should be dressed together and run parallel to each other. The wires in a cable should always be straight and parallel, crossed or kinked wires are not acceptable. See Fig. 5-13.

Wires that break-out together should be grouped together in the cable and should never be abruptly pulled out disregarding their

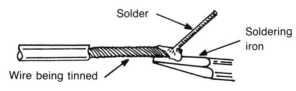

Fig. 5-12. Tinning wire.

Fig. 5-13. Crossed wires in cable.

previous position. The routing should be planned so that the wires veer gradually toward the cable breakout. When wires cross each other in a cable, they should cross inside the trunk. See Fig. 5-14. Cable breakouts should be kept symmetrical whenever possible.

Cable connections should be made before the general assembly and installation of components whenever possible. As the cable is being made, care must be taken to insure that sufficient allowance is provided for bends and service loops.

Warning: Splicing in Cables Always Requires Quality Assurance Approvals.

Cable assemblies that may be disconnected at both ends must be identified at both ends.

Extreme right angle bends must be made by bending one wire at a time, and tools such as pliers are not to be used for bending wires in a cable under any circumstances.

Wires should not be interwound with each other unless the engineering drawing specifies twisting, as in the case of twisted pairs, and then the twist must continue to the terminating point. Cable connections to free floating terminals should not permit the cable weight to be supported by the electrical connections, and they must provide enough slack to allow the terminal to remain free in its normal movement. Lacing should not be used to secure a cable to a support. Cable clamps are required.

Cables that are prepared for installation into a chassis assembly should terminate the leads with at least 6 inches of extra length.

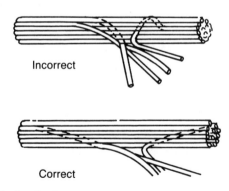
Incorrect

Correct

Fig. 5-14. Wire breakout.

This will insure having enough lead length at installation for potential variations and service loops.

HARNESSING AND CABLING

Groups of wires are usually harnessed or cabled so that they form a sturdy and compact unit that can be more easily dressed than the individual wires, and the harness or cable can be installed as a single assembly.

Chassis wiring is laced to form a "wiring harness" and is fabricated by the manufacturer to suit a particular wiring layout. Harnesses should be layed out so that the circuit tracing is accomplished simply, and accessibility to components which may require replacement is not limited. The individual wires in a harness should be positioned to run parallel or at right angles to each other whenever possible. Sharp bends must be avoided since they will cause insulation damage.

Harnesses are normally fabricated on a "harness jig" or "forming board." The board is marked with numbers and symbols to indicate the wire sizes, color coding, routing terminations and wiring sequence. Pegs or nails are used to form a pattern which follows a pictorial wiring diagram and serves to locate the wire runs. During the manufacturing of the harness assembly, the wire ends may be anchored by wrapping them around a nail or by fanning them out for easier dressing and using tape or a simple clamp, or by drilling holes in the board. See Fig. 5-15.

Another method of anchoring the wires during a build is to attach a spring to the harness board at the termination point. The pitch of the spring is determined by the wire size and must not be so tight that the insulation may be damaged. The spring method is simple, fast and inexpensive. See Fig. 5-16.

The harness may be laid out on the harness board with the bot-

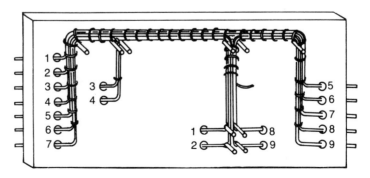

Fig. 5-15. Harness forming board.

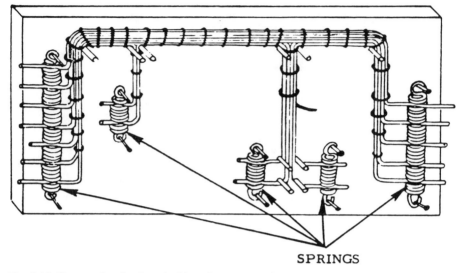

SPRINGS

Fig. 5-16. Harness forming board with springs.

tom side facing up for ease of lacing. When this is done and the harness is installed into a unit the lacing knots and splices are not visible and the wiring has a neat and orderly appearance. In some instances, harness boards are designed with electrical checking points to speed up testing and reducing rework in the manufacturing cycle. See Fig. 5-17.

Clamping

Wires and Cables that are over 6 inches long should always be mechanically tied to the chassis to prevent any movement. Standard commercially available cable clamps, shown in Fig. 5-18, are normally used for this function. The most common clamp is a loop type nylon device.

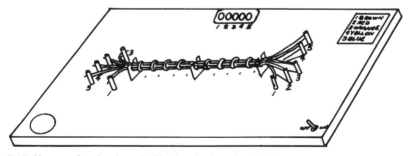

Fig. 5-17. Harness forming board with electrical testing devices.

Fig. 5-18. Standard cable clamp.

Wire and cable routing should be planned early in the chassis design stage so that holes may be provided for the mounting hardware.

The following points should be taken into consideration when clamping wires and cables.

- The number of clamping points must be sufficient to prevent any motion that may cause abrasion to the wires or cables.
- When shielded wire or cable is used, it should have a vinyl sleeve placed around the shield at the clamp area. It is often desired to sleeve the entire length of exposed shielding to prevent potential shorting to the chassis or nearby components.
- Clamps should always be located at least one inch away from any cable breakouts to eliminate the possibility of placing a strain on the breakout.
- Clamps should never be located too close to a connector. Allowance must be made to avoid stressing the connector terminations.
- When metal clamps are used, an insulating cushion should be inserted under the clamp to prevent wire or cable damage.
- Clamps are always required on each side of a hinged assembly, except when a cable tray is used.
- Clamps should be installed at least every 12 inches on an extended cable run.

Clamps with a mounting hole provided for securing cables to the chassis or final unit are available in many forms, as shown in Figs. 5-19 through 5-30.

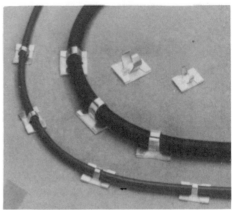

Fig. 5-19. Assorted cable clamps.

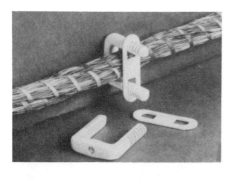
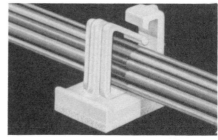

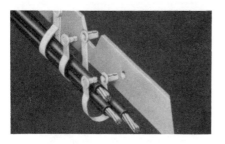
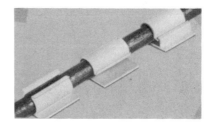

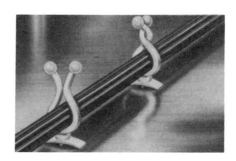

Fig. 5-20. Assorted cable clamps.

Lacing Methods

Ribbon type lacing cord is preferred to the round in order to reduce the cutting into the wire insulation. When round cord is used it should follow the sizes shown in Table 5-1.

The process of lacing a harness is started at one end with a "starting" tie, (lacing can also be started at the center with a lock stitch and a terminating wrap at each end). See Fig. 5-31.

Lacing is started by cutting a length of cord that is two and one-half times the length of the cable or harness being assembled. One end of the lacing cord is laid over the wire group and is held

93

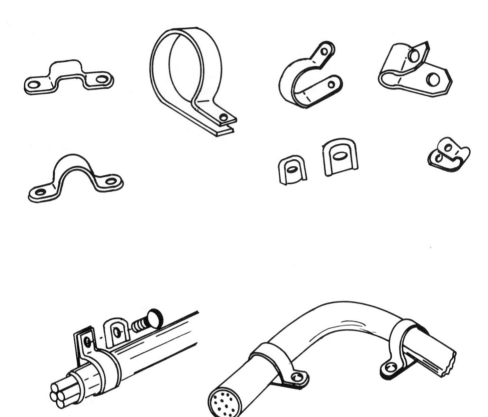

Fig. 5-21. Assorted cable clamps.

as approximately four turns of cord are wound over it, continue wrapping the cord until 12 turns have been wound around the wire group. See Fig. 5-32.

This starting wrap is secured by a lock stitch. The lock stitch is made by forming a loop, passing the cord over and through the loop and pulling the cord tight. See Fig. 5-33.

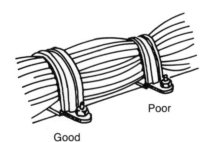

Poor

Good

Fig. 5-22. Use of cable clamps.

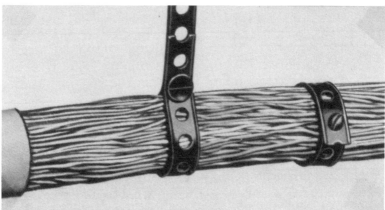

Fig. 5-23. Flat cable clamps and cable straps.

A secure stitch can be made only by passing the cord over the loop, never under it. In this method the cord is always locked under each loop. See Fig. 5-34.

After the starting wrap and lock stitch, a lock stitch is made at intervals of not less than 1/2 inch spacings. See Fig. 5-35.

As the lacing is advanced, the wire bundles should be re-formed to insure a neat and firmly bound cable. All of the conductors should be laying parallel with no twisting or crossovers. This method of lacing is known as the "regulation cablemans knot."

Terminating the harness lacing is accomplished by making four wraps of cord at the last lock stitch, forming a separate piece of

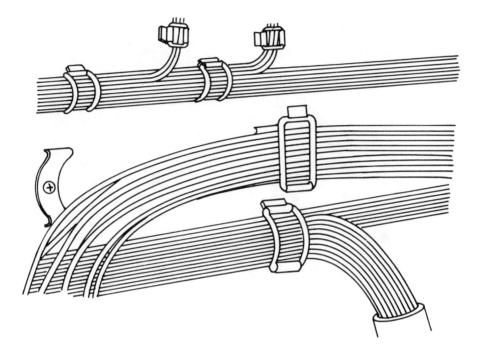

Fig. 5-24. Assorted cable clamps.

cord into a two inch loop, and laying it along side the wires. Then eight turns of the original cord are wrapped over the loop and the end of the lacing cord is passed through the loop. See Fig. 5-36.

To complete the securing of the lacing termination, both ends of the loop are pulled together to pull the lacing cord under and through the wrap and the lacing cord is pulled tight locking the wrap, the exposed end of the lacing cord is cut approximately 1/8 to 1/4 inch from the final wrap.

The lacing methods shown in Figs. 5-38 through 5-45 use single-

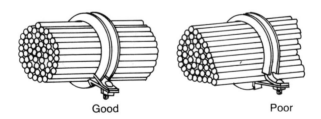

Good   Poor

Fig. 5-25. Use of cable clamps.

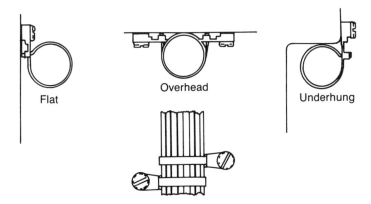

Flat

Overhead

Underhung

Fig. 5-26. Installation of mounting straps.

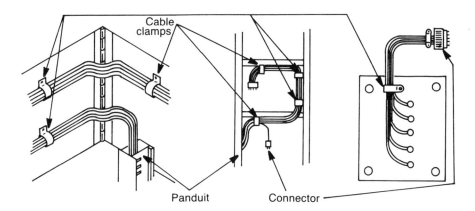

Cable clamps

Panduit

Connector

Fig. 5-27. Use of cable clamps and a panduit.

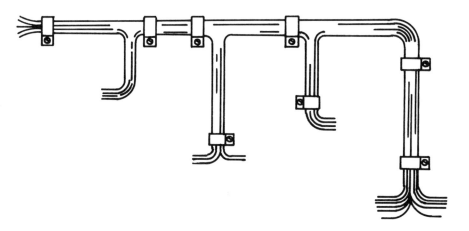

Fig. 5-28. Clamping harness assembly.

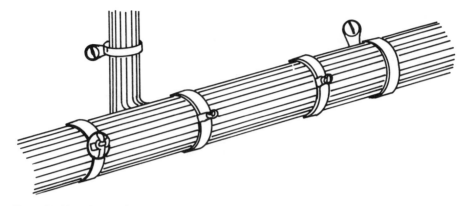

Fig. 5-29. Use of mounting straps.

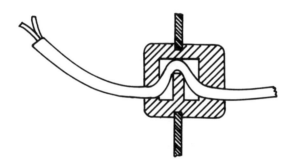

Fig. 5-30. Strain relief device.

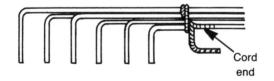

Cord
end

Fig. 5-31. Lacing a harness, step 1.

Fig. 5-32. Lacing a harness, step 2.

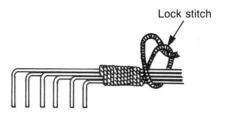

Fig. 5-33. Lacing a harness, step 3.

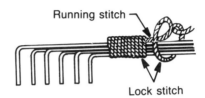

Fig. 5-34. Lacing a harness, step 4.

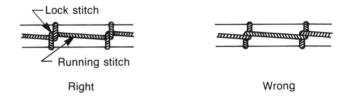

Right   Wrong

Fig. 5-35. Running stitch.

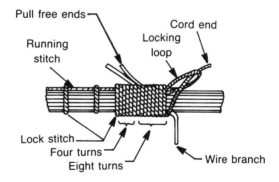

Fig. 5-36. Ending a running stitch, step 1.

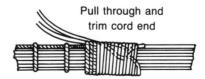

Fig. 5-37. Ending a running stitch, step 2.

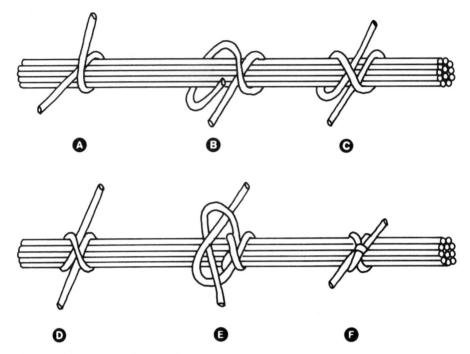

Ⓐ   **Ⓑ**   **Ⓒ**

Ⓓ   **Ⓔ**   **Ⓕ**

Fig. 5-38. Clove hitch and square knot.

Correct   Incorrect

Fig. 5-39. Spot tie at breakout.

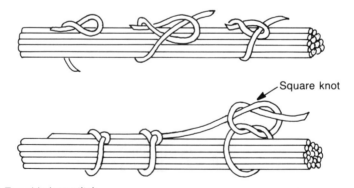

Square knot

Fig. 5-40. Top side lace stitch.

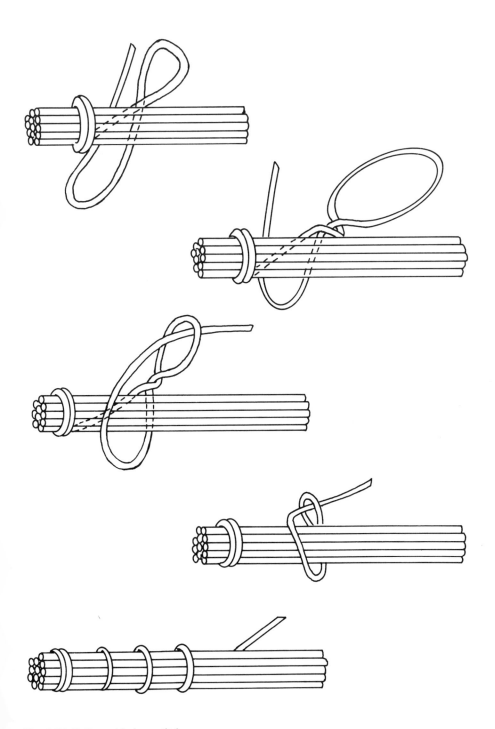

Fig. 5-41. Bottom side lace stitch.

Cable diameter	Cord size
up to 3/8 inch	#4
5/16 to 3/4 inch	#6
5/8 to 1 inch	#9
1 inch & over	#12

Table 5-1. Round Lacing Cord Sizes.

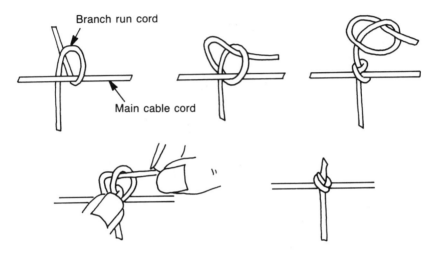

Fig. 5-42. Branch run tie.

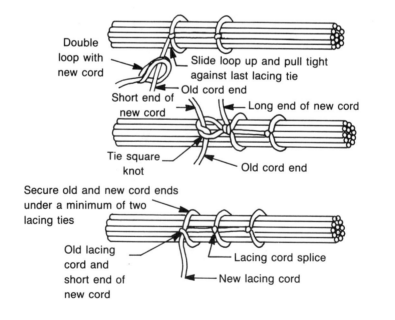

Fig. 5-43. Splicing lacing cord.

lacing. The methods are the same when using a double cord. The ties must always be tight around a wire or cable group, but care must be taken to prevent the lacing from damaging the wire or cable insulation.

The most popular lacing tie is the clove hitch with a square knot to retain it. See Fig. 5-38. Spot ties made in this manner should be spaced approximately twice the cable diameter apart, or at least 1 inch, whichever is greater. This type of spot tie must immediately precede each cable breakout. See Fig. 5-44. The following figures present various other types of cable lacing, and includes the lock-type lace stitch.

BREAKOUTS

Branches and sub-branches, including individual wires are normally referred to as breakouts.

All single lead breakouts should always be preceded by a lock

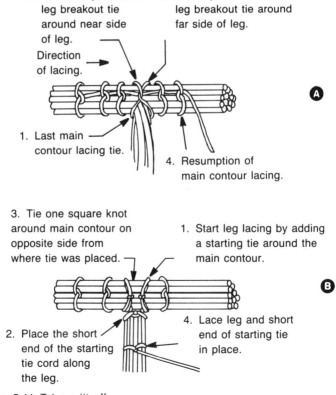

3. Second square knot leg breakout tie around near side of leg.

2. First square knot leg breakout tie around far side of leg.

Direction of lacing.

A

1. Last main contour lacing tie.

4. Resumption of main contour lacing.

3. Tie one square knot around main contour on opposite side from where tie was placed.

1. Start leg lacing by adding a starting tie around the main contour.

B

2. Place the short end of the starting tie cord along the leg.

4. Lace leg and short end of starting tie in place.

Fig. 5-44. Tying a "tee".

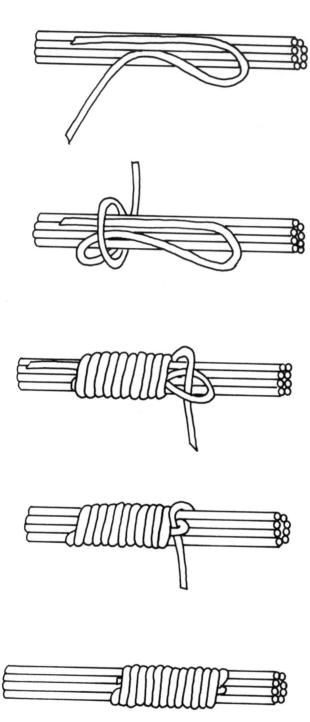

Fig. 5-45. Tying a serve.

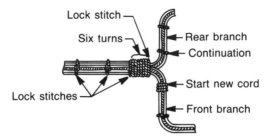

Fig. 5-46. Tying a branch.

stitch in a position that does not create a variation in the distance between stitches.

When groups of wires are branched from a harness they should be laced. Every breakout of two or more wires should be laced. When a group of wires is branched from a cable it is secured with a lock stitch. Six turns around the principal cable adjacent to the new lock stitch and a second lock stitch is made adjacent to the turns. After the branch is secured in this manner, the running stitch is continued along the main cable. See Fig. 5-46. Lacing may also begin with a square knot followed by two lock stitches and then followed by the method described above. See Fig. 5-47.

Another method of lacing a harness is by making a series of individually bound wraps at points equidistant along the harness. Lacing cord that is two inches longer than the length required for 12 turns around the wire group is cut. One end of the cord is formed into a one-inch loop which is positioned onto the wire group parallel to the lay of the wires and twelve turns of the lacing cord are wound around the loop. At the last turn the cord end is passed through the loop which extends from under the wrap and the end of the cord is pulled until the loop is under the wrap, but should be pulled until the two loops are approximately positioned at the center of the wrap. The loose ends of cord are then trimmed. See Fig. 5-48.

Fig. 5-47. Lacing beginning with a square knot.

105

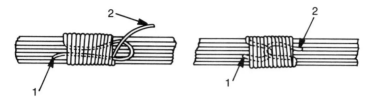

Fig. 5-48. Wherever a lacing should break a required splicing, a square knot should be used to connect the ends.

Zippered Tubing

Another method of forming a harness is to group the wires neatly and encase them in a commercially available plastic zippered tubing. This method is useful for custom cabling and in applications where a replaceable jacket is desired. The major advantage of zippered tubing is that it is much less time-consuming than lacing or tying, and the zippered tubing allows repeated access to work points. Zippered tubing facilitates the addition or removal of individual wires with a minimum of rework time. The jacket may be easily removed, the rework completed and the jacket replaced in a matter of minutes. Zippered tubing also provides definite advantages in external cabling where the tying or lacing results in a cable that is too stiff and where protection against abrasion is required.

When wires are soldered to a connector, zipper tubing proves to be very useful. The tubing can be unzipped and folded back to expose the work area, then be zipped back to cover the soldered area and sealed. See Fig. 5-49.

Zipper tubing is easily and effectively terminated using connector backshell clamps, pressure sensitive tapes or by potting.

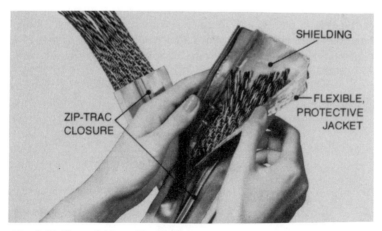

Fig. 5-49. Zipper tubing with shielding.

106

Zipper tubing that will shield a harness or cable from electrostatic and electromagnetic radiation is commercially available. The shielded zipper tubing installation is a one-step operation that will eliminate the laborious hand wrapping or expensive braiding necessary to shield cables and harness. The shielded zipper tubing can be grounded by using the standard connector backshell clamps or by the installation of grounding wires similar to those used in grounding other types of shielded cable.

Perforated zipper tubing is available for applications where wire branch outs are required or where moisture condensation must be avoided.

Zipper tubing may be purchased in the following compositions:

- Vinyl
- Vinyl-coated fiberglass
- Vinyl saturated fiberglass laminated to aluminum foil
- Vinyl backed butyl rubber
- Lead-saturated vinyl
- Mylar
- Polyethylene

The operating temperature range for zipper tubing can be as high as 2000 F, depending on the materials selected. Special fittings are available for branching and routing with zipper cable shielding such as "Y" and "T" shapes. See Fig. 5-50.

Tie Wraps

Tie wraps are one-piece molded plastic devices used for cable tying that are capable of meeting high temperature conditions, and are easily installed. They permit light weight, rapid and effective lacing of harnesses, and may be purchased in many sizes. These straps resist fungus and corrosion, do not support combustion, and have good dielectric characteristics. Larger wire bundles may be tied by using two straps together by inserting the end of one strap through the eye of the second, locking the two together. The manufacturers of tie wraps also provide tools for rapid installation and trimming in a single operation. In many applications the tie wrap may be used to secure the harness directly to the chassis.

Another form of the tie wrap is the band clamp. The band clamp is made with ratchet-like teeth along the strap that engage into the eye of the strap forming a tight bond around the wire.

Cable Clips

Cable clips are often used in manufacturing harnesses. They

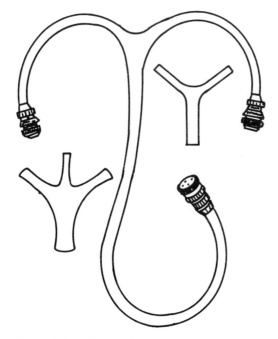

Fig. 5-50. Y- and T-shaped zipper tubing.

consist of a flat or "U" shaped base and a plastic strap. See Figs. 5-51 through 5-56 for types and applications of tie wraps and band clamps.

INSPECTION

All of the following defects should be corrected before releasing the harness to inspection.

• Frequent cord splices, indicating that the cord was pulled

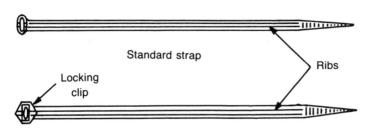

Standard strap

Ribs

Locking
clip

Self-clinching strap

Fig. 5-51. Tie straps.

Fig. 5-52. Band clamps.

too tight or the cord length was too short for the cable diameter.

- Frayed lacing cord. Fraying indicates that the original cord length was too long.
- All knots and splices should not be visible from the top of the harness.
- The wire insulation should not be frayed at the ends.
- The lacing should not be damaged by the soldering operation. There should be no evidence of burning or solder splatter on the lacing.

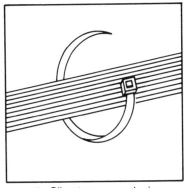

1. Slip strap around wire bundle, rib side inside

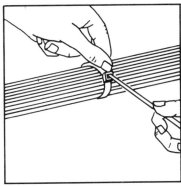

2. Pull tight and clip off excess

Fig. 5-53. Installation of self-cinching straps.

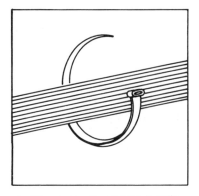

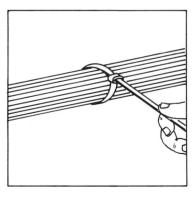

1. Slip strap around wire bundle, rib side inside

2. Thread tip through eye and draw up tight

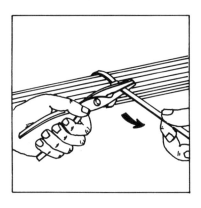

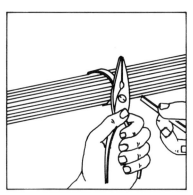

3. Apply pliers; twist 120°

4. Clip off excess

Fig. 5-54. Installation of tie straps.

Inspection of Routing and Dressing

The inspector should consider the following defects very carefully to insure that a reliable harness assembly is being released for installation into the final unit.

- Broken strands which could result in a system malfunction.
- The improper placement of wiring that may interfere with normal operation.
- Wires that are pinched, frayed or burned to the extent that a break or short could result.
- Improper terminations that could result in a loose connection.

 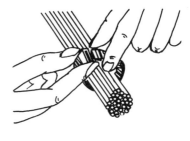

1. Select right length band clamp

2. Insert tab through loop so tab is between wires and clamp

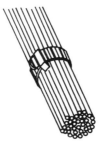

3. Push clamp together until it fits snugly around the wires and the ratchet teeth engage

Fig. 5-55. Installation of band clamps.

- Improper support which could result in breaking due to fatigue.

The following defects are considered minor, but should be noted so the same defects will not reoccur.

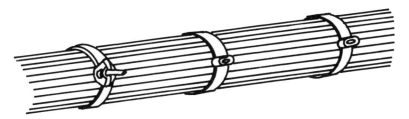

Fig. 5-56. Use of tie straps in service.

- Broken strands which would not be likely to cause a malfunction.
- Spacing between movable elements and uninsulated wires is greater than 1/16 inch but less than 1/8 inch.
- The wire insulation is chafed but not likely to result in a short.
- Wire that is drawn too taut, but not enough to place a strain on the wire, components or terminals.
- Insulation that is back more than 1/8 inch from a connection, but cannot result in a short.

Chapter 6

Flexible Circuits

Before specifying the use of flexible circuits it should be determined if a suitable application exists. There are three major areas to be considered prior to making the decision to use flexible circuits:

Cost. The total design, manufacturing, reliability, and maintenance cost should be reviewed, not simply the cost of the circuitry as comnpared to standard wiring.

Function. Evaluate the purpose of the circuit and decide whether another wiring method would be more appropriate based on all factors of use, reliability, maintainability, etc.

Wiring. Evaluate the capability of the circuit to reduce manufacturing time and eliminate wiring errors.

The final consideration in the selection of flexible circuits is the configuration complexity. This is considered against the number of circuits required. Where the total quantities are relatively small, the complexity must be high to be economically worthwhile. In large production quantities very simple as well as the highly complex assemblies will pay for themselves. An example of a flexible circuit is shown in Fig. 6-1.

DESIGN CHECKLIST

Many factors will affect the use of flexible circuits, and major cost advantages can be gained when a preliminary analysis indi-

Fig. 6-1. Typical flexible circuit.

cates that the application of the circuit meets the basic considerations.

The selection and design of flexible circuits should begin with
the following check list.

1. Operating and maximum temperature requirements.
2. Moisture absorption.
3. Flexing and tensile strength. Has the flexible wire been properly supported at adequate intervals?
4. Distributed capacitance and shielding.
5. Flammability.
6. Dielectric requirements between layers.
7. Dielectric requirements between conductors.
8. Termination system and applications of connectors.
9. Selection of standard materials and thicknesses.
10. Non-critical tolerances are loose enough to use automated
    production.

FEATURES AND CHARACTERISTICS

The advantages in flexible circuits encompass every aspect of
interconnection concerns.

Thermal Control, Reduced Weight and Space. The

larger surface area created by the flat profile configuration of the printed flexible circuit enhances the heat dissipation and allows higher current capacities. This permits smaller and lighter conductors to be used without compromising performance. The availability of materials with high temperature and insulation values allow for reduced thickness and weight without a loss in the physical and electrical characteristics.

Material Consistency. Tight control is maintained on the material properties by the processes used during manufacturing. Due to these manufacturing controls, flexible circuits maintain consistent and predictable mechanical and electrical characteristics such as dielectric strength, dielectric constant, dissipation, volume and surface resistivity.

Repeatability. Flexible circuits are always exact replicas of the master artwork. After the artwork is tested and verified, duplicate circuits are made in large quantities without any errors. The repeatability and elimination of wiring errors is a significant economic advantage for flexible circuits.

Lower Installation Cost and Higher Reliability. Flexible circuitry significantly reduces assembly and installation labor costs as compared to conventional wiring due to the unitized structure. In addition to this an important added benefit is the increased strength and resistance to damage in handling and use.

In summation we find that flexible circuitry with its limitless adaptability to most applications continues to draw attention for its many attractive features.

As a functional replacement for conventional wiring flexible circuits are far superior. Standard wire harneses are individually hand assembled, space consuming, heavy, costly, and troubled by cross-talk. Flexible circuits are highly engineered, repeatable and volume produced units that are light weight, lower cost and very highly reliable.

The use of flexible circuits allows the design engineer greater conceptual freedom in the design. The thin cross-section with its ability to fold and conform to tight and irregular spaces eliminates many problems encountered with conventional wiring. The consideration of space is of great importance where weight and size are critical, particularly in miniaturized packages. Originally flexible circuits were used only in wire harness applications. However, in recent years it has become an efficient means of interconnecting an entire subsystem or system by creating an integral assembly which carries the circuit components together with the mother board and interconnection components.

TYPES AND VARIATIONS OF FLEXIBLE CIRCUITS

In further discussions on flexible circuits the terms *dielectric, insulation,* and *laminate* are totally interchangeable and refer to the material used between the layers of conductors in the construction of the flexible cable or wire harness. Flexible circuits may be designed in three basic configurations, and can be modified to satisfy a large number of unique packaging requirements.

Single Sided Circuits

The single layer flexible circuit is the simplest and easiest to manufacture. It consists only of a single layer of copper foil laminated to a dielectric material. A second layer of insulating material is often laminated over the bare copper foil, encapsulating the conductors.

This type of printed wiring may be divided in subclasses.

Single Access Uncovered. This is the least expensive type of flexible circuit. It consists of a dielectric supporting a single exposed layer of copper circuit. This type of circuit finds applications where the circuit will not be exposed to mechanical abuse or environmental contamination. The components are mounted on the dielectric side with the terminations on the circuit side. Single access uncovered flexible circuits are found in such items as telephones, relays, small motors and other assemblies that are enclosed. See Fig. 6-2.

Single Access Covered. Figure 6-3 shows this type circuit, which consists of three layers, two layers of dielectric with a single copper circuit bonded between them. The dielectric is selectively removed from the areas where subsequent electrical connections will be made to the circuit. The covercoat (top dielectric) provides protection from moisture and is an insulation barrier

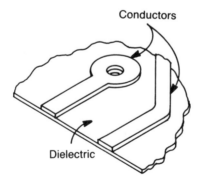

Conductors

Dielectric

Fig. 6-2. Single access uncovered flexible circuit.

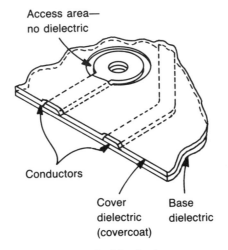

Fig. 6-3. Single access covered flexible circuit.

between the conductors. It also insulates the circuit from the associated chassis and hardware.

Double Access Uncovered. Figure 6-4 shows this type of circuit, which allows access to the circuitry from either side of the single circuit structure. The dielectric layer is manufactured with predetermined holes and the circuitry is suspended across the holes allowing access to either side. This type of flexible wiring is most frequently used where the production quantities are high, and inexpensive electrical connections are required and must provide for the installation of components from either side.

Double Access Covered. Figure 6-5 shows this flexible circuit, which consists of two layers of dielectric with a single copper circuit between. The dielectric surfaces contain pre-drilled holes on both sides of the wiring structure, allowing access to the circuit

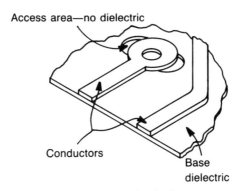

Fig. 6-4. Double access uncovered flexible circuit.

from either side. The access holes may be offset or opposing as required for the particular design application. The applications of this type of flexible circuit is the most versatile. Components may be mounted on either side of the circuit and it also lends itself to point-to-point wiring.

Double Sided Circuits

The double sided circuit consists of a layer of dielectric material with copper foil laminated to both sides. A cover layer of insulating material is then laminated over the bare copper foil on both sides fully encapsulating the conductors. See Fig. 6-6. The most common method of communication between the conductor layers is plated-through-hole used in standard printed circuit manufacturing. There are other methods of interconnecting the conductor layers which will be discussed later.

Multilayer Flexible Circuits

Perhaps the most effective mechanism for overcoming the problems encountered in designing highly complex and densely packaged circuits is the multilayer flexible printed circuit. It is frequently used in applications where:

- Unavoidable cross-overs are encountered.
- Terminals and connectors do not allow sufficient space for routing conductors between pins.

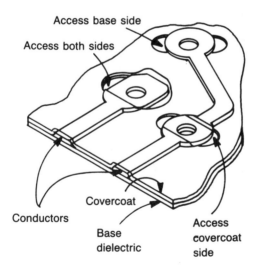

Fig. 6-5. Double access covered flexible circuit.

118

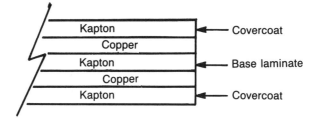

Fig. 6-6. Double sided flexible circuit.

- It is required as a means of controlling the characteristic impedance.
- Separation of sensitive circuits becomes a requirement to prevent cross-talk.
- The circuit must be shielded.
- Ground and voltage planes are desirable.
- Circuits have extreme component densities.

The multilayer flexible circuit consists of several layers of copper foil and insulating materials. It is manufactured similarly to the double sided circuit. See Fig. 6-7. The flexible circuits commonly in use include all of the types previously presented with all of the layers completely flexible, or the flexible layers manufactured with rigid printed circuit boards used as the outer layers to stiffen the assembly for support of connectors and/or electronic components. In some applications the bend areas are left unbonded and the component or connector areas are supported by using rigid printed circuit board material as a stiffener. See Fig. 6-8.

Shielded Multilayer Cables

The multilayer cable in its simplest form is a structure with three conductor layers. The center layer being the discreet wiring paths, and two outer conductor layers of solid copper foil. When

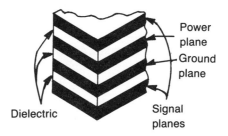

Fig. 6-7. Multilayer flexible circuit.

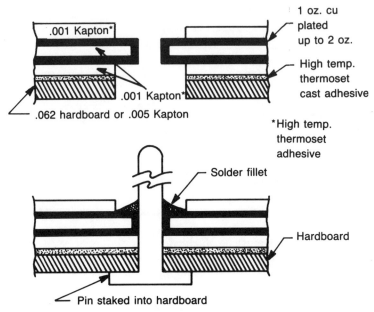

.001 Kapton*

1 oz. cu plated up to 2 oz.

High temp. thermoset cast adhesive

.001 Kapton*

.062 hardboard or .005 Kapton

*High temp. thermoset adhesive

Solder fillet

Hardboard

Pin staked into hardboard

Fig. 6-8. Supporting methods for flexible circuits.

the three conductor layers are laminated with the dielectric insulators between them they become directly equivalent to the shielded and co-axial wire configurations.

Moving or Rolling Flexible Cables

The most common application for a moving or rolling flexible cable is a chassis mounted unit with slides. The use of the flexible cable permits the designer to control the position of the cable during the opening and closing (sliding) of the unit in its cabinet or rack. The service loop that is required to protect the cable from excessive bending is eliminated by the use of the flexible cable which rolls into itself, thus saving considerable space. In this application the best results are obtained by the single layer construction with fully annealed copper conductors on the neutral axis of the roll layer. Here, the selection of the dielectric is limited to those materials that can be post treated to create the memory for the cable roll-up.

Mylar films with a flame-retardant adhesive are recommended for formed roll-up cables.

FLEXIBLE CIRCUIT MATERIALS

Flexible circuitry was invented in 1953, only a few short years

120

after the development of the standard rigid printed circuit board. But it did not gain popularity as fast as the rigid printed circuit because of several problems. The major concern was the availability of acceptable materials that would satisfy both the mechanical and electrical parameters and still yield producible circuits economically.

Most of the available materials in the 1950's were thermoplastics that would support only relatively low temperature ranges. Their suitability for flexible circuits was limited due to low melting temperatures and extreme instability.

As the complexity of the electronic systems increased and the space limitations became more severe, a series of highly reliable and economically suitable materials were developed.

The properties of the materials selected for use in flexible circuits is as critical as all of the other design factors. Based on the design requirements of the circuit, the metal foil (conductor) is selected to be either conductive or resistive. The conductive foils are typically electrodeposited or rolled copper, (occasionally aluminum is used), and the resistive foils are variations of nickel/copper and nickel/iron alloys. Most of the flexible circuits manufactured today use copper foil which is available from 1/2 ounce to 5 ounce annealed copper. (1 ounce copper = 0.0014 inch thick). The basis for the selection of the insulation materials are, 1) cost, 2) dimensional stability, 3) thermal properties, 4) toughness, 5) electrical and mechanical properties, 6) moisture absorption, and 7) radiation resistance.

The properties of many materials used in flexible wiring are given in Tables 6-1 through 6-4.

Insulation films are available in thicknesses from 0.0005 to 0.005, however, the most commonly used material ranges from 0.001 to 0.002. Not all of these materials are available in every thickness.

The temperatures listed here are the long-term operating temperatures that the insulation materials can withstand. The temperature capability of the adhesives used to bond the circuit foil to the insulation material are generally somewhere below that of the insulation material itself. However, in most of the applications today, the highest temperature attained will be during the soldering operation, usually 500 °F for 3 seconds. In general, the lower the thermal requirements, the lower the cost. However, the low temperature group of insulations will impose some design and manufacturing limitations. As an example this group requires a high degree of skill when soldering operations are performed. Direct contact with the soldering iron will melt or shrink the insulation. Extreme

Table 6-1. Flexible Printed Wiring-Material Selection Guide.

Cable Characteristic	Polyimide Film	Polyimide FEP Plastic	FEP Plastic	FEP Glass	FEP-C Plastic	FEP-C Epoxy Adh.	Monochloro-tri-fluoro-ethylene	Polyester	PVC (Self-Ext.)	Polyimide Epoxy-Phenoic Butyral	TFE Plastic
Construction Bond											
Fusion Bond	X	X	X	X	X		X				X
Adhesive Bond					X	X		X	X	X	
Environment											
Service Temperature °C	1	4	5	3	8	7	8	9	10	6	2
Radiation Absorption	1	4	10	9	10	10	10	3	6	2	5
Physical Factors											
Dimensional Stability	4	3	8	3	5	6	7	2	10	1	7
Flexibility	7	5	1	8	1	3	3	4	2	6	3
Circuit Thickness (.006/.025")	4	2	6	7	3	5	5	1	8	2	7
Stripping Ease	7	4	1	6	2	4	1	3	2	5	2
Pad Bearing Ease	5	3	1	4	1	2	1	2	NR	5	NR
Solderability	1	3	4	2	4	2	5	6	7	2	1
Welding Thru Ease	NR	NR	3	NR	3	3	3	2	1	NR	3
Potting Bondability	3	3	6	3	1	1	5	2	4	3	6
Cost Factors											
Cost—Raw Material	9	10	4	7	5	6	74	3	1	8	2
Cost—Continuous Cbl. (without connectors)	NR	6	5	NR	4	NR	7	2	1	NR	3
Cost—Etched Cable (without connectors)	9	5	7	6	2	3	8	1	NR	4	NR

Legend: 1 = Best Factor; NR = Not Recommended

Table 6-2. Thermal Resistances of Flexible Circuit Materials.

Material	Thermal Resistance
Polyester film	100 C
Non-woven Dacron epoxy	150 C
Non-woven Polyimide epoxy	150 C
FEP Teflon®film	200 C
Polyamide-imide film	240 C
TFE Teflon ®film	260 C
Polyimide film	300 C

care must be used to remove the iron immediately after the solder has flowed.

Thermoplastic Insulations

The thermoplastic materials are the lowest in cost, but these materials have very limited applications due to the extremely low operating temperature range. They are acceptable where the soldering operation is not required. The thermoplastic materials include:

Vinyl. This is the lowest cost material available. Used where temperature is not a limiting factor. Functional operating temperature = 35 °F to 149 °F.

Polyethylene. This material is a polyester with a polyethylene coat to permit heat sealing of the conductor to the dielectric. The extremely low thermal expansion rate of 0.27 mil/ C/inch facilitates fine line circuitry during manufacturing. However, its relatively low temperature characteristics (302 °F) eliminate the use of all soldering operations.

Fluorocarbons. This material is acceptable for applications for temperature ranges from −185 °F to 302 °F. Fluorocarbons are acceptable for military and commercial circuits where the use of such materials as acids, alkalies, and organic chemicals are used (although they will show slight swelling when exposed to halogenated compounds). They offer unique physical memory characteristics for retracting and self-winding and are readily hand soldered.

Thermosetting Plastics

The thermosetting plastics are a group of high temperature materials that will permit the use of high volume techniques such as dip or wave soldering. These materials can withstand many desoldering operations before they become seriously damaged. Applications using high terminal pin densities may require high tem-

Table 6-3. Detailed Characteristics of Various Insulations.

	TFE Plastic	TFE Glass Cloth	FEP Plastic	FEP Glass Cloth	Polyimide Film
Spec. Gr.	2.15	2.2	2.15	2.2	1.42
Flammable	No	No	No	No	Self-Ext
Appearance	Translucent	Tan	Clear Bluish	Tan	Amber
Bondability with Adhesives	Good[a]	Good[a]	Good[a]	Good[a]	Good
Bondability to Itself	Good	Poor	Good	Good	Poor
Chemical Resistance	Exc.	Exc.	Exc.	Exc.	Exc.
Sunlight Resistance	Exc.	Exc.	Exc.	Exc.	Exc.
Water Absorption (%)	<0.01 /24 hr	0.10 /0.68[b]	<0.01 /24 hr	0.18 /0.30[b]	3/24 hr
Volume Resistivity ohm-cm	$>10^{15}$	10^{16}	$>2 \times 10^{18}$	10^{16}	10^{16}
Dielectric Constant 10^2-10^8 Hz	2.2	$2.5/5^{[b]}$	2.1	$2.5/5^{[b]}$	3.5
Dissipation factor 10^2-10^8 Hz	2×10^{-4}	7×10^{-4} 10^{-3} [b]	2×10^{-4}	10^{-4} $10^{-3[b]}$	3×10^{-3} 14×10^{-3}
Service Temp. Min. (°C)	−200	−70	−200	−70	−200
Max. (°C)	250	250	200	200	300
Tensile Str. psi @ 25 °C	3000	$20,000^{[b]}$	3000	$20,000^{[b]}$	25,000
N/m² × 10⁸ @ 25 °C	0.2067	1.378	0.2067	1.378	1.697
Modulus of Elasticity psi	58,000	$4.0^{[b]}$	50,000	$4.0^{[b]}$	510,000
N/m² × 10⁸	3.930	0.0003	3.394	0.0003	34.623
Thermal Expansion in/in /°F × 10⁻⁶	55 (−30 °C to 30 °C)	Low[b]	50 (−30 °C to 30 °C)	Low[b]	11 (−14 °C to 38 °C)
cm/cm /°C × 10⁻⁶	100		90		20
Dielectric Strength Volts/mil	600	650 1600[b]	2800	650 1600	7000
Sample Size (mils)	15	3	5	3	2

[a] Must be treated
[b] Depends on % of glass cloth
[c] Depends on formulation (plasticizer)

PCTFE	Epoxy Dacron	Poly-propylene	Polyester Film	Poly-vinyl-Chloride	Poly-ethylene
2.10	1.38	0.905	1.395	1.25	0.93
No	Yes	Slow Burning	Yes	Self-Ext	Yes
White & Opaque	Trans-lucent	Clear	Clear	Trans-lucent	Clear
Good[a]	Good[a]	Poor	Good	Good	Poor
Good	Good	Good	Poor	Good	Good
Exc.	Good	Good	Exc.	Good	Good
Exc.	Fair	Low	Fair	Fair	Low
0	1.5	0.01	0.8/24 hr	0.10	0.01 /24 hrs
3.1×10^{16}	1×10^{10}	10^{16}	10^{15}	10^{10}	10^{16}
2.5		2.0	2.8-3.7	3.6-4.0	2.2
15×10^{-3}	70×10^{-3}	2×10^{-4} 3×10^{-4}	2×10^{-3} $16 \times 10^{10-3}$	14×10^{-2}	6×10^{-4}
−70	−20	−55	−60	−30	−20
125	100	100	105	85	60
4500	300	5700	20,000	3000	2000
0.31	0.8825	0.3927	1.378	0.2067	0.1378
190,000	12,000	170,000	550,000		50,000
12.90		11.713	37.895		3.445
(−195 °C to 90 °C)	(−30 °C to 30 °C)	(−30 °C to 30 °C)	(21 °C to 50 °C)		(−30 °C to 30 °C)
48	11	61	15	[c]	100
82	20	110	27		180
1100	900	600	700	800[c]	585
19.2		125	1		125

Table 6-4. Recommended Insulation Service Temperatures.

Material	High Temp.*** °C	Low Temp. °C
I. Adhesive Bonded		
Polyimide film—polyimide adhesive*..	300	−200
Polyimide film—phenolic butyral.....	150	−100
FEP "C"—epoxy.................	135	−55
Polyimide film—epoxy.............	135	−55
Polyester film—polyester..........	100	−100
Polyimide film—polyester..........	100	−100
Polyvinyl chloride**..............	85	−30
Polyimide-Acrylic................	200	−100
II. Heat Fused		
TFE plastic.....................	250	−200
FEP Fluorocarbon Resin...........	200	−200
TFE-Glass-FEP-Bonded plastic......	200	−70
Polyimide-film-FEP	150	−200
FEP "C" plastic................	150	−55
Polycarbonate	125	−55
Monochloro-tri-fluro-ethylene	125	−70
Polyvinyl chloride**..............	85	−30
Polyester-polyethylene**	60	−20
Polyethylene**	60	−20

perature materials since the normal soldering temperature range is from 375 °F to 500 °F.

FEP Plastic. This material essentially displays a flat dielectric constant from 60 Hz to 1 MHz and an absolute maximum operating temperature of 563 °F. It is not quite as satisfactory in the low temperature applications as the fluorocarbons (−85 °F). "Swimming" of the conductors during the thermoplastic manufacturing operations limits the conductor spacing to 0.015 inches under normal conditions. The FEP plastics have excellent resistance to acids, alkalies, and organic solvents, and are readily hand soldered.

Film Polyimide. The most stable of the thermoplastic materials contains a thin film of FEP plastic which permits heat sealing. The extremely stable base permits etched line accuracies up to 60% greater than the non-polyimide types. This material accepts all methods of soldering. However, dip and wave soldering require a 1 hour bake-out at 150 °F to 175 °F to remove all moisture. The dimensional stability and electrical characteristics are dependent only on delaminating which will occur at temperatures above 314 °F and altitudes above 70,000 feet.

The high heat that is applied during the manufacturing operations and the heat applied during high volume soldering at assembly tend to increase the adherence of the bonds in all of the thermosetting materials. The "float" or "swim" of the conductors during manufacturing and assembly of the wiring and cabling is almost totally eliminated.

Film/Polyimide. This material is used extensively in military and high reliability commercial applications because of its high tensile strength, (10,000 PSI), and dielectric strength, (3300 VDC). Film/polyimide has a very low thermal expansion of 0.02 inch to 0.04 inches. However, long periods of exposure to high temperatures will cause a cosmetic change. The film will become so dense that it appears to be black, this change is in appearance only and does not effect the physical or electrical characteristics.

Design and Producibility

The limitations and applications of some of the flexible circuit materials in frequent use today are:

- Mylar (Polyethylene Terepthalate) - MIL-I-631, type G: The primary applications for this material are flexible circuits in calculators, automotive, and other low cost units where little or no soldering is required. The operating temperature is 106 °C. A polyester adhesive or vinyl is used for bonding the conductor surfaces.
- Teflon® FEP type A (Fluorinated Ethylene Propalene) L-P-523B: Due to the unpredictable and erratic shrinkage characteristics during bonding at the thermoplastic temperature (515 °F), this material is seldom used by itself. It is often specified for circuits requiring a low dielectric constant (2.2), but must be used with a modified adhesive system.

When extra flexibility is required with the Kapton® circuits, a covercoat of FEP is often used. FEP is not recommended in applications where plated-through-holes are required due to its known lubricity.

- Teflon® FEP Type C (with modified adhesive): The FEP surface must be pretreated with a C treatment (C10 is one side only and C20 is two sides) to insure a favorable bond of the adhesive system to the Teflon® .
- HF Film - Kapton® MIL-P-46112, Type 2: HF Film is a Kapton® F with FEP on one or two sides depending on the application. Before the development of the new adhesive systems this film was used extensively for flexible circuits. How-

ever, problems were encountered in circuit movement (swimming) and shrinkage. Because of the high temperatures required for bonding a thermal plastic, additional surface treatments of the conductor (copper) foil were necessary. The Black Oxide and Ebonal C processes were the most widely used for treating the copper foil for bonding. These processes caused a surface condition known as "Dendrites" which allowed the FEP to lock around the irregularities in the surfaces. This material is rarely in use today due to the problems stated above.

- H Film Kapton® MIL-P-46112 Type 1: This material replaces the Type 2 HF film described above. Several suppliers apply their own modified versions of adhesive, in epoxy or acrylic, to the Kapton® film. In this form the bond strength and extended operating temperature ranges, along with the lower thermal setting bonding temperatures allow circuits to be manufactured with greater ease. It also provides the ability to meet the requirements of MIL-P-50884B.

My recommendation to users of flexible wire assemblies in selecting materials is to address the unique requirements of their specific application rather than simply selecting the lowest cost material. The good designer will seek the advice of a reputable flexible circuit manufacturer to avoid costly misjudgements.

FLEXIBLE CIRCUIT COVERCOAT

After the flexible circuit has been etched or formed it must be protected from moisture, contamination, and many other potential damaging effects. This is usually accomplished by bonding an adhesive coated dielectric film to the surface of the circuit. There are other less common methods of bonding the covercoat, but due to the cost and the problems encountered they will not be discussed here.

Melt-Bonded and Adhesive-Bonded Covercoats

In melt-bonding (fusion-bonding), the thermoplastic film is adhered to the metal foil in a platen press or roll laminator. Heat and pressure are applied to melt the film momentarily, then it is cooled while still under pressure to resolidify it. The metal foil must be specially treated prior to bonding, to insure an acceptable adhesion by melt bonding. The fluorocarbon and polyvinyl chloride flexible circuits are generally melt-bonded.

Adhesive Bonding

A number of factors led to development of newer circuit types based on the adhesive bonded construction. One of the major advantages of adhesive bonding is the ability to utilize high quality insulating materials such as polyester and polyimide films. These films are not suitable for melt-bonding. A second advantage of adhesive-bonds is the improved dimensional control of the circuit pattern resulting when the etched circuit is not remelted in the covercoat lamination step. In the adhesive-bonded circuits, standard practice is to use the same dielectric film material in both the base laminate and the covercoat film.

Liquid Covercoats

Flexible circuit assemblies where a liquid covercoat is formed from a solution will eliminate the need for the lamination of a prepunched and preformed film over the circuit and will also eliminate the high heat and pressure of the laminating process. The liquid covercoat has a number of advantages in cost, freedom of design, reliability and repairability.

The cost savings gained with the liquid covercoat represent a major advantage since the plastic films are very expensive compared to the liquid coating materials. The plastic films must be pre-cut and pre-punched prior to lamination and these operations add considerably to cost in terms of equipment, labor, and material loss in scrap from the cutting. The lamination in the platen press or roll press is another expensive operation and the heat and pressure can be harmful to the base material. In addition, there is the possibility of undesirable dimensional changes. A second advantage in the liquid covercoat is the acceptability of materials that are not satisfactory in the plastic films. The melt-bonded insulations are limited to the thermoplastic films. The liquid covercoats may be applied using thermosetting materials.

Flexible circuits constructed with the liquid covercoat are very repairable since they can be selectively stripped with chemical solvent, and easily repaired by brushing on a new covercoat in the damaged area. Enhanced repairability may also result from the use of low-melting solder-through covercoats which melt or vaporize under the heat of the soldering iron.

The elimination of the high heat and pressure cycle required in the plastic film covercoat process permits closer conductor spacing, does not adversely affect the bond between the conductor and the base circuit dielectric, provides better dimensional control, and results in less damage to the plated-through holes in double sided and multilayer constructions. The liquid covercoats, demonstrate more ability to fill the space between closely spaced conductors, where the laminated films have a tendency to "bridge" over these spaces leaving the conductor edges incompletely sealed against wicking of moisture and contaminates, (some manufacturers have overcome this problem by increasing the thickness of the adhesive when using film overcoat.)

On the other hand, the plastic laminated films can be completely free of pinholes and porosity which are problems common to covercoats. For the highest dielectric strength and integrity the laminated films will no doubt prove superior for some time to come.

During the application and curing cycle of the liquid covercoat the liquid is converted to a polymer film. The properties of this film must meet the following general requirements.

- Good adhesion to the base circuit material.
- Sufficient flexibility and flexibility life for the specific application.
- Provide environmental protection against moisture and contamination.
- Provide required electrical properties (dielectric strength, dielectric constant, dissipation factor, etc.)
- Must maintain all of its physical properties throughout the product life.
- Provide solder resistance properties and resist solder flux solvents.
- Provide a good apperance when completed.
- Meet any additional requirements imposed by the customer.

A unique requirement of the coatings used in flexible circuits is the requirement for a high degree of flexibility. This factor sets these coatings apart from the conventional solder-resistant coatings and conformal coatings used for rigid printed circuits. The coatings used for rigid printed circuits require only sufficient flexibility to prevent cracking during thermal cycling due to the expansion and contraction of the circuit. This allows the use of almost brittle materials such as alkyd-melamine, rigid epoxy, or similar systems. In the construction of flexible circuits, the degree of flexibility is not the same in all applications. In some applications where the circuit is not flexed in service, its flexibility need only be sufficient to permit normal handling in assembly and servicing. Where the flexible circuit will be exposed to frequent folding or rolling particulary at low temperatures, the materials must be selected to withstand such abuse.

The capability of the polymer films used in the construction of flexible circuits to meet the requirements at the low temperatures are specified by the Institute of Printed Circuits. See Table

6-5. The thermoplastic films have a high degree of ductility which is hard to attain in the thermosetting polymer films or the thermosetting polymers used in the liquid coating formulations. Polyurethane, butyl, and the silicone elastomers have proven to be very successful in the liquid coatings where the dimensional support is provided by the film used for the circuit base.

Covercoats for Polyimide Circuits

The polyimide materials combine excellent overall properties with a high temperature capability. In many applications, the dimensional stability, toughness, low temperature flexibility, and flame resistance is of greater concern than heat resistance, although polyimides are capable of operating up to 250 °C. The Polyimide-FEP (fluoronated ethylene propylene) melt bonded construction with a laminated film covercoat is a much simpler product and will operate at temperatures up to 200 °C. In order to reduce manufacturing costs, epoxy adhesives and other heat resistant adhesives have been developed. These adhesives will reduce the upper temperature range slightly, but will maintain other desirable properties. Table 6-6 presents test data on four types of covercoats developed for use with adhesive bonded polyimide constructions. A silicone coating provides the best heat resistance. Epoxy has the best moisture and abrasion resistance, and the polyurethane provides a good combination of low temperature flexibility and moisture protection. Butyl rubber coatings give excellent low temperature flexibility and moisture resistance, but they lack heat resistance. The polyimide films, however, are not the best selection for high humidity applications.

Table 6-5. Cable Type Specifications.

Type	Temperature Range	Self-Extinguishing	Materials
AN	0 to 65 C	No	Polyvinyl Chloride
AS	−20 C to 105 C	Yes	Polyvinyl Chloride
BN	−20 C to 105 C	No	Polyester (Heterogeneous)
BS		Yes	Polyester (Heterogeneous) or FEP ("C" bond)
C*	−40 C to 200 C	Yes	FEP (Melt bond) or polyimide FEP (Melt bond) or TFE (Homogeneous)
D*	−40 C to 250 C	Yes	TFE (Homogeneous) or Polyimide (Polyimide bond)

*Plated conductors are recommended at this temperature.

Covercoats for Polyester Circuits

The polyester construction using the adhesive bonding methods constitute the largest volume of flexible circuit and flexible cable sales. This type of circuit construction provides acceptable stability at a low cost. The service temperature range is limited to -20 °C to 105 °C. Since these circuits are generally used in highly competitive applications, the use of the liquid covercoat appears to be very attractive. Table 6-7 gives the test results of several promising liquid covercoats. The polyester and acrylic covercoats allow solder connections to be made directly through the coating since the heat from the soldering iron is sufficient to melt through the coating material. This must be done with extreme care so that the base circuit is not damaged. Stripping the acrylic coating may also be accomplished with solvents that will not attack the polyester film base materials.

Covercoats for PVC Circuits

PVC is even less expensive than the polyester materials and it is capable of providing good environmental protection within its temperature range. The major limitation of this type of construction in the more complex circuits is its dimensional instability. This problem occurs in the covercoat lamination process where high heat and pressure are required to melt the covercoat and force it between the etched conductors and fuse it with the base film. Conductor "swimming" becomes a serious problem and is difficult to control. The use of a low temperature curing liquid covercoat eliminates this step. The base laminate is formed by melt bonding or adhesive bonding and the covercoat is applied after etching by spraying or screening. Table 6-8 shows the test results of one type of system that promises adequate performance at a relatively low cost.

ADHESIVES

The adhesives used in the manufacturing of flexible circuits and cables fall into two general categories:

Thermoplastics	Thermosetting
FEP	Phenolic-butynal
Polyester	Epoxy
Polyethylene	Polyimide
	Cross-linked polyester
	Acrylic

132

Table 6-6. Liquid Covercoats on Polyimide Circuits.

Covercoat material	Low temp. flexibility (1/8" mandrel bend at temp. shown)	Insulation resistance in humidity (IPC-FC-240A comb pattern 96 hrs @ 35 °C & 90% R.H. megohms)	Insulation Resistance at elevated temp. (IPC-FC-240A comb pattern Megohms)			Solderability
			105 °C	130 °C	155 °C	
Silicone RTV	Passes −65 °C	100	6,000	400	40	Solder resist
Flexible epoxy	Passes −35 °C	200,000	4,500	530	150	Solder resist
Polyurethane	Passes −65 °C	1,000	1,800	100	50	Solder resist
Butyl rubber	Passes −65 °C	30,000	350	50	20	Not a resist
No covercoat	Passes −65 °C	30	1,600	130	20	Solderable

Table 6-7. Liquid Covercoats on Polyester Circuits.

Covercoat material	Low temp. flexibility (1/8" mandrel bend at temp. shown)	Insulation resistance in humidity (IPC-FC-240A comb pattern 96 hrs @ 35 °C & 90% R.H. megohms)	Insulation Resistance at elevated temp. (IPC-FC-240A comb pattern Megohms)			Solderability
			90 °C	105 °C	130 °C	
Polyester	Passes −65 °C	2,500	3,000	1,000	160	Solder through
Acrylic	Passes −20 °C	200,000	30,000	30,000	2,700	Solder through
Polyurethane	Passes −65 °C	50,000	2,600	1,000	300	Solder through
No covercoat	Passes −65 °C	20,000	4,500	1,400	220	Non-solderable

133

Table 6-8. Liquid Covercoats on PVC Circuits.

Property/test method	Liquid Vinyl covercoat	No covercoat
Low temp. flexibility (1/8″ mandrel bend test)	Passes – 20 °C	Passes – 20 °C
Insulation resistance in humidity (IPC-FC-240A comb pattern (megohms) 96 hrs @ 35 °C & 90% R.H.)	2,500	30,000
Insulation resistance at elevated temperature (IPC-FC-240A comb pattern) (megohms)		
at 70 °C	1,900	2,100
at 90 °C	600	410
at 105 °C	280	200
Flammability	Self extinguishing	Self extinguishing

The designer must keep informed of the adhesives that are commercially available since the adhesives are the most researched and developed of all of the materials used in the manufacturing of flexible circuits. Figure 6-9 presents a comparative analysis of the dielectrics and adhesives available.

LAYOUT

Unfortunately, no formal training is available for the design, layout and tape-up of flexible circuits. The designer must approach this task using his or her experience in printed circuit board design, enhanced by a knowledge of the materials and processes used in the manufacturing of flexible circuits and cables.

Since most flexible circuits and flexible cables are custom designed for specific applications, the designers must develop the following information before beginning the initial layouts.

- Wire list
- Schematic diagram
- Current and voltage drop permitted for each conductor
- Capacitance limitations
- Shielding requirements
- Mechanical and environmental requirements

All of the above data is basic to deciding which of many available production techniques and materials combinations will best meet the application at the lowest cost.

There are four generally used flexible circuit dielectrics. These are Kapton, Teflon, Polyester, and Arramid paper. The adhesive systems that are used to create a homo- genious laminate are generally the least understood of the package. The table below will define some of the impor- tant factors for the everyday flex user.

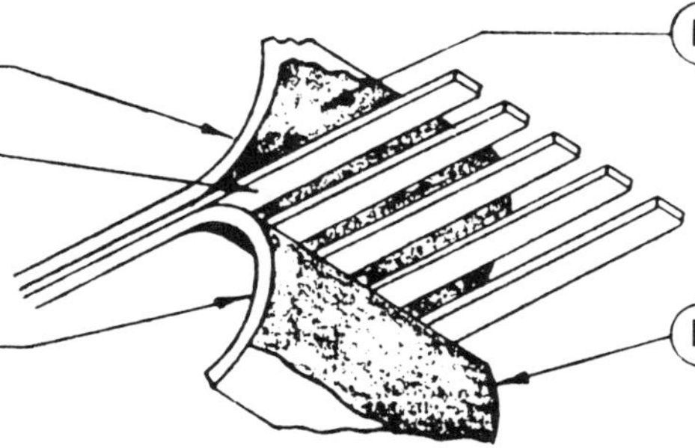

	HOW BONDED	SOLDER ABILITY	SOLVENTS RESISTANCE	MOISTURE ABSORPTION	DIMENSIONAL STABILITY
Kapton* A	Thermoset adh.	Exc.	Exc.	OK MIL-P-50884B	Exc.
Kapton* M/E	Thermo-plastic adh.	Marginal	Fair	OK MIL-P-50884B	Exc.
Kapton* F	F.E.P. Fusion to Kapton	Good	Exc.	Exc.	Fair
Nomex* M/E	Thermo-Plastic adh.	Marginal	Fair	Fair	Poor
Polyester M/E	Thermo-Plastic adh.	Poor	Poor	Fair	Poor
Teflon* A	Thermoset adh.	Good	Exc.	Exc.	Poor
Teflon* fusion	F.E.P. fusion	Good	Exc.	Exc.	Poor

*MIL-1-50884-B—No failures during tests to mil spec encountered.

© Registered Trademark DuPont Co.

Fig. 6-9. Comparison of dielectrics and adhesives.

135

Electrical Parameters

The electrical requirements that will influence the design must be fully established.

- The schematic diagram must be complete, the circuit components selected, current, voltage, and the signals identified for each conductor, as well as any shielding requirements. This information establishes the criteria governing the layout and is the basis for the design (where the designer is allowed the freedom of pin address, the layout is usually simplified and can be generated at a lower cost, and the design may be greatly enhanced).
- A wire list and/or wiring diagram (though not always available), is the most useful tool to use in generating the layout of the flexible circuit since it identifies each conductor of the circuit.

Mechanical Parameters

The mechanical requirements are also necessary to insure that the layout and artwork will be accurate.

- The chassis configuration defining the locations of all of the connectors and components, and their installation tie-down requirements.
- Drilling data and hole tabulations must be established to insure an accurate and producible circuit.
- Component specification sheets must be supplied to the designer with all of the dimensional data.
- The environmental requirements, operating temperatures, altitude, storage life, moisture, etc.

Documentation

The complete documentation package will consist of the artwork masters (photographed on 0.007 mil stable based mylar or glass), schematic diagram, wire lists, wiring diagram, mechanical drawings and specifications, and the top assembly drawing. With the design parameters available and understood, the mechanical layout is the place to start making the cost savings in the design.

The finished circuit or cable size is primarily governed by the space available in the using unit. The selection of materials is governed by the intended application of the unit into which it will be installed.

The layout is simplified when the wire list calls out terminals rather than pin-to-pin conductor runs. The designer should attempt to keep the conductor cross-overs to a minimum to reduce the number of flexible circuit layers required.

Conductor Spacing

Once the conductor width is selected, using Fig. 6-10, the space between the conductors is the next consideration. The conductor spacing is often chosen by the manufacturing considerations rather than the electrical performance requirements, since the voltages are normally very low and most materials used in flexible circuits can withstand 300 V/mil or greater. Normally the conductor spacing will be between 0.010 and 0.050 inches, but when required, spacing has been as little as 0.003 inches.

The Layout

Working at any convenient scale, place all of the connectors

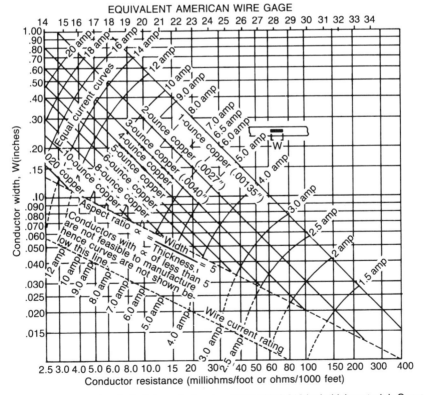

Fig. 6-10. Design chart for single flat conductors insulated with 0.010 inch thick material. Curves shown allow a 10 degrees C rise a 20 degrees C ambient temperature.

137

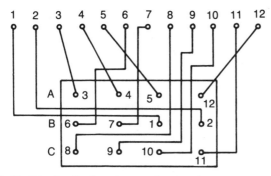

Fig. 6-11. Flexible circuitry layout example, step 1.

and circuit components in their relative positions, and determine the physical restrictions of the circuit (clearance at the edges for the card guides, etc.). Using the schematic, interconnect the various points. At this time it will become evident where the need for cross-overs will be required, and if a multilayer circuit must be used.

Begin the layout by reducing the number of layers at the points of the greatest concentration. This is usually at a connector. First find, identify, and list all of the common terminals. Then arrange the layers to minimize the cross-overs at the area of the highest density. Continue the reduction of the cross-overs to the less dense areas until they are at an absolute minimum.

Figure 6-11 shows 12 wires from various points routed to the connector using four layers of circuitry. Figure 6-12 demonstrates one solution to the crossover problem using 3 layers of circuitry, but uses added circuit area. Figure 6-13 shows the hookup in 3 layers with a reduction in circuit area. The final pass, in Fig. 6-14 shows the crossover problem solved and a minimum circuit area required. Thus, the principal of fanning out from the areas of highest conductor density to the areas of lesser conductor density proves best and at lowest cost.

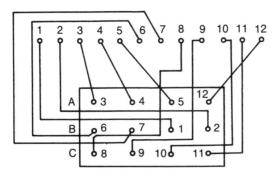

Fig. 6-12. Flexible circuitry layout example, step 2.

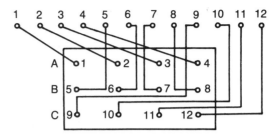

Fig. 6-13. Flexible circuitry layout example, step 3.

Terminal Areas (Pads)

All of the pads should be made as large as possible without violating the space requirements. Whenever possible, the following standards should be used.

- Pad a minimum of three times the hole size (absolute minimum of 0.005 inches of copper around the hole).
- Whenever possible, tie the pads down with ears.
- Fillet all sharp bends to reduce stress concentrations.
- Specify the hole size to $+/-0.005$ inches.

Since most circuits terminate in copper pads, consideration should be given to typical hardware shapes and mating with the connector pins. An annular ring must be provided completely around the hole to insure an acceptable solder junction. In some instances, the pad and hole cannot be designed in this manner and an alternate geometry must be used. Odd shaped pads are acceptable when they provide sufficient surface area for the solder joint, however, they must have at least 0.005 inches of copper completely surrounding the hole.

Access Windows

Most flexible circuits are insulated on both sides and access

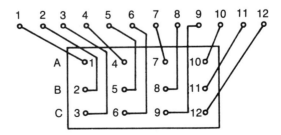

Fig. 6-14. Flexible circuitry layout example, step 4.

windows must be added to facilitate soldering the circuit components to the circuit. These insulation windows should overlap the circuit pads as much as possible, to provide additional hold-down for the pads. This technique helps strengthen the circuit. Access to the pads can be made by chemical milling in some materials.

Other insulation (such as Teflon®) must be end-milled. The accuracy of the hole size and position is best when the circuit is manufactured on N.C. equipment. Many manufacturers use prepunched covercoats which, when properly aligned, will eliminate both the chemical milling and the end mill operations.

Folding and Rolling

For cables that are to be folded or rolled, a radius of 10 to 12 times the circuit thickness should be provided. A cable that is slightly too long will still function, but a cable that is too short and too tight will be likely to crack. As the number of layers increases, the necessary radius will vary, and a section at the bend area should be left unbonded. When several layers are unlaminated at a tight bend, each layer should be progressively longer to create a book binder effect which results in a more uniform radius with reduced stresses. Avoid the "I" beam affect which results when conductors lay parallel with eyelets or feed-through holes at a bend area. In applications where the flexible cable will not see constant flexing in service and only minor flexing during assembly and maintenance, avoid specifying unnecessry testing and test fixtures which add considerably to the manufacturing cost.

Tear Resistance

Attention to the tear resistance of a cable or circuit is an extremely important consideration. Many flexible circuit users demonstrate little appreciation for the handling of these circuits. It is essential to design anti-tear features into the circuits to enable them to withstand the rigorous handling during the production phase. Some of the common features include:

- Largest possible radius at all internal corners.
- Attach backer boards at the connector and component areas.
- Potting of the connectors to the cable.
- Apply a bead of soft potting material at the board to flex interface to provide a strain relief.
- Include a glass-cloth in the laminate at all internal corners.
- Add an FEP type C film (with adhesive) to the outside surface at all internal corners.

140

Training of the manufacturing personnel in the proper handling and care of flexible circuits and cables will pay off by the reduction or elimination of tearing attributed to abusive handling.

SHIELDING

Many shielding requirements can be avoided by close attention to the conductor locations within the flexible circuit. Sensitive conductors can be positioned away from radiating lines during the artwork layout to avoid "cross-talk". Also, grounded shield conductors can be placed adjacent to the sensitive conductors to provide the required isolation. When additional shielding is required, it can be accomplished by the use of thin copper foils, copper mesh foils, or screened-on silver filled epoxy in the external surfaces. Care must be taken in the multilayer applications where the shields must be positioned between the layers. To maintain proper flexibility, the layer stack-up is critical. A cross-hatch pattern in the artwork provides a means of controlling the flexibility when the shielding is needed at the inner layers. This cross-hatching circuit functions best when it is made of dead soft copper foil.

Twisted Pairs

Flexible circuits have effectively coped with the requirements of twisted shielded pairs by implementing one or more c: the following methods:

Transposed Pair. This is a zig-zag crossing network with plated-through holes that achieve a twisted pair condition.

Isolated Conductors. Parallel conductors are placed with an isolating ground conductor on both sides of the signal conductor.

Coincident Straight Pair. Paired conductors are placed in a one-over-one configuration which positions them approximately 0.004 inches apart due to the insulation thickness of the base laminate.

Although the coincident method displays favorable electrical characteristics, the construction forms an "I" beam which will reduce the flexibility of the circuit in the bend areas.

PRODUCIBILITY

The dimension and tolerances used for rigid components and metal parts cannot be used in the design of flexible circuitry due to the many varibles and material instabilities. Process step tolerances that have a direct bearing on the flexible circuit are:

• Artwork master pattern: +/– 0.002 to +/– 0.005 (+/–

0.002 is preferred for layer to layer alignment)
- Programming: +/ 0.002
- Drilling machine & drift: +/− 0.0015
- Artwork composite: +/= 0.002
- Lamination: built in stresses
- Etching: removes copper and stress relieves but may cause circuit position to change.
- Lamination of covercoat
- Punching and die cutting
- Solder coat: causes temperature cycling.

Several of the items listed above represent inconsistencies which contribute to the instability of the flexible circuit. In addition, the hydroscopic nature of Kapton® can vary the thickness by +/− 0.0015 inch/inch. Care must be taken when tolerancing the flexible circuit as shown here.

FLEXIBLE CABLE CONNECTORS

The following figures present data on some of the common connectors in use with flexible cables and how they are addressd. Before designing the cable connector termination the dimensional data for the connector is required. This information must include the pin diameter, pin length, and pin spacing.

Round - Radial Pins

The connectors with a round radial pin pattern offer two methods of addressing the cable. When the pin spacing is relatively large, (0.150 to 0.200 inches) the conductors can be routed between the pins of the outer ring for a simple right-angled address, as shown in Fig. 6-15, or they may be addressed by the right-angled bilateral address technique as shown in Fig. 6-16. When the pin density does not allow routing between the pins of the outer ring pattern, a fold-out technique may be employed to reach the inner ring of pins, Fig. 6-17. More than one layer of circuit can be attached to the same pin pattern providing that the layers do not have the same pin address, i.e., all of the connections to pin 1 will be on the same layer, and all of the connections to pin 2 will be the same layer, and so on.

Fig. 6-15. Right-angled address to a round connector with radial rows. Conductors must pass between pins.

142

Fig. 6-16. Right-angled bilateral address to a round connector with radial rows. Conductors must pass between pins.

Round - Straight Pins

The connectors with straight rows of pins offer a greater variety of address techniques. They can be addressed by any of the techniques shown in Figs. 6-18 through 6-20.

Rectangular - Staggered

The rectangular connectors, with the pins in staggered rows on 0.100 inch spacing or greater, are easily addressed with a single layer right angle address as shown in Fig. 6-21, or by branching the cable to achieve in-line or everted modes as shown in Figs. 6-22 and 6-23.

Rectangular - Straight

Connectors with two rows of pins on 0.100 inch centers will generally permit routing of the conductors through the first row to an angled connection to the back row of pins as shown in Fig. 6-24. The connectors with more than two rows of pins should employ the branched cables with in-line or everted style addressing. See Fig. 6-25.

Board Edge

Flexible circuits can be terminated to a rigid printed circuit to make an effective removable unit which will mate with standard

Fold-out

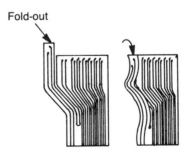

Fig. 6-17. Fold-out flexible circuit to reach the inner pins.

143

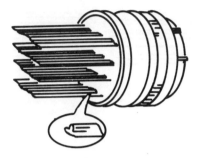

Fig. 6-18. In-line address to a round connector with straight rows of pins.

Fig. 6-19. Everted address to a round connector with straight rows of pins.

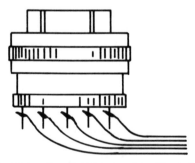

Fig. 6-20. Everted address to a round connector with straight rows of pins, using cables grouped horizontally.

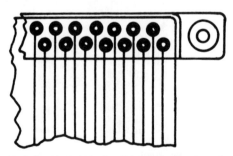

Fig. 6-21. Rectangular connector in staggered row geometry.

144

Fig. 6-22. In-line address to a rectangular multirow connector.

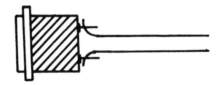

Fig. 6-23. Everted address to a rectangular multirow connector.

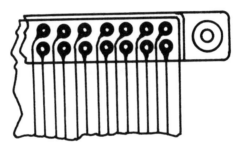

Fig. 6-24. Rectangular connectors with straight row pin layout.

Fig. 6-25. In-line address refers to the parallel geometry of pin and conductor.

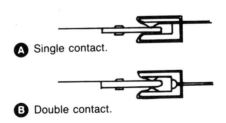

Fig. 6-26. Typical female recepticals used with flexible circuit male plugs.

printed circuit edge connector types. This can be accomplished in two ways. The flexible circuit can be lap soldered and adhesive bonded for structural support, or the flexible circuit can be wrapped around the rigid backing board. Both types will mate with either the single row contact connector or a double row contact connector. See Fig. 6-26.

Other types of flexible cable connections are shown in Figs. 6-27 through 6-29. Permanent connections can be made to flexible

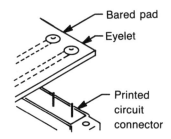

Fig. 6-27. Flexible circuit connection with bared pad and eyelet.

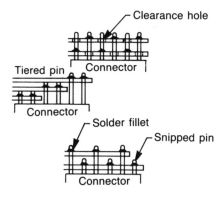

Fig. 6-28. Multilayer cable connector approaches.

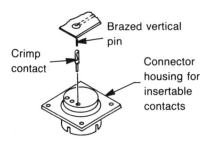

Fig. 6-29. Crimp insertable connector.

146

circuits by soldering, crimping, or welding external leads directly to the circuit land areas or eyelets. Terminal posts or solderless terminals are also installed in the flexible circuits to reinforce the points of termination.

Chapter 7

Coaxial Cables

Coaxial cable is the most versatile type of cable in use today. Its development is one of the truly great milestones in the science of long distance communications.

Coaxial cable is used when the distributed capacity must be held constant over the entire length of the line. Coaxial cable is a variant of multiconductor wire. In coaxial cable, one conductor follows a precise concentric path through another and the space between is filled by an insulating material. It is extremely important that the concentricity be maintained over the entire length of cable. If the relationship between the shielding and the inner wire is permitted to vary the circuit efficiency will be affected.

When a coaxial cable is bent, the minimum bend radius should never be less than ten times the outside diameter of the cable, since a tighter bend will cause the dielectric to cold flow, which will cause creeping of the inner wire at the bend.

Coaxial cables are selected with regard to the impedance and attenuation of the specified design frequencies. A large number of forms are commercially available. The most common type is the cable consisting of a stranded or solid inner conductor, a dielectric, an outer conductor of braided shielding, and a protective insulating material covering the braid.

In a low-capacity coaxial line, the dielectric is air. The inner and outer conductors are separated by widely spaced insulators. The effect of this construction is to lower the effective capacitance. The RG- 62/U coaxial cable is an example of the air dielectric cable.

In a delay line, the high impedance is achieved by spiraling the inner conductor. A single foot of this cable may have an impedance that is equivalent to 15 feet of a standard coaxial cable.

Using a telephone line with conventional wire as an example for explaining the functions of coaxial cables, the wires are paired on the telephone poles, one pair being used for each phone circuit. The transmission of signals over wire lines requires two conductors to complete the circuit, one is the "go" wire and the other is the "return" wire. On some telephone circuits only the "go" wire is mounted on the poles and the earth is used for the return. Often the pairs of wires for phone circuits are bundled together in groups of 1800 pairs (3600 separate wires) and jacketed to form a "multipair cable". In each of these methods the wires carrying the conversation signals are exposed to external interference. Lightning will cause static, moisture (rain) can cause leakage across the insulators and result in a frying noise in the telephone receiver, faults on power transmission lines cause other noises that interfere with the conversation. The proximity of the pairs of wires carrying signals, particularly in multipair cables will often result in cross-talk, and the listener will faintly hear another conversation being picked up from a nearby pair.

Another problem in communication on conventional wire pairs is high attenuation. The signals get weaker as they travel along the wire and amplifiers are required to boost the signal energy along the path so the signal will remain above the line noise. The second problem, and the most economically important, is the bandwidth. A phone conversation can be carried if the circuit transmits audible tones in the range of 300 hertz to 2500 hertz. It is also possible to carry more than one conversation at the same time on a single pair of wires by *frequency multiplexing*. While the conversation is carried on the 300 Hertz to 2500 Hertz band, frequency multiplexing causes the second conversation to be carried on the 3000 Hertz to 5200 Hertz band, the third on the 5700 Hertz to 7900 Hertz band, and so on. Each conversation requires 2200 Hertz with a "guard band" of 500 Hertz between to prevent mixing (cross-talk). Each of the signals is converted back to the 300 Hertz to 2500 Hertz band at the telephone receiver. The number of conversations that a pair of wires can carry is limited by the relatively low upper limit of frequency that conventional wires can transmit. Coaxial cable was developed as a solution to these problems.

DESIGN OF COAXIAL CABLES

In coaxial cable the "go" conductor is the inner (center) wire, a solid or stranded copper wire of comparatively small diameter, surrounded by a very heavy insulation—the dielectric. But the return conductor is not a wire in the coaxial cable. It is a copper tube or shield completely surrounding the "go" wire and the dielectric. It is concentric with the center conductor, hence the term coaxial. No external interference can affect the signal because it is carried by currents completely shielded by the "return" conductor. Figure 7-1 shows the makeup of coaxial cable.

Coaxial cable has an extremely broad bandwidth and will transmit signals from zero (direct current) to millions of Hertz. Literally hundreds of messages can be frequency multiplexed and transmitted simultaneously over a single coaxial cable. Even a television program can be transmitted simultaneously with hundreds of telephone conversations.

Coaxial cable with its low attenuation needs fewer amplifiers than conventional wire pairs. Fewer amplifiers are required since a single unit simultaneously boosts hundreds of signals on the cable.

Beyond its importance to the telephone industry, coaxial cable is used extensively in radio, television, radar, navigation, fire control, aircraft, shipbuilding, underwater sound, computers, and many other types of transmitting equipment. Community and cable TV systems use miles of this type of cable. Sophisticated TV systems use large diameter single or double shielded cable as a main transmission line with smaller size coaxial cables as a tapoff, and a third cable to carry the signal directly to the receiver.

The uses of coaxial cable extend to any application where signal loss and attenuation must be kept to a minimum, and where the elimination of external interference is desirable or important. The newest application for coaxial cables is in the field of instrumentation and computers where many coaxial cables contained in a common jacket form an integral unit frequently used in the computerized instrumentation field.

HOW COAXIAL CABLES ARE IDENTIFIED

Cables manufactured for the government are identified with the RG legend,

R - RADIO FREQUENCY
G - GOVERNMENT
8 - number assigned to the government approval
/U - UNIVERSAL SPECIFICATION

The letters A, B, or C before the / indicate a specification modifi-

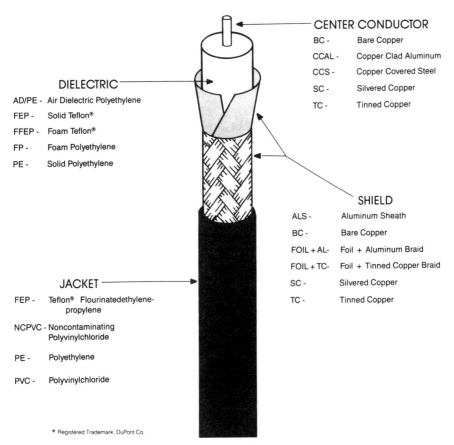

CENTER CONDUCTOR

BC -	Bare Copper
CCAL -	Copper Clad Aluminum
CCS -	Copper Covered Steel
SC -	Silvered Copper
TC -	Tinned Copper

DIELECTRIC

AD/PE -	Air Dielectric Polyethylene
FEP -	Solid Teflon®
FFEP -	Foam Teflon®
FP -	Foam Polyethylene
PE -	Solid Polyethylene

SHIELD

ALS -	Aluminum Sheath
BC -	Bare Copper
FOIL + AL-	Foil + Aluminum Braid
FOIL + TC-	Foil + Tinned Copper Braid
SC -	Silvered Copper
TC -	Tinned Copper

JACKET

FEP -	Teflon® Flourinatedethylene-propylene
NCPVC -	Noncontaminating Polyvinylchloride
PE -	Polyethylene
PVC -	Polyvinylchloride

® Registered Trademark, DuPont Co.

Fig. 7-1. Coaxial cable construction.

cation or revision. As an example: RG 8/U is superceded by RG 8A/U, but both types are still being used.

Types of coaxial cables that are not identified by the RG system are primarily intended for use in applications where government specifications are not required. There are many types of commercial cables available for specific applications where each type is identified by the vendor part numbers.

APPLICATIONS

For the selection of coaxial cables for specific design requirements, considerations of the proper materials are tabulated in Table 7-1.

Another important consideration in the selection of a coaxial cable is the required attenuation. The theoretical attenuation (A)

Table 7-1. Selection of Coaxial Cables.

	Inner conductors						Dielectrics			Outer conductors					Jackets					
	Soft bare CU	Tinned soft CU	Silver plated CU	Nickel plated CU	Tinned CAD. BRZ.	Copperweld	Polyethylene	Teflon® TFE	Butyl rubber	Soft bare CU	Tinned soft CU	Silver plated CU	Aluminum tube	Copper tube	Polyethylene	Teflon® TFE	Teflon® FEP	PVC	Neoprene	Glass braid
Max. oper. temp. °C.	200	150	200	250	150	200	80	260	80	200	150	200	—	—	80	260	200	105	90	260
Resistivity at 20 °C. ohm-cm/ft.	10.371	11.133	10.371	12.50	11.92	25.928														
Avg. tensile psi 10³	37	37	37.5	37.5	45	130	1.9	3.5	1.1						1.9	3.5	2.7	2.5	3.2	
Flexibility	Exc.	Exc.	Exc.	Exc.	Good	Good	Good	Good	Exc.	Exc.	Exc.	Exc.	Poor	Poor	Good	Good	Good	Good	Exc.	Exc.
Resist. to org. solv.							Poor	Exc.	Good						Poor	Exc.	Exc.	Poor	Good	Exc.
Resist. to acids and alkalies							Exc.	Exc.	Good						Exc.	Exc.	Exc.	Fair	Good	Exc.
Abrasion resist.															Good	Exc.	Exc.	Good	Exc.	Poor
Flame resist.															Slow burn.	Non-flam.	Non-flam.	Self ext.	Self ext.	Non-flam.

is the attenuation due to the conductors plus the attenuation of the dielectric;

$$A = 4.35 \frac{R_t}{Z_o} + 2.78 \sqrt{E} \; pF = dB \text{ per } 100 \text{ ft.}$$

Where:

R_t = Total line Resistance ohms/1000 ft.

$$R_t = 0.1 \frac{1}{d} + \frac{1}{D} \sqrt{F} \text{ (for single copper line)}$$

p = Power factor of dielectric (.0005 for Polyethylene)

F = Frequency in megahertz (MHz)

As shown in equation 7-1, the attenuation will increase as the frequency increases. In a perfect cable, the pattern of increasing attenuation would be exact and regular, however, in practical applications this is difficult to achieve, and therefore tolerances are specified as shown in Table 7-2.

The military RG specifications define the tolerances permitted on the various electrical characteristics. These tolerances will vary from cable to cable depending on the cable size and the dielectric material used. Since manufacturing coaxial cable is a "continuous" process, rather than a "batch" process, variations are encountered. To insure that there is no place in the line which could cause a high attenuation, the cable is "swept" at various frequencies at or near its intended application.

A review of the basic equation for the Characteristic Impedance:

$$Z_o = \frac{138}{\sqrt{E}} \log_{10} \frac{D}{d}$$

Where:

Z_o = Characteristic Impedance

E = Dielectric constant (air is 1).

D = Inside diameter of the *"return"* (outer) conductor (conductive metal tube or one or more braids).

d = Outside diameter of the *"go"* (inner) conductor.

indicates that a difference in the inside diameter (D) of the return line of only a few thousandths of an inch will significantly affect the impedance. In the 50 ohm group of miniature cables, the tolerances become even more important.

Even with a perfect design there still remains the practical installation and use which the cable will be subjected to. The power rating, as well as other characteristics will be affected by applica-

Table 7-2. Attenuation of Coaxial Cables.

RG/U CABLE	NOM. ATTENUATION dB/100 FT. AT THE FOLLOWING FREQUENCIES (MHZ) :									
	1	10	50	100	200	400	1000	3000	5000	10000
5, 6, 6A	—	—	—	2.7	4.2	6.4	11.3	22.0	30.0	43.0
5A, 5B, 212	.24	.78	1.8	2.6	3.9	5.5	9.1	17.8	25.0	—
7	.18	.64	1.6	2.4	3.5	5.2	—	—	—	—
8, 8A, 10, 10A, 213, 215	.15	.55	1.33	2.0	3.5	4.6	8.0	16.5	27.0	—
9	.16	.57	1.38	2.0	2.9	4.25	7.3	15.5	23.0	36.0
9A, 9B, 214	.175	.61	1.47	2.1	3.2	5.0	9.0	18.0	25.0	38.0
11, 11A, 12, 12A, 13, 13A, 216	.187	.66	1.59	2.3	3.25	4.75	7.8	16.5	26.5	—
14, 14A, 74, 74A, 217, 224	.12	.41	.98	1.4	2.05	3.10	5.5	12.4	19.0	51.
17, 17A, 18, 18A, 177, 218, 219	—	.24	.62	.95	1.5	2.4	4.4	9.5	15.3	—
19, 19A, 20, 20A, 220, 221	—	—	—	.69	1.12	1.85	3.6	7.7	—	—
21, 21A, 222	1.48	4.4	9.3	13.0	18.0	26.0	43.0	85.0	—	—
22	—	—	—	4.6	6.2	8.7	—	—	—	—
22B, 111, 111A	—	—	—	3.9	5.6	7.7	12.0	25.0	—	—
23A, 24A	—	—	—	—	—	5.2 ea.	—	—	—	—
25, 25A, 26, 26A, 27A, 28B, 64, 64A, 88, 88A	.7	—	—	—	—	—	—	—	—	—
29	—	1.20	2.95	4.4	6.5	9.6	16.2	30.0	—	—
34, 34A, 34B	—	—	.85	1.4	2.12	3.28	5.85	16.0	—	—
35, 35A, 35B, 164	—	.235	.58	.85	1.27	1.95	3.5	8.6	15.5	18.0
54, 54A	—	—	—	3.2	4.7	6.8	11.5	25.0	—	—
55, 55A, 55B, 223	—	1.2	3.2	4.8	7.0	10.3	16.7	30.7	46.0	130.
57, 57A, 130, 131	—	—	—	—	—	6.0	—	—	—	—
58, 58B	.33	1.25	3.13	4.6	6.9	10.4	17.8	37.5	60.0	—

				6.0	9.0	13.5	24.0	54.0	83.0	247.
58A, 58C	–	–	–	–	–	–	–	–	–	–
59, 59A, 59B	.335	1.07	2.4	3.4	4.85	7.0	12.0	26.5	42.0	–
62, 62A, 71, 71A, 71B	.25	.85	1.9	2.7	3.8	5.3	8.7	18.5	30.0	83.0
62B	–	–	–	–	–	7.3	–	–	–	–
62C, 317	–	–	–	–	–	8.0	–	–	–	–
63, 63B, 79, 79B	–	.62	1.39	1.99	2.8	4.0	6.4	12.2	–	–
65A	5.4	21.2	–	–	–	–	–	–	–	–
81	–	–	–	–	–	5.5	–	–	–	–
82	–	–	–	–	–	3.5	–	–	–	–
84A, 85A	–	–	–	–	–	2.8	–	–	–	–
87A, 116, 165, 166, 225, 227	.18	.60	1.42	2.07	3.05	4.45	7.60	15.0	21.5	36.5
94	–	–	–	2.2	3.3	5.0	9.0	20.	–	–
94A, 226	–	–	–	–	–	3.5	–	–	–	–
108, 108A	–	–	–	–	–	16.8	–	–	–	–
114, 114A	.95	1.34	2.05	2.9	5.4	–	–	–	–	–
115, 115A, 235	.17	.59	1.4	2.05	3.0	4.4	7.3	14.0	20.0	33.0
117, 118, 211, 228	–	.245	.61	.90	1.35	2.4	3.55	7.6	12.0	38.0
117A, 118A	–	–	–	–	–	2.3	–	–	–	–
119, 120	–	.43	1.2	1.5	2.2	3.25	5.6	11.8	17.8	56.0
122	.4	1.7	4.48	7.0	10.8	16.5	29.0	57.0	–	–
125	–	.49	1.1	1.6	2.3	3.4	5.7	13.4	–	–
126, 301	–	–	–	–	–	–	70.	116.	–	–
133A	–	–	–	–	–	5.7	–	–	–	–
140, 302	–	–	–	3.3	4.7	6.9	12.8	26.0	–	–
141, 141A, 142, 142A, 142B, 303	.34	1.13	2.68	3.85	5.6	8.5	13.8	27.0	39.0	70.0
143, 143A, 304	.25	.83	1.9	2.8	4.0	5.8	9.6	18.2	25.5	42.0

Table 7-2. Attenuation of Coaxial Cables. (Cont.)

NOM. ATTENUATION dB/100 FT. AT THE FOLLOWING FREQUENCIES (MHZ):										
RG/U CABLE	1	10	50	100	200	400	1000	3000	5000	10000
144	–	–	–	1.8	2.6	3.9	6.9	14.8	–	–
149, 150	–	–	–	–	–	8.5	–	–	–	–
156	.21	–	–	–	–	–	–	–	–	–
157	.19	–	–	–	–	–	–	–	–	–
158	.20	–	–	–	–	–	–	–	–	–
161	–	–	–	–	–	17.4	–	–	–	–
174	2.3	3.9	6.6	8.9	12.2	17.4	30.0	64.	99.	190.
178, 178A, 196	2.6	5.6	10.2	13.8	19.5	28.	46.	76.	114.	170.
178B	–	–	–	–	–	29.0	–	–	–	–
179, 179A, 187	3.0	5.3	8.1	10.0	12.6	16.0	24.	44.	64.	139.
179B	–	–	–	–	–	21.0	–	–	–	–
180, 180A	2.4	3.3	4.6	5.7	7.6	10.8	17.	35.	50.	88.
180B	–	–	–	–	–	17.0	–	–	–	–
181	–	–	–	–	–	6.0 ea.	–	–	–	–
188, 188A, 316	3.1	6.0	9.6	11.4	14.2	16.7	31.	60.	82.	136.
190, 329	.40	–	–	–	–	–	–	–	–	–
191, 230, 328	.50	–	–	–	–	–	–	–	–	–
192	.26	2.0	–	–	–	–	–	–	–	–
193, 194	.20	1.0	–	–	–	–	–	–	–	–
195A	–	2.2	–	6.6	9.5	13.3	22.5	46.0	–	–
197, 232	–	.14	.32	.4	.6	1.0	11.0	13.5	15.0	–
209	–	–	–	–	–	2.5	–	9.4	–	–

210	—	—	—	—	—	7.0	—	—	—	—
211A, 228A	—	—	—	—	—	2.3	—	10.0	—	—
231, 331, 334, 335	—	—	—	—	—	2.3	4.2	—	—	—
233, 240	—	.07	.16	.25	.33	.5	.9	2.0	—	—
234, 242	—	.035	.09	.13	.2	.29	.5	—	—	—
236, 237	—	.125	.16	.19	1.2	1.8	3.0	6.0	8.0	14.0
244, 245	—	.24	.51	.8	1.1	1.7	2.7	4.5	6.0	—
252, 253	—	.23	.51	.9	1.2	1.8	2.8	5.0	7.7	10.2
254, 255	—	.13	.27	.38	.55	.85	1.5	2.3	4.5	—
257, 258, 270, 319	—	.06	.15	.22	.31	.45	.8	1.8	—	—
264B, 264C	—	—	—	—	—	12.0	—	—	—	—
265	—	.06	.11	.18	.27	.58	1.0	—	—	—
267	—	.12	.3	.47	.68	1.0	1.7	3.0	—	—
268	—	.27	.6	.89	1.4	1.8	2.8	5.0	7.2	12.5
269, 318	—	.12	.28	.40	.6	.85	1.5	2.6	—	—
280	—	—	1.1	—	2.35	3.5	6.0	11.0	—	—
281	—	.23	.8	1.2	1.8	2.5	4.1	8.0	—	—
293	—	—	—	—	—	5.0	—	16.0	—	—
293A	—	—	—	—	—	4.0	—	15.0	—	—
294, 294A	—	—	—	—	—	10.0	—	—	—	—
295	—	—	—	—	—	3.0	—	12.5	—	—
296	—	—	—	—	—	11.0	—	—	—	—
306A, 332, 333, 336	.05	.15	.35	.5	.8	1.2	2.2	4.0	7.0	—
307A	—	—	—	—	—	7.5	—	—	—	—
360	—	.19	.40	.6	.9	1.5	2.8	6.0	9.0	—

tion factors such as flexing, bending (particularly into a radius smaller than 20 times the diameter) and variations in the atmospheric pressure (altitude).

The overall size of the cable as related to the dielectric will be influenced by the operating voltage requirements. Power rating, one of the important considerations in design is significantly influenced by the value D/d. This is the governing ratio, assuming matched lines and a 40 °C ambient temperature. Conductor temperatures are normally operated between 65 °C and 80 °C. As an example of what happens to power in relation to ambient and conductor temperature, see Fig. 7-2. To calculate an accurate power rating, consideration must be given to both the ambient and conductor temperatures. See Fig. 7-3. When the specified ambient is above 40 °C, the design should derate the cable accordingly. As an example, RG 17 has an approximate power rating of 930 Watts at 500 MHz. If the specified ambient temperature is 50 °C, the cable must be derated to 75% (a power rating of 700 watts).

THE MANUFACTURING PROCESS

The manufacturing of the RG 62/U and the RG 71/U groups requires several operations. In the first operation a polyethylene thread is spiralled around the conductor. In the second operation, the dielectric is extruded over the conductor and the spiralled thread. There is a possibility of breaking the conductor during this process due to the fact that the spiralled thread is not always constant in diameter and may cause the extruder tip to jam. This jam causes a momentary stoppage and the resulting jerking motion will result in conductor breakage.

After the extruded dielectric is completed, it is "spark tested" as part of the extrusion operation to insure that there are no holes or voids in the dielectric (the inner conductor is at ground poten-

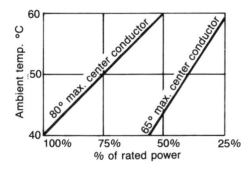

Fig. 7-2. Relation of power to ambient temperature in coaxial cable.

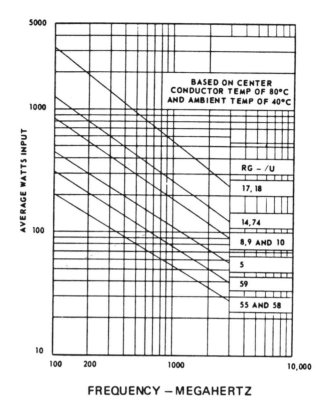

Fig. 7-3. Relation of power to frequency and temperature.

tial). Any holes or voids will create a spark failure, which will be recorded with the location and reel number so that it can be cut out before entering the next operations.

Braiding

After the extruded dielectric is completed and inspected, the next operation is braiding. As required for the specific applications of the coaxial cable by the specification, the extruded cable is braided with one or two shields. During this, and all remaining operations, the cable is kept under constant tension. After completion of the braiding operation, the cable is covered by a second extruded jacket, and is again passed through a chain electrode at high potential to detect insulation deficiencies (this time the braiding is at ground potential). When the polyethylene dielectric (solid or semi-solid) is extruded, strains may develop in the material. Theoretically, these strains will be reduced by the use of hot water in the cooling trough. As the cable is run through the trough it is taken

159

Table 7-3. Coaxial Cables Specifications.

RG/U Number	Catalog No.	Nominal Impedance	Capacitance pF/FT	Dielectric Material	Size and Type of Inner Cond.	Jacket	Shield	O/A Diameter	Wt. per 100 Ft.	Remarks
1				WAVE GUIDE						
2				WAVE GUIDE						
3				WAVE GUIDE						
4	507-4	50	30	Poly	20 BC	Blk. PVC	2BC	.226	2.5	Superseded by RG 58/U
5	507-5	52.5	28.5	Poly	16 BC	Blk. PVC	2BC	.332	8.6	Superseded by RG 5 B/U
5A	507-5A	50	29	Poly	16 S	Grey PVC	2S	.328	8.3	Superseded by RG 5 B/U
*5B	507-5B	50	28.5	Poly	16 S	Blk. L.T. PVC	2S	.332	8.7	Micro Wave Cable
6	507-6	75	20	Poly	21 CW	Grey PVC	BC-S	.332	8.0	Superseded by RG 6A/U
*6A	507-6A	75	20	Poly	21 CW	Blk. L.T. PVC	BC-S	.332	8.0	Video & Comm. Cable
7	507-7	95	12.5	SS Poly	19 BC	Blk. PVC	BC	.370	8.0	
8	507-8	52	29.5	Poly	7/21 BC	Blk. PVC	BC	.405	10.5	
*8A	507-8A	52	29.5	Poly	7/21 BC	Blk. L.T. PVC	BC	.405	10.3	
9	507-9	50	30	Poly	7/21 S	Grey PVC	BC-S	.420	13.0	
9A	507-9A	50	30	Poly	7/21 S	Grey PVC	2S	.420	13.1	
*9B	507-9B	50	30	Poly	7/21 S	Blk. L.T. PVC	2S	.420	13.2	
10	507-10	52	29.5	Poly	7/21 BC	Grey PVC	BC	.475	12.6	Superseded by RG 10A/U
*10A	507-10A	52	29.5	Poly	7/21 BC	Blk. L.T. PVC	BC	.475	12.8	RG 8A/U with Armor
11	507-11	75	20.5	Poly	7/26 TC	Blk. PVC	BC	.405	9.7	
*11A	507-11A	75	20.5	Poly	7/26 TC	Blk. L.T. PVC	BC	.405	9.3	Flex. Video & Comm.
12	507-12	75	20.5	Poly	7/26 TC	Grey PVC	BC	.475	11.6	Superseded by RG 12A/U
*12A	507-12A	75	20.5	Poly	7/26 TC	Blk. L.T. PVC	BC	.475	11.7	RG 11A/U with Armor
13	507-13	74	20.5	Poly	7/26 TC	Blk. PVC	2BC	.425	12.1	

*13A	507-13A	74	20.5	Poly	7/26 TC	Blk. L.T. PVC	2BC	.420	12.1	Flex. Video & Comm.
14	507-14	52	29.5	Poly	10 BC	Grey PVC	2BC	.545	20.3	Superseded by RG 14A/U
*14A	507-14A	52	29.5	Poly	10 BC	Blk. L.T. PVC	2BC	.545	20.5	Power Trans.
15	507-15	76	20	Poly	15 CW	Blk. PVC	2BC	.545	19.6	Superseded by RG 11A/U. RG 12A/U
16	507-16	52	29.5	Poly	.125 BC Tube	Blk. PVC	BC	.630	25.4	
17	507-17	52	29.8	Poly	.188 BC	Grey PVC	BC	.870	46.3	
*17A	507-17A	52	29.8	Poly	.188 BC	Blk. L.T. PVC	BC	.870	46.7	Low Atten.–High Power Transm.
17B	507-17B	52	29.5	Poly	.188 BC	Blk. L.T. PVC	2S	.940	47.0	Cancelled: Reassigned as RG 177/U
18	507-18	52	29.5	Poly	.188 BC	Grey PVC	BC	.945	51.5	RG 17/U with Armor
*18A	507-18A	52	29.5	Poly	.188 BC	Blk. L.T. PVC	BC	.945	51.9	RG 17A/U with Armor
19	507-19	52	29.5	Poly	.250 BC	Grey PVC	BC	1.120	74.5	
*19A	507-19A	52	29.5	Poly	.250 BC	Blk. L.T. PVC	BC	1.120	74.0	Low Atten.–High Power Transm.
20	507-20	52	29.5	Poly	.250 BC	Grey PVC	BC	1.195	92.5	RG 19/U with Armor
*20A	507-20A	52	29.5	Poly	.250 BC	Blk. L.T. PVC	BC	1.195	92.5	RG 19A/U with Armor
21	507-21	53	29	Poly	16N	Grey PVC	2S	.332	8.3	
*21A	507-21A	53	29	Poly	16N	Blk. L.T. PVC	2S	.332	8.4	High A tten. w/Small Temp. Coeff of Atten.
22	507-22	95	16	Poly	Two 7/.0152 BC	Blk. PVC	TC	.405	10.3	
22A	507-22A	95	16	Poly	Two 7/.0152 BC	Grey PVC	2TC	.420	11.9	Superseded by RG 22B/U
*22B	507-22B	95	16	Poly	Two 7/.0152 BC	Blk. L.T. PVC	2TC	.420	12.0	Balanced Twin Cond.
23	507-23	125	12	Poly	Two 7/21 BC	Blk. PVC	2BC	.650 x.945	38.0	Superseded by RG 23A/U
*23A	507-23A	125	12	Poly	Two 7/21 BC	Blk. L.T. PVC	2BC	.650 x.945	36.0	
24	507-24	125	12	Poly	Two 7/21 BC	Blk. PVC	2BC	.735 x1.034	43.0	Superseded by RG 24A/U
*24A	507-24A	125	12	Poly	Two 7/21 BC	Blk. L.T. PVC	2BC	.735 x1.034	41.0	RG 23A/U with Armor
*25	507-25	48	50	Rub.	19/.0117 TC	CHLORO.	2TC	.565	20.5	H.V. Pulse Cable

* Covered by Spec. Mil-C-17

● STANDARD WIRE & CABLE CO.

Table 7-3. Coaxial Cables Specifications. (Cont.)

RG/U Number	Catalog No.	Nominal Impedance	Capacitance pF/FT	Dielectric Material	Size and Type of Inner Cond.	Jacket	Shield	O/A Diameter	Wt. per 100 Ft.	Remarks
*25A	507-25A	48	50	Rub.	19/.0117TC	CHLORO.	2TC	.505	20.5	H.V. Pulse Cable
*26	507-26	48	50	Rub.	19/.0117TC	CHLORO.	TC	.525	18.9	Pulse Cable — Armored
*26A	507-26A	48	50	Rub.	19/.0117TC	CHLORO.	TC	.505	18.9	Pulse Cable — Armored
27	507-27	48	50	Rub.	19/.0185TC	Blk. PVC	TC	.675	30.4	H.V. Pulse Cable
*27A	507-27A	48	50	Rub.	19/.0185TC	CHLORO.	TC	.670	30.4	H.V. Pulse Cable
28	507-28	50	50	Rub.	19/.0185TC	CHLORO.	TC-GW	.805	37.0	Pulse Cable
28A	507-28A	50	50	Rub.	19/.0185TC	Rub. over Armor	TC	.805	37.0	Pulse Cable 55°C Use
*28B	507-28B	48	50	Rub.	19/.0185TC	CHLORO.	TC-GW	Max. .750	37.0	
29	507-29	53.5	28.5	Poly	20 BC	Poly	TC	.184	2.2	Superseded by RG 58/U
30	507-30	50	27	Copo.	7/26 BC	Blk. PVC	BC	.250	4.4	Superseded by RG 58/U
31	507-31	51	31	Copo.	7/21 BC	Blk. PVC	BC	.405	10.6	Superseded by RG 8/U
32	507-32	51	29	Copo.	7/21 BC	Blk. PVC	BC	.465	14.1	Superseded by RG 10A/U
33	507-33	51	30	Poly	10 BC	Lead	None	.470	39.0	
34	507-34	71	21.5	Poly	7/21 BC	Blk. PVC	BC	.625	22.9	Superseded by RG 34B/U
34A	507-34A	71	21.5	Poly	7/.0249 BC	Blk. L.T. PVC	BC	.630	22.9	High Power, Low Atten. Flex. Superseded by RG 34B/U
*34B	507-34B	75	21.5	Poly	7/.0249 BC	Blk. L.T. PVC	BC	.630	22.4	
35	507-35	71	21.5	Poly	9 BC	Grey PVC	BC	.945	45.4	Armored
35A	507-35A	71	21.5	Poly	9 BC	Blk. L.T. PVC	BC	.945	45.8	Armored—High Power Low Atten.
*35B	507-35B	75	21.5	Poly	.1045 BC	Blk. L.T. PVC	BC	Max. .945	52.5	Armored
36	507-36	69	22	Poly	6 BC	Blk. PVC	BC	1.180	80.5	Armored
37	507-37	52.5	38	Rub.	20 TC	Poly	TC	.210	4.0	Superseded by RG 58/U
38	507-38	52.5	38	Rub.	17 TC	Poly	2TC	.312	11.0	Superseded by RG 5/U

39	507-39	72.5	28.6	Rub.	22 TCW	Poly	2TC	.312	10.0	Superseded by RG 6/U, RG 59/U
40	507-40	72.5	28	Rub.	22 TCW	CHLORO.	2TC	.420	15.0	Superseded by RG 6/U
41	507-41	67.5	27.6	Rub.	16/30 TC	CHLORO.	TC	.425	15.0	
42	507-42	78.6	20	Poly	21 N	Grey PVC	2S	.342	5.6	Superseded by RG 21A/U
43	507-43	95	17.6	Copo.	Two-7/21 BC	Blk. PVC	BC	.617	—	Superseded by RG 57A/U
44	507-44	Stub Supported Coaxial								
45	507-45	Stub Supported Coaxial								
46	507-46	Stub Supported Coaxial								
47	507-47	Stub Supported Coaxial								
48	507-48			WAVE GUIDE						
49	507-49			WAVE GUIDE						
50	507-50			WAVE GUIDE						
51	507-51			WAVE GUIDE						
52	507-52			WAVE GUIDE						
53	507-53			WAVE GUIDE						
54	507-54	58	27	Poly	7/26 BC	Blk. PVC	BC	.275	4.4	Superseded by RG 54A/U
54A	507-54A	58	26.5	Poly	7/.0152 BC	Poly	TC	.250	4.4	
55	507-55	53.5	28.5	Poly	20 BC	Poly	2TC	.206	3.6	
55A	507-55A	50	28.5	Poly	.035 S	Blk. L.T. PVC	2S	.216	3.6	
*55B	507-55B	53	28.5	Poly	.032 S	Poly	2TC	Max. .206	3.6	
56	507-56	48	50	Rub.	19/.0117 BC	Blk. PVC	2BC	.535	24.3	Pulse Cable W.E. KS 9351
57	507-57	95	17	Poly	Two 7/21 BC	Blk. PVC	TC	.625	24.8	Superseded by RG 57A/U
*57A	507-57A	95	17	Poly	Two 7/21 BC	Blk. L.T. PVC	TC	.625	24.1	
58	507-58	53.5	28.5	Poly	20 BC	Blk. PVC	TC	.195	2.7	

* Covered by Spec. Mil-C-17

© STANDARD WIRE & CABLE CO.

163

Table 7-3. Coaxial Cables Specifications. (Cont.)

RG/U Number	Catalog No.	Nominal Impedance	Capacitance pF/FT	Dielectric Material	Size and Type of Inner Cond.	Jacket	Shield	O/A Diameter	Wt. per 100 Ft.	Remarks
58A	507-58A	50	30	Poly	19/33 TC	Blk. PVC	TC	.195	2.7	
58B	507-58B	53.5	28.5	Poly	20 BC	Blk. L.T.PVC	TC	.195	2.6	Deleted
*58C	507-58C	50	30	Poly	19/33 TC	Blk. L.T.PVC	TC	.195	2.6	
59	507-59	73	21	Poly	22 CW	Blk. PVC	BC	.242	4.1	
59A	507-59A	75	21	Poly	22 CW	Blk. L.T.PVC	BC	.242	3.9	
*59B	507-59B	75	21	Poly	.023 CW	Blk. L.T.PVC	BC	.242	3.2	
60	507-60	50	39	Rub.	Stranded BC	CHLORO.	BC	.425	15.0	Pulse Cable
61	507-61			Special 500 Ohm Line						
62	507-62	93	13.5	SS Poly	22 CW	Blk. PVC	BC	.242	3.7	
*62A	507-62A	93	13.5	SS Poly	22 CW	Blk. L.T.PVC	BC	.242	3.5	Similar to RG 62A/U Except Str. Cnd
*62B	507-62B	93	13.5	SS Poly	7/32 CW	Blk. L.T.PVC	BC	.242	3.0	
62C	507-62C	93	13.5	SS TFE	22 SCW	Fiber Glass	S	.242	4.0	
63	507-63	125	10	SS Poly	22 CW	Blk. PVC	BC	.405	8.8	
63A	507-63A	125	10	Poly	22 BC	Blk. PVC	BC	.405	8.8	Superseded by RG 63B/U
*63B	507-63B	125	10	SS Poly	22 CW	Blk. L.T.PVC	BC	.405	8.4	Low Cap. Air Spaced
*64	507-64	48	50	Rub.	19/.0117 TC	CHLORO.	2TC	.495	22.5	Pulse Cable
*64A	507-64A	48	50	Rub.	19/.0117 TC	CHLORO.	2TC	.475	20.5	Pulse Cable
65	507-65	950	44	Poly	32 Formex F	Blk. PVC	BC	.405	9.6	Delay Cable Hi Imp. Video
*65A	507-65A	950	44	Poly	32 Formex F	L.T. PVC	BC	.405	9.6	Delay Cable Hi Imp. Video
66	507-66			WAVE GUIDE						
67	507-67			WAVE GUIDE						
68	507-68			WAVE GUIDE						

No.	Spec.	Imp.	Cap.	Dielectric	Conductor	Jacket	Shield	O.D.	Wt.	Remarks
69	507-69			WAVE GUIDE						
70	507-70			UNASSIGNED						
71	507-71	93	13.5	SS Poly	22 CW	Poly	TC & BC	.250	4.3	
71A	507-71A	93	13.5	SS Poly	22 CW	Blk. L.T.PVC	TC & BC	.245	4.3	
*71B	507-71B	93	Max. 14.5	SS Poly	22 CW	Poly	TC & BC	Max. .250	4.6	
72	507-72	150	7.8	SS Poly	22 CW	Blk. PVC	BC	.630	16.9	
73	507-73	25	61.8	Poly	20 BC	None	2BC	.275	3.1	
74	507-74	50	29.5	Poly	10 BC	Grey PVC	2BC	.615	23.4	Superseded by RG 74A/U
*74A	507-74A	52	29.5	Poly	10 BC	Blk. L.T.PVC	2BC	.615	23.6	RG 14A/U with Armor Superseded by RG 224/U
75	507-75			WAVE GUIDE						
76	507-76			Stub Supported Coaxial						
77A	507-77A	48	50	Rub.	19/.0117 TC	Poly	2TC	.415	19.5	Pulse Cable
78A	507-78A	48	50	Rub.	19/.0117 TC	Poly	TC	.385	14.9	Pulse Cable
79	507-79	125	10	SS Poly	22 CW	Blk. PVC	BC	.475	11.4	Superseded by RG 79B/U
79A	507-79A	125	Max. 11	SS Poly	22 CW	Blk. PVC	BC	.475	13.0	Superseded by RG 79B/U
*79B	507-79B	125	Max. 11	SS Poly	22 CW	Blk. L.T.PVC	BC	.475	13.6	RG 63B/U with Armor
80	507-80			Bead Supported Coaxial						
*81	507-81	50	37	Mag. Ox.	.0625 BC	None	BC Tube	.375	17.2	Semi-Rigid High Temp.
*82	507-82	50	38	Mag. Ox.	.125 BC	None	BC Tube	.750	69.8	Semi-Rigid High Temp.
83	507-83	35	44	Poly	10 BC	Blk. PVC	BC	.405	12.2	Deleted
*84A	507-84A	75	21.5	Poly	.1045 BC	Lead	BC	1.000	132.5	RG 35B/U with Lead Jacket
*85A	507-85A	75	21.5	Poly	.1045 BC	Lead	BC	1.565	291.0	RG 84/U w/Special Armor
*86	507-86	200	7.8	Poly	Two 7/21 BC	None	None	.650 x.300	10.3	Twin-Lead
87	507-87	50	29.5	TFE	7/21 S	Fiber Glass	BC & S	.425	13.9	Superseded by RG 87A/U

* Covered by Spec. Mil-C-17

© STANDARD WIRE & CABLE CO.

Table 7-3. Coaxial Cables Specifications. (Cont.)

RG/U Number	Catalog No.	Nominal Impedance	Capacitance pF/FT	Dielectric Material	Size and Type of Inner Cond.	Jacket	Shield	O/A Diameter	Wt. per 100 Ft.	Remarks
*87A	507-87A	50	29.5	TFE	7/20 S	Fiber Glass	2S	.425	17.4	
*88	507-88	48	50	Rub.	19/.0117 TC	Blk. PVC	4TC	Max. .515	21.1	H.V. Pulse Cable
*88A	507-88A	48	50	Rub.	19/.0117 TC	Blk. L.T. PVC	4TC	Max. .515	21.1	H.V. Pulse Cable
88B	507-88B	50	50	Rub.	19/.0117 TC	CHLORO.	4TC	.565	23.8	H.V. Pulse Cable
89	507-89	125	10	Poly	22 CW	Blk. PVC	BC	.632	20.0	Deleted
90	507-90	50	30.8	Poly	7/24 TC or S	L.T. PVC	2TC-1GW	.425		Carrier Freq. Comm.
91	507-91	WAVE	GUIDE							
92	507-92	46	--	SS TFE	.375 BC	None	BC Tube	--	--	TFE Bead Supported Coaxial Line
93	507-93	50	29	TFE Tape	19/18 BC	Fiber Glass	BC	.710	47.5	Replaced by RG 117/U
*94	507-94	50	29	TFE Tape	19/23 S	Fiber Glass	2BC	.445	26.5	Superseded by RG 94A/U
94A	507-94A	50	29	TFE Tape	19/22 S	Fiber Glass	2BC	.470	22.5	For Use Where Expansion & Contraction Are Problem
95	507-95	WAVE	GUIDE							
96	507-96	WAVE	GUIDE							
97	507-97	WAVE	GUIDE							
98	507-98	WAVE	GUIDE							
99	507-99	WAVE	GUIDE							
100	507-100	35	44	Poly	19/.0147 BC	Blk. PVC	BC	.242	6.5	FTR — K1366
101	507-101	75	--	Rub.	14 BC	--	TC	.588	--	
102	507-102	140	--	Rub.	Two 12 BC	--	TC	1.088	--	
103	507-103	WAVE	GUIDE							
104	507-104	WAVE	GUIDE							
105	507-105	WAVE	GUIDE							

106	507-106		WAVE GUIDE							
107	507-107		WAVE GUIDE							
108	507-108	78	Poly	24.5	Two 7/28 TC	Blk. PVC	TC	.245	3.1	
*108A	507-108A	78	Poly	24.5	Two 7/28 TC	Blk. L.T. PVC	TC	.235	2.9	Shielded Twisted Pair
109	507-109		WAVE GUIDE							
110	507-110		WAVE GUIDE							
111	507-111	95	SS Poly	16	Two 7/.0152 BC	Grey PVC	2TC	.490	14.5	RG 22A/U with Armor
*111A	507-111A	95	SS Poly	16	Two 7/.0152 BC	Blk. L.T. PVC	2TC	.490	14.5	RG 22B/U with Armor
112	507-112		WAVE GUIDE							
113	507-113		WAVE GUIDE							
114	507-114	185	SS Poly	6.5	33 CW	Blk. PVC	BC	.405	8.7	
*114A	507-114A	185	SS Poly	6.5	33 CW	Blk. L.T. PVC	BC	.405	8.7	For Use Where Expansion & Contraction Are Problem
*115	507-115	50	TFE Tape	29.5	7/21 S	Fiber Glass	2S	.375	18.0	
*115A	507-115A	50	TFE Tape	29.5	7/21 S	Fiber Glass	2S	.415	18.0	
*116	507-116	50	TFE	29.5	7/20 S	Fiber Glass	2S	.475	22.4	RG 87A/U with Armor
*117	507-117	50	TFE	29.5	.188 BC	Fiber Glass	BC	.730	45.0	
*117A	507-117A	50	TFE	29.5	.188 BC	Fiber Glass	BC	.730	44.6	
*118	507-118	50	TFE	29	.188 BC	Fiber Glass	BC	.780	60.0	RG 117/U with Armor
*118A	507-118A	50	TFE	29	.188 BC	Fiber Glass	BC	.780	58.0	
*119	507-119	50	TFE	29	.102 BC	Fiber Glass	2BC	.465	22.5	High Temperature
*120	507-120	50	TFE	29	.102 BC	Fiber Glass	2BC	.515	28.2	RG 119/U with Armor
121	507-121		WAVE GUIDE							
*122	507-122	50	Poly	29.3	27/36 TC	Blk. L.T. PVC	TC	.160	2.0	Same as RG 58A/U Except Smaller & Lighter
123	507-123		Not Assigned							

* Covered by Spec. Mil-C-17

● STANDARD WIRE & CABLE CO.

Table 7-3. Coaxial Cables Specifications. (Cont.)

RG/U Number	Catalog No.	Nominal Impedance	Capacitance pF/FT	Dielectric Material	Size and Type of Inner Cond.	Jacket	Shield	O/A Diameter	Wt. per 100 Ft.	Remarks
124	507-124	73	20.3	TFE Tape	22 TCW	Fiber Glass	TC	.240	21.0	Replaced by RG 140/U
125	507-125	150	7.8	SS Poly	26 CW	Blk. L.T. PVC	BC	.600	18.0	FTR-SP53
*126	507-126	50	29	TFE	7/24 K	Fiber Glass	K	.280	7.6	High Atten. Cable
127	507-127			WAVE GUIDE						
128	507-128	50		SS TFE	.644 BC	None	BC Tube	1.625	—	TFE Bead Supported Coaxial Line
129	507-129			Flexible Wave Guide						
*130	507-130	95	17	Poly	Two 7/21 BC	Blk. PVC	TC	.625	22.0	RG 57A/U with Twisted Inner Conductors Flex.
*131	507-131	95	17	Poly	Two 7/21 BC	Blk. PVC	TC	.710	29.5	RG 130/U with Armor
132	507-132			WAVE GUIDE						
133	507-133	95	16.2	Poly	21 BC	Blk. PVC	BC	.405	9.4	USAF 51B 14092
*133A	507-133A	95	16.2	Poly	22 BC	Blk. L.T. PVC	BC	.405	8.9	NATO Type NWR-7
134	507-134	185	6.5	SS TFE	28 BC	None	Brass	.450		TFE Bead Supported Coaxial Line
135	507-135			WAVE GUIDE						
136	507-136			WAVE GUIDE						
137	507-137			WAVE GUIDE						
138	507-138			WAVE GUIDE						
139	507-139			WAVE GUIDE						
*140	507-140	75	21	TFE	.025 SCW	Fiber Glass	S	.233	4.5	Sim. to RG 59/U w/TFE Core
141	507-141	50	28.5	TFE	19 SCW	Fiber Glass	S	.190	3.5	Sim. to RG 58/U w/TFE Core
*141A	507-141A	50	28.5	TFE	.039 SCW	Fiber Glass	S	.190	3.5	High Temp. Similar to RG 58C/U
142	507-142	50	28.5	TFE	19 SCW	Fiber Glass	2S	.206	4.5	Sim. to RG 55/U w/TFE Core

*142A	507-142A	50	28.5	TFE	.039 SCW	Fiber Glass	2S	.206	4.5	High Temp. Similar to RG 55A/U
*142B	507-142B	50	28.5	TFE	.039 SCW	FEP	2S	.195	4.2	NATO Type NWR-25
143	507-143	50	28.5	TFE	15 SCW	Fiber Glass	2S	.325	10.2	Sim. to RG5/U w/TFE Core
*143A	507-143A	50	28.5	TFE	.059 SCW	Fiber Glass	2S	.325	10.2	High Temp. Similar to RG 5 B/U
*144	507-144	75	20.5	TFE	7/25 SCW	Fiber Glass	S	.410	12.0	Sim. to RG 11/U w/TFE Core
145	507-145	76	14.6	SS Poly	Two/13 BC	Lead-Ter	BC Tube			
146	507-146	190	6.0	SS TFE	33 CW	Fiber Glass	BC	.375	10.8	Cancelled
147	507-147	62	29.5	Poly	.250 BC	Blk. PVC	BC	1.937		RG 19/U w/Spiral Armor
148	507-148	52	29.5	Poly	7/21 BC	Blk. PVC	BC	.800		RG 8/U w/Spiral Armor
*149	507-149	75	20.5	Poly	7/26 TC	Blk. PVC	BC	.405	10.0	RG 11/U Low Noise
*150	507-150	75	20.5	Poly	7/26 TC	Blk. PVC	BC	.475	11.7	RG 149/U with Armor
£151	507-151	50	—	—	.125 BC Tube	None	BC Tube	.375	—	Bead Supported Coaxial Line
£152	507-152	50	—	—	2.60 BC Tube	None	BC Tube	6.125	—	Bead Supported Coaxial Line
£153	507-153	50	—	—	.664 BC Tube	None	BC Tube	1.625	—	Bead Supported Coaxial Line
£154	507-154	50	—	—	1.315 BC Tube	None	BC Tube	3.125	—	Bead Supported Coaxial Line
£155	507-155	50	—	—	.341 BC Tube	None	BC Tube	.875	—	Bead Supported Coaxial Line
*156	507-156	60	30	Poly & Syn. Rub.	7/21 TC	Blk. L.T. PVC	3TC 1GW	.540	21.1	Poly Tape between GW Braid and Outer Braided Tinned Copper Shield
*157	507-157	60	38	Poly & Syn. Rub.	19/24 TC	Blk. L.T. PVC	3TC 1GW	.725	31.7	Poly Tape between GW Braid and Outer Braided Tinned Copper Shield
*158	507-158	25	78	Poly & Syn. Rub.	37/21 TC	Blk. L.T. PVC	3TC 1GW	.725	38.0	Poly Tape between GW Braid and Outer Braided Tinned Copper Shield
159	507-159	50	29.0	TFE Tape	20 S	Fiber Glass	S	.195	3.5	Replaced by RG 142/U
160	507-160	125	12.0	Poly	Two 19/27 TC, Two 19/27 BC	Blk. PVC	BC	1.055	—	Special Flexible 4 Cond. Twinax (2 Tin'd.—2 Cop.)
*160A	507-160A	125	12.0	Poly	Two 19/27 TC, Two 19/27 BC	Blk. PVC	BC	1.055		Same as RG 160/U except Copper Ribbon Braid Shield & Mylar Tape
161	507-161	70	20	TFE	7/38 SCB	Blk. Nylon	S	.090	.7	Miniature
162	507-162	175	—	SS TFE	.156 BC Tube	None	BC Tube	3.065	—	TFE Bead Supported Coaxial Line
163	507-163									WAVE GUIDE

* Covered by Spec. Mil-C-17   £ Covered by Spec. Mil-L-3890   ● STANDARD WIRE & CABLE CO.

Table 7-3. Coaxial Cables Specifications. (Cont.)

RG/U Number	Catalog No.	Nominal Impedance	Capacitance pF/FT	Dielectric Material	Size and Type of Inner Cond.	Jacket	Shield	O/A Diameter	Wt. per 100 Ft.	Remarks
*164	507-164	75	21.5	Poly	.1045 BC	Blk. L.T. PVC	BC	.870	49.0	Same as RG 35A/U w/o Armor
*165	507-165	50	29.5	TFE	7/20 S	Fiber Glass	S	.410	12.0	
*166	507-166	50	29.5	TFE	7/20 S	Fiber Glass	S	.460	14.4	RG 165/U with Armor
167	507-167		WAVE GUIDE							
168	507-168		WAVE GUIDE							
169	507-169		WAVE GUIDE							
170	507-170		WAVE GUIDE							
171	507-171		WAVE GUIDE							
172	507-172		WAVE GUIDE							
173	507-173		WAVE GUIDE							
*174	507-174	50	30	Poly	7/34 CW	Blk. PVC	TC	.100	.75	
*174A	507-174A	50	30	Poly	7/34 CW	Blk. L.T. PVC	TC	.100	.75	
175	507-175	Bead Supported Coaxial Line								
*176	507-176	2240	49	Poly	.135 BC Helix	PVC	BC	.405	12.0	High Impedance Delay
*177	507-177	50	30	Poly	.195 BC	Blk. L.T. PVC	25	.895	47.0	
178	507-178	50	27.9	TFE	7/38 SCW	Kel F or Equal	S	Max. .079	.9	Mil-C-8721
*178A	507-178A	50	27.9	TFE	7/38 SCW	Kel F	S	Max. .075	.9	Supersedes RG 178/U
*178B	507-178B	50	27.9	TFE	7/38 SCW	FEP	S	Max. .075	.625	Supersedes RG 178A/U
179	507-179	70	20.4	TFE	7/38 SCW	Kel F or Equal	S	Max. .094	1.7	Mil-C-8721
*179A	507-179A	75	20.4	TFE	7/38 SCW	Kel F	S	Max. .105	1.7	Supersedes RG 179/U
*179B	507-179B	75	20.4	TFE	7/38 SCW	FEP	S	Max. .105	1.7	Supersedes RG 179A/U
180	507-180	93	15.3	TFE	7/38 SCW	Kel F or Equal	S	Max. .141	1.9	Mil-C-8721

*180A	507-180A	95	14.5	TFE	7/38 SCW	Kel F	S	Max. .145	1.9	Supersedes RG 180/U
*180B	507-180B	95	14.5	TFE	7/38 SCW	FEP	S	Max. .145	1.98	Supersedes RG 180A/U
*181	507-181	125	12	Poly	Two 7/26 BC	Blk. L.T. PVC	BC	.640	19.8	Transmission Unbalanced Cable
182	507-182	125 Each	12 Each	Poly	Two 19/.0066 TC / Two 19/27 BC	Blk. L.T. PVC	BC	1.055	—	Dual Twinax
183	507-183	50	23	SS PS	.0251 BC	None	Al Tube	.750	38.0	
184	507-184		WAVE GUIDE							
185	507-185	2000	—	SS Poly	40 R.I.M. Helix	Blk. L.T. PVC	Magnet Wire	.282	—	Delay Cable
186	507-186	1000	—	SS Poly	32 TFE Magnet Wire Helix	Blk. L.T. PVC	Magnet Wire	.405	—	Delay Cable
*187	507-187	75	19.5	TFE	7/38 SCW	TFE	S	Max. .110	1.13	H.T. Miniature
*187A	507-187A	75	19.5	TFE	7/38 SCW	TFE	S	Max. .110	1.13	Supersedes RG 187/U
*188	507-188	50	29.0	TFE	7/.0067 SCW	TFE	S	Max. .110	1.11	H.T. Miniature
*188A	507-188A	50	29.0	TFE	7/.0067 SCW	TFE	S	Max. .110	1.11	Supersedes RG 188/U
189	507-189	50	23.0	Special	.251 BC	Blk. Poly	2S	.875	57.0	Partially Air Supported by Cross Linked Polystyrene
190	507-190	50	50	Rub.	19/.0117 TC	CHLORO.	3TC-GW	.700	35.3	Pulse Cable
*191	507-191	25	85	Rub.	TC Braid .485	CHLORO.	3TC-GW	1.460	146.9	Cancelled
192	507-192	12.5	175	Butyl Rub.	TC Braid GW Tube	RUB	3TC-GW	2.165	—	Pulse Cable
193	507-193	12.5	159	SR	TC Braid GW Tube	RUB	3TC-GW	2.165	—	Pulse Cable
194	507-194	12.5	159	SR	TC Braid GW Tube	Al Armor	2TC-GW	Max. 2.01	—	Pulse Cable
*195	507-195	95	15	TFE	7/38 SCW	TFE	S	Max. .155	1.8	Supersedes RG 195/U
*195A	507-195A	95	15	TFE	7/38 SCW	TFE	S	Max. .155	1.8	Supersedes RG 195/U
*196	507-196	50	28.5	TFE	7/38 SCW	TFE	S	Max. .080	.6	Supersedes RG 196/U
*196A	507-196A	50	28.5	TFE	7/38 SCW	TFE	S	Max. .080	.6	Supersedes RG 196/U
197	507-197	50	22	SS PS	.300 BC	None	Al Tube	.875	49.9	Semi Rigid Mil-C-22931/2A
198	507-198	70	16	SS PS	.114 BC	Poly	Al Tube	.600	15.7	

* Covered by Spec. Mil-C-17

© STANDARD WIRE & CABLE CO.

Table 7-3. Coaxial Cables Specifications. (Cont.)

RG/U Number	Catalog No.	Nominal Impedance	Capacitance pF/FT	Dielectric Material	Size and Type of Inner Cond.	Jacket	Shield	O/A Diameter	Wt. per 100 Ft.	Remarks
199	507-199	70	16	SS PS	.209 BC	Poly	Al Tube	1.015	44.5	
200	507-200	70	16	SS PS	.403 BC	Poly	Al Tube	1.765	93.0	
201	507-201			RIGID WAVE GUIDE						
202	507-202			RIGID WAVE GUIDE						
203	507-203			RIGID WAVE GUIDE						
204	507-204			RIGID WAVE GUIDE						
205	507-205			RIGID WAVE GUIDE						
206	507-206			RIGID WAVE GUIDE						
207	507-207			RIGID WAVE GUIDE						
208	507-208			RIGID WAVE GUIDE						
*209	507-209	50	26.5	Taped TFE	19/.038 S	Silicone Rubber & Fiber Glass	2S	Max. .750	43.2	
*210	507-210	93	14.5	SS TFE	.0253 SCW	Fiber Glass	S	.242	4.0	Formerly RG 62C/U
*211	507-211	50	29	TFE	.190 BC	Fiber Glass	BC	.730	45.0	Formerly RG 117/U
*211A	507-211A	50		TFE	.190 BC	Fiber Glass	BC	.730	45.0	Formerly RG 117A/U
*212	507-212	50	28.5	Poly	.0556 S	Blk. L.T. PVC	2S	.332	8.3	Formerly RG 58/U
*213	507-213	50	29.5	Poly	7/.0296 BC	Blk. L.T. PVC	BC	.405	9.9	Formerly RG 8A/U
*214	507-214	50	29.5	Poly	7/.0296 S	Blk. L.T. PVC	2S	.425	12.6	Formerly RG 9B/U
*215	507-215	50	29.5	Poly	7/.0296 BC	Blk. L.T. PVC w/Armor	BC	.475	14.9	Formerly RG 10A/U
*216	507-216	75	20.5	Poly	7/26 TC	Blk. L.T. PVC	2BC	.425	11.4	Formerly RG 13A/U
*217	507-217	50	29.5	Poly	.106 BC	Blk. L.T. PVC	2BC	.545	20.1	Formerly RG 14A/U
*218	507-218	50	29.5	Poly	.195 BC	Blk. L.T. PVC	BC	.870	44.6	Formerly RG 17A/U
*219	507-219	50	29.5	Poly	.195 BC	Blk. L.T. PVC w/Armor	BC	Max. .945	49.6	Formerly RG 18A/U

*220	507-220	50	29.5	Poly	.260 BC	Blk. L.T. PVC	BC	1.12	72.0	Formerly RG 19A/U
*221	507-221	50	29.5	Poly	.260 BC	Blk. L.T. PVC w/Armor	BC	1.195	78.6	Formerly RG 20A/U
*222	507-222	50	29	Poly	.0656 Resist.	Blk. L.T. PVC	25	.332	8.0	Formerly RG 21A/U
*223	507-223	50	28.5	Poly	.035 S	Blk. L.T. PVC	25	.216	3.6	Formerly RG 55A/U
*224	507-224	50	29.5	Poly	.106 BC	Blk. L.T. PVC w/Armor	2BC	Max. .615	23.0	Formerly RG 74A/U
*225	507-225	50	29.5	TFE	7/.0312 S	Fiber Glass	25	.430	17.4	Formerly RG 87A/U
*226	507-226	50	29	Taped TFE	19/.0254 S	Fiber Glass w/Armor	2BC	.500	24.7	Formerly RG 94A/U
*227	507-227	50	29.5	TFE	7/.0312 S	Fiber Glass w/Armor	25	Max. .460	22.4	Formerly RG 116/U
*228	507-228	50	29	TFE	.190 BC	Fiber Glass w/Armor	BC	Max. .795	62.5	Formerly RG 118/U
*228A	507-228A	50	29.4	TFE	.190 BC	Fiber Glass w/Armor	BC	Max. .795	62.5	Formerly RG 118A/U
229	507-229	50	29.5	TFE	7/20 S	Fiber Glass	S	.480	14.4	Replaced by RG 116/U
*230	507-230	25	100	Rub.	37/21 TC	CHLORO.	2TC 1GW	.740	--	Triaxial Pulse Cable
231	507-231	50	25	Poly Foam	BC Tube	None	Al Tube	.500	15.2	Mil-C-23806/1A
231A	507-231A	50	25	Poly Foam	.162 BC	Poly	Al Tube	.625	15.2	Mil-C-23806/1B
232	507-232	50	22	SS PS	.300 BC	Poly	Al Tube	1.015	58.0	Semi Rigid Mil-C-22931/2A
233	507-233	50	22	SS PS	BC Tube	Poly	Al Tube	1.765	108.0	Semi Rigid Mil-C-22931/3A
234	507-234	50	22	SS PS	BC Tube	Poly	Al Tube	3.296	311.0	Semi Rigid Mil-C-22931/4A
*235	507-235	50	29.5	TFE Tape	7/21 S	Silicone Rubber	25	Max. .470	16.0	Semi Rigid Mil-C-22931/1A
236	507-236	50	24	SS PS	.162 BC	None	Al Tube	.500	16.5	Semi Rigid Mil-C-22931/1A
237	507-237	50	24	SS PS	.162 BC	Poly	Al Tube	.600	20.0	Semi Rigid Mil-C-22931/1A
238	507-238	CANCELLED SAME AS RG 197/U								
239	507-239	CANCELLED -- SEE RG 232/U								
240	507-240	50	22	SS PS	BC Tube	None	Al Tube	1.625	93.0	Semi Rigid Mil-C-22931/3A
241	507-241	CANCELLED -- SEE RG 233/U								
242	507-242	50	22	SS PS	BC Tube	None	Al Tube	3.125	270.0	Semi Rigid Mil-C-22931/4A

* Covered by Spec. Mil-C-17

© STANDARD WIRE & CABLE CO.

Table 7-3. Coaxial Cables Specifications. (Cont.)

RG/U Number	Catalog No.	Nominal Impedance	Capacitance pF/FT	Dielectric Material	Size and Type of Inner Cond.	Jacket	Shield	O/A Diameter	Wt. per 100 Ft.	Remarks
243	507-243			CANCELLED – SEE RG 234/U						
244	507-244	75	15.5	SSPS	.102 BC	None	Al Tube	.500	11.8	Semi Rigid Mil-C-22931/1A
245	507-245	75	15.5	SSPS	.102 BC	Poly	Al Tube	.600	15.3	Semi Rigid Mil-C-22931/1A
246	507-246	75	15.5	SSPS	.188 BC	None	Al Tube	.875	34.3	Semi Rigid Mil-C-22931/2A
247	507-247	75	15.5	SSPS	.188 BC	Poly	Al Tube	1.015	42.3	Semi Rigid Mil-C-22931/2A
248	507-248	75	15	SSPS	.370 BC	None	Al Tube	1.625	94.8	Semi Rigid Mil-C-22931/3A
249	507-249	75	15	SSPS	.370 BC	Poly	Al Tube	1.765	109.8	Semi Rigid Mil-C-22931/3A
250	507-250	75	15	SSPS	.717 BC	None	Al Tube	3.125	239.5	Semi Rigid Mil-C-22931/4A
251	507-251	75	15	SSPS	.717 BC	Poly	Al Tube	3.295	280.5	Semi Rigid Mil-C-22931/4A
252	507-252	75	24.4	Poly Tubes	.165 BC	None	Al Tube	.530	17.5	Semi Rigid Mil-C-22931/1A
253	507-253	75	24.4	Poly Tubes	.165 BC	Poly	Al Tube	Max. .635	19.0	Semi Rigid Mil-C-22931/1A
254	507-254	50	24.4	Poly Tubes	.311 BC	Poly	Al Tube	Max. 1.100	65.5	Semi Rigid Mil-C-22931/2A
255	507-255	50	24.4	Poly Tubes	.311 BC	None	Al Tube	.953	55.5	Semi Rigid Mil-C-22931/2A
256	507-256	50	23.5	TFE Tubes	S Tube	None	Al Tube	.953	55.0	
257	507-257	50	24.4	Poly Tubes	BC Tube	None	Al Tube	1.786	120.0	Semi Rigid Mil-C-22931/3A
258	507-258	50	24.4	Poly Tubes	BC Tube	Poly	Al Tube	Max. 1.936	138.0	Semi Rigid Mil-C-22931/3A
259	507-259	50	23.5	Poly Tubes	.115 BC	None	Al Tube	.390	10.0	
260	507-260	50	23.5	Poly Tubes	.115 BC	Poly	Al Tube	.450	14.0	
261	507-261	50	23.5	Poly Tubes	BC Tube	None	Al Tube	3.37	--	CANCELLED
262	507-262	50	23.5	Poly Tubes	BC Tube	Poly	Al Tube	3.52	--	CANCELLED
263	507-263	50	21.5	SS TFE	.172 BC	None	Al Tube	.500	17.0	
264	507-264	40	38	Poly	4 x 19/27 BC	PVC	2BC-2TC	.750	33.6	Quad Cable

174

No.	Part No.									
264A	507-264A	40	38	Poly	4 x 19/27 BC	Blk. L.T. PVC	2BC-2TC	.750	32.7	Quad Cable
264B	507-264B	40	42 Max.	Poly	4 x 19/27 BC	Poly U	2BC-2TC	.750	—	Mil-C-23020A
264C	507-264C	40	42 Max.	Poly	2 x 13 BC / 2 x 13 TC	Poly U	2BC-2TC	.750	32.7	Mil-C-23020/4
265	507-265	50	22.3	SSPS	BC Tube	Poly	BC Tube	2.070	—	Mil-C-22931/7
*266	507-266	1530	53	Poly	.144 BC Helix	PVC	BC	.400	12.0	Delay Line
267	507-267	50	22.2	SSPS	BC Tube	PVC	SS Tube	1.190	—	Mil-C-22931/6
268	507-268	50	23	SSPS	.160 BC	None	BC Tube	.500	23.4	Mil-C-22931/5
269	507-269	50	22.2	SSPS	BC Tube	None	BC Tube	1.005	42.1	Mil-C-22931/6A
270	507-270	50	22.3	SSPS	Coppered Steel Tube	None	BC Tube	1.830	87.5	Mil-C-22931/7A
271-278	507-278		WAVE GUIDES							
*279	507-279	75	17	SS TFE	19/36 SCW	Fiber Glass	S	.145	12.5	
*280	507-280	50	27.5	SS TFE	9 BC	FEP	2S	.480	20.0	
281	507-281	50	29	SS TFE	19/.0378 S	SR & Braid	2S	.750	40.0	
282	507-282	54.6	28.2	1 Poly	22 S	FEP	2S	.200	3.1	
283	507-283	46	50	RUB.	19/.117 S	CHLORO.	2S	Max. .475	14.2	
284A	507-284A	75	15	SS TFE	.220 BC	—	BC Tube	1.005	41.0	
285A	507-285A	100	13	TFE	.1144 BC	—	BC Tube	1.005	43.0	
286	507-286	75	15.1	SS Poly	BC Tube	None	BC Tube	1.830	72.0	
287	507-287	100	13.5	6S Poly	.197 BC	None	BC Tube	1.830	75.0	
288	507-288	50	21.6	SS Poly / SSPS	BC Tube	PVC	BC Tube	3.750	300.0	
289	507-289	75	14.7	SS Poly / SSPS	BC Tube over Steel Tube	PVC	BC Tube	3.750	300.0	
290	507-290	75	15.1	SS Poly	BC Tube	Poly	BC Tube	1.990	—	
291	507-291		WAVE GUIDE							
292	507-292	75	15.1	SS Poly	BC Tube	Poly FC	BC Tube	1.830	104.0	

* Covered by Spec. Mil-C-17

● STANDARD WIRE & CABLE CO.

Table 7-3. Coaxial Cables Specifications. (Cont.)

RG/U Number	Catalog No.	Nominal Impedance	Capacitance pF/FT	Dielectric Material	Size and Type of Inner Cond.	Jacket	Shield	O/A Diameter	Wt. per 100 Ft.	Remarks
293	507-293	50	30.8	Poly	.106 BC	CHLORO.	S	.545	16.0	Mil-C-23020 A
293A	507-293A	50	30.8	Poly	.106 BC	Blk. Poly	S	.545	16.0	Mil-C-23020/2
294	507-294	95	16.3	Poly	12BC - 12TC	CHLORO.	TC	.630	20.5	Twin-Axial
294A	507-294A	95	16.3	Poly	12 BC - 12TC	Poly	S	.630	20.5	Twin-Axial for Submarine Use
295	507-295	50	—	Poly	.195 BC	Blk. Poly	BC	.895	42.0	Mil-C-23020/3
*296	507-296	50	36.4	SR	37/.0336 S	Neoprene	S	1.190	—	
297	507-297	50	21.4	SS TFE	BC Tube	None	BC Tube	1.005	—	
298	507-298			Poly	7/24 CW	Poly Foam	None	.650	9.0	Mil-C-22667 A
*301	507-301	50	29	TFE	7/.0203 K	FEP	K	.245	7.4	Same as RG 126/U with FEP Jacket
*302	507-302	75	21	TFE	.025 SCW	FEP	S	Max. .206	4.4	Same as RG 140/U with FEP Jacket
*303	507-303	50	28.5	TFE	.039 SCW	FEP	S	.170	3.0	Same as RG 141A/U with FEP Jacket
*304	507-304	50	28.5	TFE	.059 SCW	FEP	2S	.280	10.2	Same as RG 143A/U with FEP Jacket
305	507-305	75	14.4	FEP	BC Tube	Poly	BC Tube	1.990	—	Similar to RG 298/U
306A	507-306A	75	16.5	Poly Foam	.173 BC	Poly	Al Tube	1.015	54.5	Mil-C-23806/2A
*307A	507-307A	75	16.7	Poly Foam	19/.0058 S	Poly	2S	Max. .270	7.0	
*316	507-316	50	29	TFE	7/.0067 SCW	FEP	S	.102	1.2	Same as RG 188A/U with FEP Jacket
317	507-317	95	15.4	FEP	Two 7/.029 BC	Neoprene	TC	.710	—	Mil-C-23020/5A
318	507-318	50	22.2	SS PS	BC Tube	Poly	BC Tube	1.10	53.0	Mil-C-22931/6A
319	507-319	50	22.3	SS PS	Coppered Steel Tube	Poly	BC Tube	1.97	104.0	Mil-C-22931/7A
321	507-321	50	21.7	SS Poly	BC Tube	None	BC Tube	2.850	121.0	
322	507-322	50	21.7	SS Poly	BC Tube	Poly FC	BC Tube	3.040	178.0	
323	507-323	50	25.6	Poly F	BC Tube	Poly FC	BC Tube	1.06	42.0	

324	507-324	50	25.6	Poly F	BC Tube	None	BC Tube	.980	32.0	
325	507-325	50	26.3	TFE	19 Strd S	Poly	S	Max. .465	10.0	
326	507-326	50	26.3	TFE	19 Strd S	Poly	S	Max. .779	24.0	
327	507-327	50	26.3	TFE	19 Strd S	Poly	S	Max. 1.18	55.0	
*328	507-328	25	85	RUB.	TC Braid	CHLORO.	2TC-GW	1.460	146.9	
*329	507-329	50	50	RUB.	19/.0117 TC	CHLORO.	2TC-GW	.700	35.3	
330	507-330	50	25.0	Poly Foam	S	None	S	.242	—	
331	507-331	50	25	Poly Foam	.162 BC	Poly	Al Tube	.625	18.7	Mil-C-23806/1A
332	507-332	50	25	Poly Foam	.288 BC	None	Al Tube	.875	48.0	Mil-C-23806/2A
333	507-333	50	25	Poly Foam	.288 BC	Poly	Al Tube	Max. 1.062	54.5	Mil-C-23806/2A
334	507-334	75	17	Poly Foam	.098 BC	None	Al Tube	.500	15.2	Mil-C-23806/1A
335	507-335	75	17	Poly Foam	.098 BC	Poly	Al Tube	.625	18.7	Mil-C-23806/1A
336	507-336	75	16.5	Poly Foam	.173 BC	None	Al Tube	.875	48.0	Mil-C-23806/1A
360	507-360	50	25	Poly Foam	.243 BC	Poly	Al Tube	.825	39.8	Mil-C-23806/3A
366	507-366	50	26.6	Poly Foam	.160 BC	Poly	Al Tube	.620	—	
367	507-367	50	21.7	Poly Helix	BC Tube	Poly	BC Tube	5.20	45.9	
369	507-369	50	23.5	Poly Tubes	.117 BC	Poly	Al Tube	.470	14.0	
370	507-370	50	24.0	Poly Tubes	.117 BC	None	Al Tube	.390	10.0	
373	507-373			Poly	16 BC	Poly Foam		.650		Mil-C-28751 (EC) Buoyant Cable
374	507-374	—	—	Poly	21 BC	Poly Foam	None	.650	9.7	Buoyant Mil-C-24301
376	507-376	50	26.0	Poly Foam	.312 BC Tube	Poly	Al Tube	1.06	39.0	
377	507-377	50	24.0	TFE Tubes	.165 S. Tube	None	Al Tube	.530	17.0	
378	507-378	50	22.1	Poly	BC Tube	Poly	Al Tube	2.000	62.0	Semi Rigid Mil-C-22931/13
382	507-382	RIGID LINE								

* Covered by Spec. Mil-C-17

© STANDARD WIRE & CABLE CO.

Table 7-3. Coaxial Cables Specifications. (Cont.)

RG/U Number	Catalog No.	Nominal Impedance	Capacitance pF/FT	Dielectric Material	Size and Type of Inner Cond.	Jacket	Shield	O/A Diameter	Wt. per 100 Ft.	Remarks
383	507-383	100.0	—	Poly	Two .0403	Poly Foam	None	.650	—	Twisted Pair High Strength Alloy Conductors
384	507-384	50	30.8	Poly	.16 BC	Poly Foam	Flat BC	.650	—	Buoyant Cable Mil-C-28726 (EC)
385	507-385	50	25	SS TFE	.153 S	Optional	Al Tube	.660	17.8	Low Loss
386	507-386	—	—	Poly	.0508 CW	Poly Foam	None	.650	—	
388	507-388	50	30.8	Poly	.1020 BC	Poly	S	.545	—	
389	507-389	50	22.8	Poly	.250 BC Al	Poly	2S	.875	36.6	Replaces RG 189/U
*391	507-391	72	—	C Poly & Poly	7/26 TC	Blk. L.T. PVC	TC	.405	9.2	Low Noise
*392	507-392	72	—	C Poly & Poly	7/26 TC	Blk. L.T. PVC	TC	.475	11.4	RG 391/U with Armor
*393	507-393	50	29.4	TFE	7/.0312S	FEP	2S	.390	16.5	
*400	507-400	50	29.3	TFE	19/.0077S	FEP	2S	.195	5.0	
*401	507-401	50	29.3	TFE	14 S	None	BC Tube	.250	8.1	
*402	507-402	50	29.3	TFE FEP	.0360 SCW	None	BC Tube	.141	3.2	
*403	507-403	50	29.3	TFE	7/38 SCW	FEP	2S	.116	.750	Tri Coaxial
*404	507-404	50	31.5	TFE	7/38 SCW	FEP	S	Max. .075	.54	Low Noise
*405	507-405	50	28.3	TFE	24 SCW	None	BC Tube	.086		Semi Rigid

* Covered by Spec. Mil-C-17

© STANDARD WIRE & CABLE CO.

from hot to cool water in graduated steps, and most of the strains should be completely relieved. However, the last operations in manufacturing the cable have all kept it under constant tension and any strains that may have been retained from the extruding operation have little or no opportunity to be relieved.

When the cable is unreeled, if any strains are present, this operation will release them and there could be conductor movement which will show up in localized areas. To detect these defects the "sweep-test" is used.

As shown in the preceding simplified explanation, there are always potential problems in manufacturing coaxial cables, some of which will lead to electrical use problems. Because of this, the manufacturers are constantly improving the process controls to insure that the highest standards are maintained.

Table 7-3 provides the electrical and physical characteristics for some of coaxial cables commonly used in military and U.L. (Underwriters Laboratories) equipment.

References

STANDARD WIRE, INC.
El Segundo, California

U.S. Defense Supply Agency
ASESA
RF Transmission Lines & Fittings, 1962

E. I. DUPONT
Journal of Teflon®

Anaconda Wire & Cable
Various catalogs and tech notes

Chapter 8

Flat Cables

Flat cables have many uses in modern electronics systems. When a wiring situation arises where a thin form-factor, superior flexibility and/or flex life, or the ability to transmit a large number of digital signals is required, it will be worthwhile to consider using one of the many forms of flat cables. The Aerospace industry pioneered flat cable as a solution to their space and weight problems. The first military specification NAS-729 was written to aid in the use of flat cables in military programs. It was later replaced by MIL-C-55543 and MIL-C-49059. Over the years the flat cables defined by these specifications have been used successfully in applications where space and flexing were major problems. In almost every case these cables were part of a custom assembly that required a transition from the flat cable into terminating devices designed for discreet wires.

Flat cable offers the ultimate in flexing applications and there are several types of termination systems available for both the commercial and military environments. The flat form fits some otherwise unuseable spaces, such as along the sides of the cabinet or chassis, where standard wire assemblies would have too much bulk and result in interference. Flat cables are manufactured such that the mechanical loads are shared by all of the conductors, and they provide greater surface to volume ratios so they can dissipate heat better than round cables. The better heat dissipation characteristics of flat cable allows the use of higher resistance, smaller conductors for the same temperature rise at a given current. The consistant wire positioning means consistent electrical characteristics without full shielding. This leads to significant improvements in signal carrying cables. However, care must be taken in selecting the proper cable since extreme thinness can lead to cable-to-cable crosstalk. Should additional shielding be required, some of the advantages of the flat cable will be lost due to the increase in thickness and loss of flexibility.

Flat Conductor Cable. This cable is manufactured in continuous lengths with solid conductors in a flat configuration. It can be reeled off of a spool to make up harness assemblies similar to those made with round wire.

Ribbon and Woven Cable. This configuration is usually made with preinsulated, round stranded wire that is bonded or woven into a flat cable.

Transmission Line Cable. Although this cable is in a flat configuration, it is made with solid conductors on closely toleranced spacings to provide characteristics that are not normally found in flat cables.

Flexible Printed Cable. This type of flat cable is produced using the printed circuit technologies. It is never made in continuous lengths. It is manufactured in specific configurations by etching away copper from a flexible substrate. A more extensive discussion of flexible cables (circuits) is presented in Chapter 6.

These four basic configurations of flat cables, shown in Fig. 8-1, cover the general types in use today, although there are many variations available. Flat cables must be considered as a total system early in the design phases of the product. Figure 8-2 shows the seven basic components of the flat cable system. All seven components need not be used in every application, but the entire wiring concept must be planned so that all of the components will interrelate into one well conceived design.

TERMINATION FOR FLAT CABLES

There are four basic methods for preparing flat cables for termination. They are: stripping, crimping through the insulation, welding through the insulation, and stripping and slitting. See Fig. 8-3.

A number of variations have been used, but most will fall into one of these four categories. The design of the cable and it's termination devices is greatly influenced by the selection of the method to be used. Each method has advantages and disadvantages. The environmental requirements and the close proximity of the conduc-

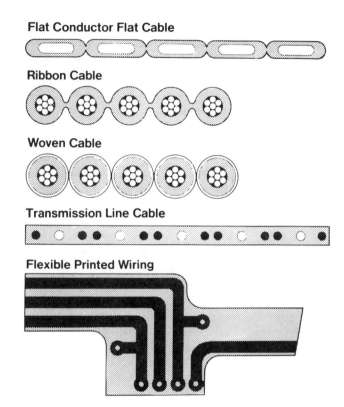

Flat Conductor Flat Cable

Ribbon Cable

Woven Cable

Transmission Line Cable

Flexible Printed Wiring

Fig. 8-1. Common flat cable configurations.

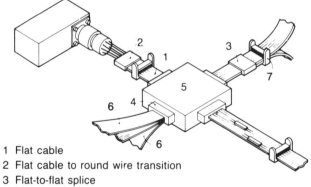

1 Flat cable
2 Flat cable to round wire transition
3 Flat-to-flat splice
4 Flat cable connector
5 Flat cable terminal junction (matrix)
6 Shielding
7 Clamping

Fig. 8-2. Flat cables and connectors.

182

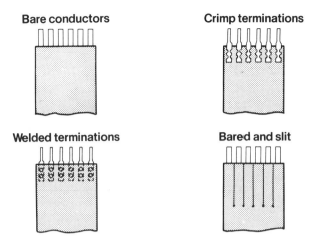

Fig. 8-3. Flat cable preparation.

tors dictate that the conductors must be sealed after termination. Stripping the cable and soldering usually is considered the most efficient method since the conductors can be isolated, sealed, and strain-relieved in one operation. The newer insulation displacement connectors are rapidly becoming more common in flat cable designs since they eliminate the stripping and soldering operations by piercing through the insulation and gripping the conductor in a single assembly operation of closing the connector (Fig. 8-4).

Flat cables designed for insulation displacement connectors (IDC) are intended to overcome the problems of discrete wire flat cables. The conductors are all insulated at the same time during manufacturing and are all terminated at once without stripping the cable. The result is the lowest cost flat cable system available. Electrical characteristics are good since the cable is consistent and the connectors are very short. Flexibility is good with the PVC insulation, but the flex-life is short. Polyester insulated cables are available for applications where flexing and mechanical strength are required. For high temperature applications and better electrical characteristics, fluorocarbon (Teflon®) cables are available. Primarily because of the low cost of the IDC system, applications for it are growing at a greater rate than for other methods. It is found in slow to medium speed computers, as well as computer peripherals and business machines.

ROUND WIRE FLAT CABLE

Round wire flat cable has a number of distinctive electrical and mechanical advantages that has made it the choice for intercon-

183

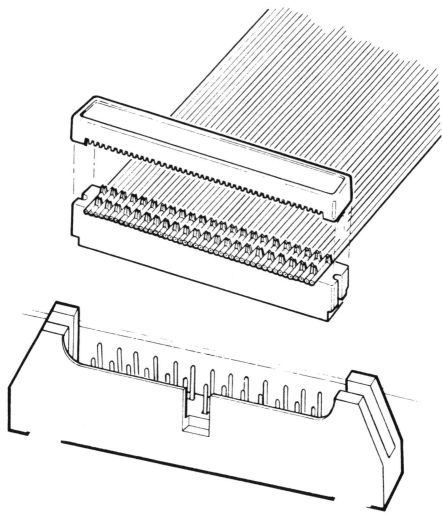

Fig. 8-4. Insulation displacement connector.

necting modern electronic systems. The conductors may be solid or stranded, and they share a common primary or secondary insulation that maintains parallel relationship between the conductors over the entire length of the cable. The cable can be folded, bent, and flexed as easily as a single wire. Since the wires are parallel over the entire length, the electrical performance is always the same at any point along the cable. The wires all lie in a single plane allowing for mass termination. They are almost impossible to miswire. See Fig. 8-5.

FLEXING APPLICATIONS

The round wire flat cable is desirable because of it's mechanical performance. The ability of this cable to flex in a predetermined manner for a great number of cycles makes it ideal for such applications as drawers, gymbals, and hinges where continual flexing is required. See Fig. 8-6. The torque required to flex the cable can be changed by different insulations, thickness, or wire specified. The most supple cable would be one made from finely stranded wire in a silicone insulation. At the other end of the flexing spectrum are power cables with TFE Teflon® insulation, which are widely used in many aerospace applications. These cables may be jacketed to provide abrasion and environmental protection.

ELECTRICAL APPLICATIONS

The round wire flat cables are commonly used in the computer and mircoprocessor industry due to their stable electrical characteristics. They have the electrical repeatability of a printed circuit and are found to be highly acceptable as transmission line cables. The cable may have a ground plane on one or both sides to improve the electrical characteristics and provide shielding when it is required. In many applications the round wire flat cables may fulfill the functions of coaxial cable, twisted-pairs, tri-leads or twisted shielded pairs. Round wire flat cables are often called *ribbon cables* since they are sometimes color coded and manufactured

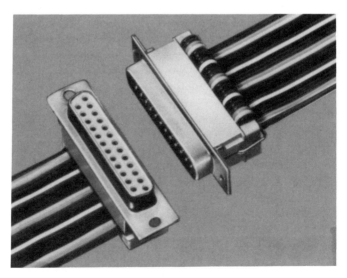

Fig. 8-5. Mass termination of flat cables.

Fig. 8-6. Application of flat cables where flexibility is important.

to look like a ribbon made up of discrete wires. These individual insulated wires are easy to split apart and terminate as though they were discrete wires. The military specification, MIL-C-49055 is the general specification for round wire flat cable. It covers flexible, flat, unshielded electrical cable with either solid or stranded inner round conductors. The cables covered by this specification are acceptable for aerospace, ground, and shipboard applications where size, and weight are prime considerations. The wires must be strippable with a Marshall Space Flight Center stripping tool and separable with a razor blade. Most of the other requirements are similar to those imposed on discrete wires.

The MIL-C-49055/1 cable uses 16 AWG wire of 0.200 inch pitch (centers). Each successive slash sheet goes to a smaller wire, down to MIL-C-49055/8, which uses 30 AWG wire on 0.050 inch pitch. The first eight slash sheets specify a 600V voltage rating at either 105 °C or 150 °C temperature rating. The MIL-C-49055/10 is a transmission line cable using 30 AWG wire on 0.030 inch centers, it is unique, because it requires a cross-talk test. It has 28 AWG wires on 0.050 centers and is rated at 300 volts with a temperature rating of 105 °C.

The conductor pitch of all of the round wire flat cables is held at + or − 0.002 to allow for mass terminations. All of these cables are compatible with the insulation displacement connectors that are available. The most common of these connectors are specified in the military standard MIL-C-83503.

FABRICATION METHODS

MIL-C-49055 does not specify the method of fabrication for round wire flat cables. They may be made from discrete insulated wires that are either bonded together with an adhesive, woven together with filaments or threads, bonded to a film on one side, or bonded between two films. This type of cable can employ some types of insulation that could not otherwise be used. It can also be used where twisted pairs or coaxial cables are desired.

Another method of fabricating round wire flat cable is to start with a set of bare wires and laminate or extrude the insulation. Where the cables are laminated, a set of grooves are used to form the proper profile around the conductors. Then the insulation is either melt-bonded or adhesive bonded over the wires. Although all of these MIL-C-49055 cables are theoretically acceptable, there is a great difference in the various insulations and methods of fabrication. Due to this lack of standardization it is recommended that an incoming inspection procedure be used to detect the defects that would make the cable unsuitable for application in specific programs.

INSULATION DISPLACEMENT CONNECTORS

The MIL-C-49055/9 round wire flat cable with the 28 AWG wire on 0.050 centers is almost perfectly matched to the interconnecting needs of modern electronic systems, but it still must be terminated in an equally acceptable method. The MIL-C-83503 specification was developed to fill this requirement. To establish the importance of this specification it is necessary to understand the principals that make insulation displacement and mass termination function so well. Prior to these new techniques, the method of terminating cables was to strip the ends and solder, weld, wrap, press, crimp, or pierce it. This method was very difficult when using 28 AWG stranded wires. The concept of insulation displacement left the insulation virtually unchanged while making a unique type of crimp or press joint. Extensive testing has shown that this method results in highly reliable connections.

Round wire flat cables are uniquely compatible with mass termination since the conductors are always in a precise position in a single plane. They can be terminated at any position along the entire length. The surface of the insulation is normally grooved so that the insulation displacing contact of the connector will align and

Table 8-1. Flat Cable Specifications.

MANUFACTURER	Circle Number	Number of Conductors (max)	Gauge Size (AWG)	Type of Insulation	Conductor Spacing (inches)	Wire Identification	Operating Temp. (°C)
ABL Electronics Supply 914-962-2253 1736 Front St, Yorktown Hts NY 10598	300	60	22 to 30	PVC	0.050 0.100	•	105 (max)
AP Products 216-354-2101 PO Box 603, 9450 Pineneedle Dr, Mentor OH 44060	301	50	28	molded	0.100		−20 to 105
Advance Electronic Mfg/Wire & Cable Div 415-592-4550 PO Box 500,1661 Industrial Way, Belmont CA 94002	302	200	6 to 32	PVC, Teflon®, Tefzel, Kinar	†	•	−50 to 260
Aero-Motive Mfg 616-381-1242 I-94 at Miller Rd, Kalamazoo MI 49001	303	†	4 to 16	PVC neoprene	0.018 0.030	•	−35 to 105
Alpha Wire Corp 201-925-8000 711 Lidgerwood Ave., Elizabeth, NJ 07207	304	60	28	PVC	0.050	•	105 (max)
***AMP** 717-564-0100 449 Eisenhower Blvd, Harrisburg PA 17105	305	60	28	PVC	0.050	•	−20 to 105
Augat 617-222-2202 33 Perry Ave, Attleboro MA 02703	306	64	30	PVC	0.050	•	−55 to 105
Belden 317-983-5200 PO Box 1980, Richmond IN 47374	307	64	18 to 30	PVC	0.050 0.100 0.156	•	105 (max)
Berg Electronics 717-975-1500 York Expressway, New Cumberland PA 17070	308	60	28 to 38	PVC	0.050	•	−20 to 105
Brand-Rex 203-423-7771 W Main St, Willimantic CT 06226	309	80	10 to 45	PVC, Polyester, Kapton®, FEP, Polyrad	0.006 to 0.750	•	−20 to 260

MANUFACTURER	Circle Number	Number of Conductors (max)	Gauge Size (AWG)	Type of Insulation	Conductor Spacing (inches)	Wire Identification	Operating Temp. (°C)
Brim Electronics 201-796-2886 8-12 Susan La, Fairlawn NJ 07410	310	30	22 to 30	PVC	†	•	105 (max)
C&M Corp 203-774-4812 PO Box 348, Waukeegan CT 06387	311	50	14 to 30	PVC	†	•	105 (max)
Calmont Energy & Electronics 714-549-0336 420 E Alton St, Santa Ana CA 92707	312	60	18 to 28	Silicone	†	•	200 (max)
Cicoil Corp 213-882-2021 20945 Plummer St, Chatsworth CA 91311	313	330	16 to 42	Silicone	0.018 to 0.150	•	260 (max)
Circuit Assembly Corp 714-540-5490 3169 Red Hill Ave, Costa Mesa CA 92626	314	64	22 to 30	PVC	0.050 0.100	•	125 (max)
Cirflex Systems 215-355-5075 Huntington Valley Industrial Park, Huntington Valley PA 19006	315	†	1 to 44	Mylar, Kapton®	†	•	150 (max)
Daburn Electronics & Cable Corp 201-768-5400 70 Oak St, Norwood NJ 07648	316	50	22 to 30	PVC	†	•	−55 to 105
*Dearborn Wire & Cable Co 312-696-1000 9299 Evenhouse Ave, Rosemont IL 60018	317	30	22 to 30	PVC	0.050	•	105 (max)
Electroweave 617-752-8932 38 Harlow St, Worcester MA 01605	318	†	10 to 30	Teflon®, Tefzel, PVC	0.025 (min)	•	−55 to 200
GSI Corp 301-252-1768 1917 Greenspring Dr, Timonium MD 21093	319	150	12 to 34	Teflon®, Tefzel, PVC	†	•	†
Gavitt Wire & Cable Co 617-867-6476 Central St, Brookfield MA 01506	320	50	16 to 32	PVC	†	•	−55 to 105

† Available in various sizes and ratings; contact manufacturer for further information.

Table 8-1. Flat Cable Specifications. (Cont.)

MANUFACTURER	Circle Number	Number of Conductors (max)	Gauge Size (AWG)	Type of Insulation	Conductor Spacing (inches)	Wire Identification	Operating Temp. (°C)
Hirose Electric USA 213-709-1247 9254 Deering Ave, Chatsworth CA 91311	321	60	24 to 28	PVC	0.050	•	−20 to 105
Hitachi 213-275-5220 1494 South Robertson Blvd, Los Angeles CA 90035	322	72	24 to 28	PVC, Polyester, Tefzel	0.0625 0.050 0.100	•	105 (max)
Hughes Aircraft 714-549-5701 PO Box 90515, 5250 W Century Blvd, Los Angeles CA 90009	323	120	†	Mylar, Kapton®	0.156 †	•	−55 to 125
JSC Wire & Cable Co 201-694-6200 Burgess Pl, Wayne NJ 07470	324	5	20 to 24	PE, PVC	†	•	†
3M Co 612-733-1110 3M Center, St Paul MN 55101	325	64	24 to 30	PVC	0.0425 0.050 0.054 0.0625 0.075	•	105 (max)
Manhattan Electric Cable Corp 914-967-8000 Station Plaza, Rye NY 10580	326	8	20 to 24	PVC	0.032	•	105 (max)
Methode Electronics 312-867-9600 7447 W Wilson Ave, Chicago IL 60656	327	30	12 to 28	Polyester, Kapton®, Nomex, PVC	0.100 0.125 0.150 0.156	•	105 (max)
MIL-Spec Wire & Cable 516-546-5454 311 N Main St, Freeport NY 11520	328	64	20 to 32	†	0.050 0.156	•	200 (max)
Minicomputer Accessories 408-737-7777 130 S Wolfe Rd, Sunnyvale CA 94086	329	60	24	PVC	0.050	•	−20 to 105
Molex 312-969-4550 2222 Wellington Ct, Lisle IL 60532	330	30	18 to 28	PVC	0.050 0.100 0.156	•	−20 to 105
*Panduit 312-532-1800 17301 Ridgeland Ave, Tinley Park IL 60477	331	64	18 to 28	PVC	0.050 0.100 0.156	•	−20 to 105

MANUFACTURER	Circle Number	Number of Conductors (max)	Gauge Size (AWG)	Type of Insulation	Conductor Spacing (inches)	Wire Identification	Operating Temp. (°C)
Parlex Corp 617-685-4341 145 Milk St, Methuen MA 01844	332	200	8 to 40	Polyester, PVC, Kapton®, Nomex	0.100	•	105 (max)
Phoenix Wire 802-372-4561 5 Flat Dr, South Hero VT 05486	333	10	20 to 60	Teflon®	†	•	260 (max)
Raychem Corp 415-361-3333 300 Constitution Dr, Menlo Park CA 94025	334	40	18 to 28	Polyolefin	0.050 0.200	•	−55 to 105
Ribbon Cable Co 714-987-0007 8753 Lion St, Cucumonga CA 91730	335	100	16 to 30	PVC, Teflon® Tefzel	†	•	260 (max)
Robinson Nugent 812-945-0211 800 E 8th St, New Albany IN 47150	336	60	28	PVC	0.050	•	−20 to 105
Rowe Industries 419-729-9761 PO Box 6877, Toledo OH 43612	337	50	12 to 22	Silicone	0.150	•	200
Shigoto Far East Ltd 212-840-8670 1500 Broadway, NY NY 10036	338	26	24 to 28	Plastic	0.100 0.200	•	†
Socapex 213-887-0750 PO Box 1535, Canoga Pk CA 91304	339	64	28	PVC	0.050	•	105 (max)
Southern Weaving 803-963-5131 PO Box 189, Mauldin SC 29662	340	72	16 to 32	PVC, Teflon®	0.050 0.100	•	−55 to 200
Stanford Applied Engineering 408-988-0700 340 Martin Ave., Santa Clara, CA 95050	341	60	26 to 30	PVC	0.050	•	105 (max)
T&B Ansley 213-223-2331 3208 Humboldt St, Los Angeles CA 90031	342	64	26 to 30	PVC	0.050	•	105 (max)
Telecommunication Devices 312-971-3460 2320 Wisconsin Ave, Downers Grove IL 60515	343	64	26 to 28	PVC	0.050 0.100	•	105 (max)
Tri-Tech Elex Corp 305-277-2131 9480 E Colonial Dr, Orlando FL 32817	344	†	†	Poly-urethane	†	•	†
Ultra Products 517-547-3161 850 Manitou Rd, Manitou Beach MI 49253	345	40	22 to 28	PVC	0.050	•	105 (max)

† Available in various sizes and ratings; contact manufacturer for further information.

precisely center the cable as it starts to displace the insulation. All of the wires are terminated at once and the insulation remains intact and retains almost all of its original tensile strength. This method of terminating cables has a high inherent reliability because the procedure is virtually operator proof. When a damaged connector must be removed and replaced, a new connector may be installed in the same position at least three times.

It should be noted that almost all of the insulation displacement connectors are made with plastic bodies and are not environmentally sealed. However, with the proper use of elastomeric sealing methods it is relatively easy to seal the connector assembly.

Table 8-1 is a listing of manufacturers of flat cable materials where additional information can be sought. It is recommended that designers involved in wiring and cabling request being placed on the mailing lists of these manufacturers to remain current with the latest advances in technology.

Chapter 9

Solderless Wrap Connections

Solderless wrapped connections (wire-wrap connections) have proven their worth in the electronics industry for some years. In billions of finished connections which have been made over the years there has never been a reported electrical connection failure. By eliminating the use of solder, the user avoids thermal damage to heat sensitive materials, the hazards of hot soldering irons, burns to personnel, fires, soldering fumes and splashes, resin joints, cold solder joints and stress concentrations.

A solderless connection is made by wrapping a specified number of turns of wire around a terminal or post with sharp corners. The sharp corners produce high pressure points that result in indentions of the wire or terminal, producing a gas-tight connection that provides highly reliable electrical continuity and mechanical stability. See Fig. 9-1.

Any terminal that has at least two sharp edges crosswise to the axis of the terminating wire is suitable for making a *wire-wrap* connection. The commonly used terminals are square, rectangular, embossed, or serrated. The square terminal has some major advantages over the other types such as:

- The natural wrapping motion of a wire over a square terminal is in a circular pattern whereas a rectangular terminal results in an elliptical wrap.

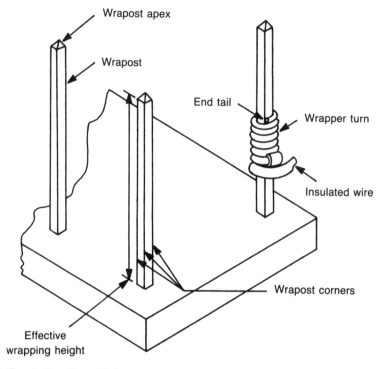

Fig. 9-1. Terminology for solderless wire-wrap connections.

- A rectangular cross section, with an elliptical wrap pattern results in the tip of the wire being wrapped projecting from the pattern. This condition, known as a pigtail is less likely to occur with the circular wrap on the square terminal. See Fig. 9-2.
- A square cross section has a uniform section modulus in all directions. This is useful in initially positioning the terminal relative to its true position and also tends to make the terminal more rigid during the wrapping operation.

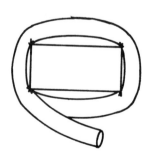

Fig. 9-2. Too much pigtail.

- The square cross section has less tendency to twist around its own axis.
- The strip force values for the square cross section is usually more consistent than the other types of terminals.
- The life of the wrapping bit tool is increased by the use of the square cross section terminals.

Most wire-wrapped connections are made using solid round wire over appropriately designed square or rectangular terminals. However, stranded wire may be used in special applications where excessive flexing is prevalent, but it must be twisted tightly and tinned prior to the wrapping operation.

There are two major classes of wire-wrapped connections (see Fig. 9-3):

Class A connections (modified solderless wrap connections)

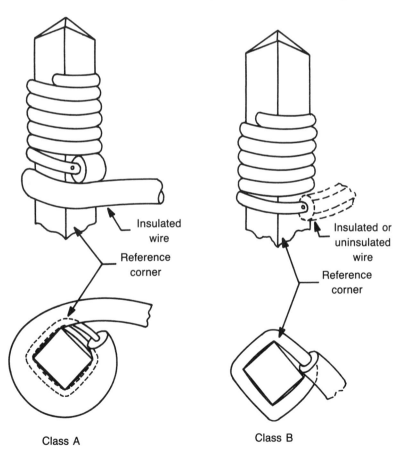

Class A   Class B

Fig. 9-3. Two classes of wire-wrap connection.

Table 9-1. Number of Wire-Wrap Turns for a .045 " Square Post.

Wire Size Designation AWG	Minimum Number of Turns	
	Class A	Class B
26	6 uninsulated and 1/2 insulated	6 uninsulated
24	5 uninsulated and 1/2 insulated	5 uninsulated
22	5 uninsulated and 1/2 insulated	5 uninsulated
20	4 uninsulated and 1/2 insulated	4 uninsulated
18	4 uninsulated	4 uninsulated

consist of a helix of continuous, solid uninsulated wire wrapped tightly around the terminal to produce a mechanically and electrically stable connection. The number of turns in the helix is dependent on the gauge of the wire used. See Tables 9-1 and 9-2. In addition to the length of uninsulated wire wrapped around the terminal, a Class A connection has an additional half turn of insulated wire to insure better vibration characteristics. The added half turn of insulated wire must be in contact with at least three of the sharp corners of the square terminal.

Class B connections (conventional wire-wrapped connections) are identical to the Class A, except that the half turn of insulated wire is not required.

The Class A connection is used in shipboard and airborne applications, and the Class B connection is acceptable for use in land based enviornments.

The terminals selected for solderless connections must be of sufficient strength to withstand the torsion applied when wrapping the wire, and should be selected to fit properly with the wrapping bit. The diagonal of the cross section of the terminal should be no greater than the wrapping tool bit minus 0.005.

As a general rule, the thickness of the terminal should be not less than one wire diameter and the terminal width should never be greater than twice the terminal thickness. The maximum ter-

Table 9-2. Number of Wire-Wrap Turns for a .025 " Square Post.

Wire Size Designation AWG	Minimum Number of Turns	
	Class A	Class B
30	7 uninsulated and 1/2 insulated	7 uninsulated
28	7 uninsulated and 1/2 insulated	7 uninsulated
26	5 uninsulated and 1/2 insulated	5 uninsulated

minal width should be no more than 3 1/2 times the conductor diameter.

Wrappable terminal length should always provide for at least one extra wrap in addition to the wraps for production in the event that an engineering change is made at a later date. The most successful materials used for making wire-wrap terminals are copper, beryllium copper, plated steel, copper-nickel alloy, tinned and untinned brass, phosphur bronze, and nickel-silver alloys. Certain finishes, particularly a hard gold plate, tend to lower the force required to slide the wrap along the terminal. To compensate for this reduction in stripping force, the wire must be wrapped under greater tension which has a tendency to reduce the life of the wrapping tool. Although plating is not a requirement for wire-wrap connections, terminals are plated for the following reasons:

- Tin plated wire is used in applications where wiring changes or repairs may be made in the field using standard soldering techniques.
- Where one end of the terminal is used as a plug-in type contact, gold plating is used for increased electrical contact reliability.

It is recommended that all wire-wrap terminals have a tapered tip. The purpose of the taper is to assist the operator in getting the terminal into the hole in the wrapping bit.

WIRE

The selection of a copper wire that conforms to the elongation listed in Table 9-3 insures that the wrap will pass the stripping force testing and the unwrap test.

HAND TOOLS

Hand tools include tools from the manual wire-wrap tool (similar

Table 9-3. Proper Wire Elongation.

AWG Number	Minimum Elongation (Percent in 10 Inches)
26	15%
24	15%
22	20%
20	20%
18	20%
16	20%

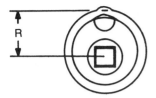

Fig. 9-4. Wire-wrap tool, end view.

to a screwdriver) to air and electrically driven tools (similar in appearance to a pistol).

The electrical design engineer will specify a certain size wire that must be used to meet the electrical requirements of the circuit. After the wire size has been selected, consideration must be given to the selection of the terminal to meet all of the physical requirements. The terminals must also meet the space limitations imposed on the application. In choosing the terminal, consideration must be given to the size of the wrapping bit (tool clearance). It is the combination of the outside diameter of the stationary sleeve plus the eccentricity of the terminal hole to wrapping bit that will determine the minimum grid or terminal spacing. See Fig. 9-4. Table 9-4 provides the dimension "R" which is referred to as the effective radius and is the minimum radius of the area around the terminal which must be clear to accommodate the wrapping bit and sleeve. Once the terminal spacing has been selected, some thought should be given to whether the spacing would be compatible with

Table 9-4. Minimum Clear Space Around a Wire Wrap Terminal.

Wire Ga. Reg.	Common Terminal Sizes	Effective Radius "R"
30-32	.020″ sq. .025″ sq. .010″ × .020″	.081
26	.016″ × .032″ .035″ × .050″ .045″ sq.	.104
24	.031″ × .062″ .035″ × .050″ .045″ sq.	.104
22	.031″ × .062″ .035″ × .050″ .045″ sq.	.125
20	.031″ × .062″ .045″ sq. 0.31″ × .062″	.150
18	.062″ sq. .062″ × .093″	.170
16	.080″ sq. .062″ × .093″	.257
14	.125″ sq. .093″ × .125″	.288

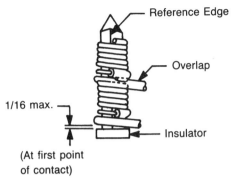

Fig. 9-5. Overlap in Class A connections.

automatic machine wrapping. Future production may dictate the use of automatic assembly, and considerable amounts of time and money could be saved with a little forethought at this time.

CONNECTIONS

The connections should be made so that the spacing between the turns of uninsulated wire, except for the first and last half turns should not be greater than 1/2 of the nominal wire diameter. There should not be any overlapping of the wires within the specified number of turns of the uninsulated wire, except that in a Class A connection, the insulated wire may overlap the last turn of insulated wire below it. See Fig. 9-5.

The first wrap on a terminal should always allow for a 1/16-inch clearance between the wrapped wire and the bottom surface of the terminal. At the termination of the last turn of a wrapped connection (end tail) the stripped wire should not pull away from the terminal by more than one stripped wire diameter. See Fig. 9-6.

The minimum number of turns of the stripped wire around the terminal is given in Table 9-5.

The minimum number of turns of insulated wire on the Class A connection is 1/2 turn and the maximum acceptable is 1 1/2 turns of insulated wire.

To insure that acceptable electrical and mechanical characteristics are maintained at each connection, the reduction in wire di-

Fig. 9-6. Maximum pullaway for Class A connections.

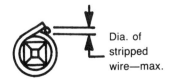

199

AWG Number	Minimum Number of Uninsulated Turns
26	6
24	5
22	5
20	4
18	4

Table 9-5. Number of Turns for Wire-Wrap Connections.

ameter due to nicks, scrapes, and deformations should not exceed the limits given in Table 9-6. Prior to making a wire-wrap connection, the wire must be free of all nicks and scrapes and the insulation must not be torn, frayed or damaged in any way.

After a wire-wrap connection is completed any attempt to move or adjust it can damage the bond between the wire and the terminal. Should it become necessary to move a completed connection, it must be completely removed and rewrapped. The completed assembly should be thoroughly cleaned and all wire clippings must be removed.

PROCESS

The sequence for making a solderless wire-wrapped connection with hand tools is as follows. See Fig. 9-7. Prior to making the wrap, the wire must be positioned radially, so that any further routing of the wire will not unwrap the connection.

- Insert the stripped wire into the feed slot.
- Bend the wire into the notch in the tool to anchor it.
- Place the larger hole in the tool over the terminal.
- Activate the tool.
- Remove the tool from the terminal.

The connection is complete. Metallic probes, tools or sharp instruments should never be used for dressing the wires.

Table 9-6. Maximum Wire Deformation.

AWG Number	Percent of Wire Diameter Reduction
30	10
26	10
24	20
22	25
20	25
18	25

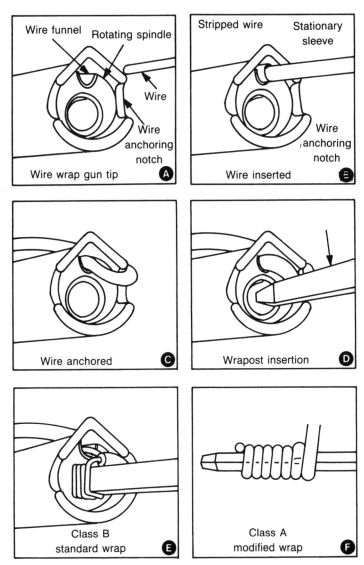

Fig. 9-7. The wire-wrap process.

BUSSING

Hand wrapped connections may be bussed by strapping. Strapping consists of wrapping a continuous uninsulated wire from terminal to terminal and requires the use of a special tool. The number of turns required for strapping is the same as for the Class B connections. Insulating sleeving is placed over the wire where the terminals are not adjacent and a potential for shorting exists.

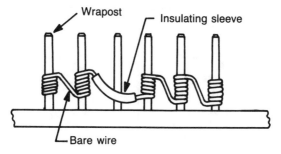

Fig. 9-8. Wire wrap strapping.

INSPECTION

Visual inspection of the wire-wrapped connections may be made under a 5x microscope. Figures 9-9 through 9-16 are provided as an aid for the visual inspection of wire-wrap connections. They show various wire-wrap imperfections.

PERFORMANCE REQUIREMENTS

Embrittlement. An unwrapping tool is used to unwrap a connection from a terminal. When the coil of wire is transferred to the tool, the tool is removed from the terminal and the wire is removed by rotating the tool. The wire need not be perfectly straight. Waves and permanent deformations are acceptable, but the wire must not break during the unwinding operation.

Strip Force. Completed wire-wrapped connections should meet the strip-force limits of Tables 9-7 and 9-8. The strip-force samples are tested using a fixture similar to that shown in Fig. 9-17. The clearance between the connection and the test fixture stripping jaws should not be greater than 0.005 inches and the stripping rate should be uniform at 1 to 10 inches per minute. The strip-force is the maximum force in pounds required to move the entire wrap a distance of 1/16 to 1/8 inches on the terminal.

Before releasing new or repaired tools to the production line they should be inspected and tested by performing a strip force and embrittlement test on at least 24 sample connections.

Fig. 9-9. Insufficient insulation wrap for a Class A connection.

Fig. 9-10. Insufficient number of turns.

Fig. 9-11. End tail.

Fig. 9-12. Overwrap.

Fig. 9-13. Wrapping over the end of the terminal post.

Fig. 9-14. Overlap.

Fig. 9-15. Spiral wrap.

Fig. 9-16. Open wrap.

GAS TIGHT CONNECTIONS

To test a wire-wrap connection for its effective gas tightness, which should be equal to or greater than the cross sectional area of the wire used in making the connection, blacken the assembly with ammonium sulphide gas after the gold plated terminals are exposed to aqua regia fumes.

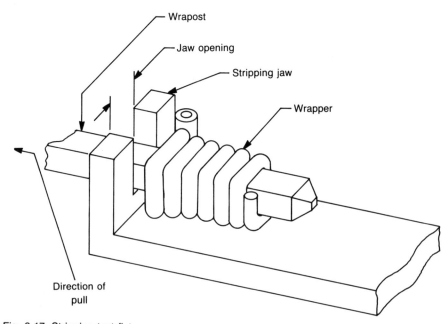

Fig. 9-17. Stripping test fixture.

204

Size AWG	Minimum Force (lbs)
26	6.0
24	7.0
22	8.0
20	9.0
18	15.0

Table 9-7. Strip Force Limits for a .045 " Square Post.

The terminal assembly is suspended and corked in a 16 by 150 millimeter test tube containing approximately 1 to 2 milliliters of aqua regia solution (1:1 concentrated hydrochloric and nitric acids). The solution must not touch the terminal assemblies and the exposure shall last for ten minutes. After the exposure to the aqua regia solution, the assembly is transferred to another 16 × 150 millimeter test tube, containing approximately one ml of concentrated ammonium sulphide solution. The assembly should be suspended

Size AWG	Minimum Strip Force (lbs)
30	2.0
28	3.0
26	4.0

Table 9-8. Strip Force Limits for a .025 " Square Post.

so that it does not touch the solution and then the test tube should be corked and the connection left until the exposed surfaces turn black. A copper and gold sulphide color will be developed on all of the areas exposed to the vapor.

Carefully remove the specimen from the test tube and unwrap the wire from the terminal. Do not scratch the blackened areas. The gas tight areas will appear bright and in sharp contrast with the blackened areas.

ELECTRICAL RESISTANCE

When tested for electrical resistance, the wire-wrap connec-

Size AWG	Current to Determine Connection Resistance
30	1.0
28	2.0
26	2.4
24	2.4
22	2.4
20	7.5
18	7.5

Table 9-9. Connection Resistance.

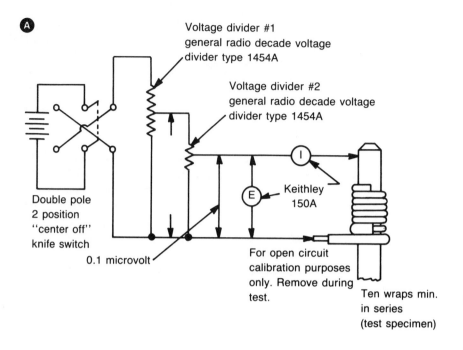

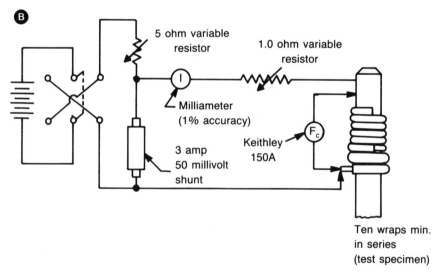

Fig. 9-18. Circuit for testing resistance of the connection.

tion should have a voltage drop across the entire wrap of not more than 4 millivolts. The test should be performed with the currents specified in Table 9-9 with the setup depicted in Figs. 9-18 and 9-19.

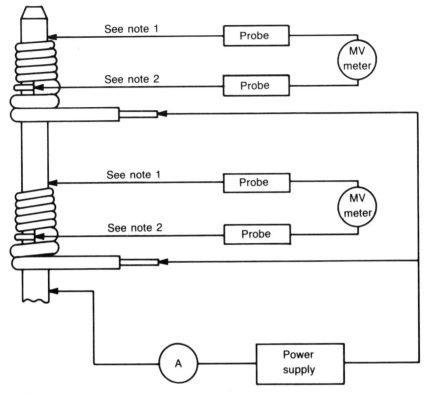

Notes:
1. This probe shall not touch the wire.
2. This probe shall be placed on the first turn of uninsulated wire.

Fig. 9-19. Circuit for testing resistance of the connection.

Chapter 10

Manufacturing Standards

The reliability of any electronic system is dependent on the quality of workmanship employed during the manufacturing phase. The production operators and inspectors are responsible for the quality and reliability of the final product.

Formal training is needed. This training can be accomplished inhouse with a comprehensive program for the qualification and certification of personnel.

The assembly worker must be taught what a reliable soldered connection is, how it is made, and the proper tools, methods and techniques required to make it.

The major cause of solder joint failures is generally attributed to poor soldering techniques such as cold joints, excessive heat, improper fluxing, etc.

Unfortunately, operators are likely to select one soldering iron and use it for all purposes. This is like using a sledge hammer to drive tacks. No one tool is suitable for all purposes. There is no one best training and certification program since all organizations are different. Each organization must decide what is most suitable for its own product and customers. To build the most reliable product at the lowest cost with maximum customer satisfaction, the following points should be considered:

- Establish soldering, wiring and assembly standards.

- Train, qualify and certify employees for adherence to these standards.
- Monitor the program and take positive actions as indicated by the changing technology.
- Ensure that only qualified personnel are performing specialized skills and processes.
- Provide employees with the required knowledge for competent job performance and evaluation of products.

The objectives from a trainee's viewpoint are to:

- Develop an understanding of their responsibilities in meeting the company standards and the customer's requirements.
- Become familiar with the company standards for wiring, soldering, and assembly.
- Demonstrate an ability to consistently meet the expected reliability and performance standards.

TOOLS

Acceptable work may occasionally be turned out with poor tools, but this is an exception. Using the wrong tool invariably requires more time, and increases the potential for poor quality. The correct tools, properly used and maintained, results in quality workmanship and contributes to the skill and pride of the worker.

A set of basic individual tools should be assigned to or owned by each operator. These tools should consist of at least:

- Round-nose bending pliers.
- Long-nose pliers.
- Diagonal cutting pliers.
- Tweezers (including a self-locking type).
- Soldering aids.
- File (for dressing soldering iron tips).
- Scissors (small, thin-blade).

The following tools should be issued as required by the tasks assigned:

- Calibrated precision wire strippers.
- Thermal wire strippers.
- Variable voltage transformer (for control of soldering iron).
- Soldering iron with spare tips.
- Heat sink (thermal shunts).

- Magnifying lamp for miniature work.
- Sponge (for cleaning soldering iron tips).

Expendable supplies are issued to specific job requirements:

- Lacing cord or cable ties.
- Core solder.
- Liquid flux.
- Alcohol or company approved solvent.
- Bristle brushes.

The following special equipment must be made available for production jobs to insure maximum productivity:

- Automatic wire strippers and cutters.
- Lead bending and cutting machines.
- Automatic component insertion equipment.
- Automatic soldering machines.
- Solder pots (for tinning wires).
- Cleaning equipment.

WORK AREA

Sufficient lighting that is properly directed at the work station is a prime requirement for quality work. This may be provided by a combination of glare-free area lighting with the addition of individual adjustable light sources at the work surface. A light level of 100 footcandles at the work place is considered necessary for adequate visibility to assemble miniature parts and connectors.

Keeping the work area neat and orderly contributes to quality work by reducing confusion. Tools and materials should always be arranged within easy reach, and each tool should be kept in a specified place. Plastic trays or shallow pans lined with industrial towels are often used for holding tools. Misplaced and inaccessible tools cause delays and often tempt the operator to use the wrong tool. Only the tools that are required by the current task should be kept at the operator's station. These simple rules can reduce or eliminate rejections, reworks, and delays.

The safety of the workplace is dependent on the development and maintenance of good safety practices by all personnel in the area. At least the following safety practices should be maintained, and other practices for special areas must be developed as required:

1. Place soldering irons where it will not be necessary to reach

over or around it. Soldering irons should be placed at the far corner of the bench when not in use.

2. When unsoldering a wire, be sure there is no tension or spring to the wire. Safety glasses should be worn to shield the eyes from hot solder splashes.

3. Always plug the soldering iron into the proper socket and be sure that there are no strands of wire clipping or metals nearby that could short the connection.

4. When cutting wire, the open face of the cutters should always face away from the eyes and body. Keep the wire cuttings in your area, protecting fellow workers.

5. Disconnect all electrical power before working on a metal chassis.

6. Be sure that blade-type screwdrivers are sharp and square. Use screwdrivers only for the work they were designed for.

7. Connect air hoses to the air supply nearest the work station and keep the hose out of the aisle. Extra hose length should be reeled up.

8. While cleaning parts with an air hose, use controlled pressure nozzles and direct the air stream away from other personnel. Never clean clothes with air pressure.

9. When cleaning with solvents, keep only a small amount at the work area in a safety can. Do not smoke or spill solvent over the work bench.

10. Safety glasses should always be worn while cutting wires or component leads, and when working with solvents.

11. Women working in an area where soldering and assembly are being performed should wear low heeled, closed toe shoes.

SOLDERING IRONS

Research has shown that the most reliable solder connections are achieved within a narrow range of temperature and application time. Junction temperatures of 500 °F to 550 °F, applied for 1 to 2 seconds produce the strongest connections. Size, wattage, and the shape of the soldering iron tip should be selected to achieve these conditions as closely as possible. When the soldering iron tip is applied, it should heat the connection to the desired temperature rapidly. The heat capacity of the soldering iron tip is dependent on its mass, the mass of the soldering iron tip should be large with respect to the mass of the metal being heated for solder application.

The soldering iron tip should not be so large that it obscures visibility of the workpiece, or cause damage to nearby parts or wire insulation.

The shape of the soldering iron tip, spade, chisel, or pyramid should be compatible with the workpiece. Keeping an assortment of spare tips, and changing tips as they wear is always good practice.

By the proper selection of soldering iron tips and a variable voltage supply, a single 50 watt pencil type soldering iron can be used for soldering anything, from printed circuits to relatively large terminals. Thermostatically controlled soldering irons require less-skilled operators, but are somewhat less versatile. Unplated copper soldering iron tips produce the best results, and are therefore recommended. This does not exclude plated tips for production work, provided the quality of the solder connections can be maintained. Copper tips should be dressed with a suitable file while in the unheated condition. After the tip has been filed and shaped, the temperature should be brought up to the minimum for melting the solder, the solder should be applied to the tip and the tip should be wiped on a damp sponge. During soldering operations, the tip should be wiped on a wet sponge before each solder connection is made.

Note: Do not change from an unplated tip to a plated tip during a single operation without allowing the extra time required for the heat to transfer from the plated tip.

Heat Application with Soldering Irons

The soldering iron tip should be positioned against the metal part having the largest mass. See Fig. 10-1. Normally, when sol-

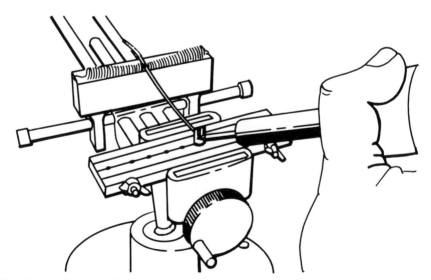

Fig. 10-1. Position the soldering iron tip against the metal part with the greatest mass.

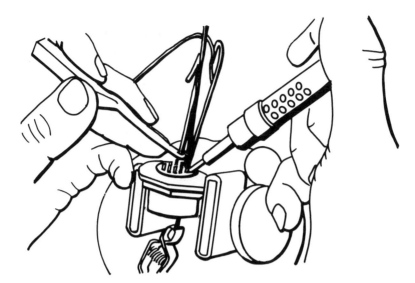

Fig. 10-2. Typical resistance soldering.

dering a wire to a terminal, the greatest mass will be at the terminal. Fresh tinning of the tip will provide faster transfer of heat to the workpiece. The solder should always be applied to the junction materials, not the soldering iron tip. The soldering iron should be removed as soon as the connection is complete to avoid overheating the solder. The surface temperature of both metals at the connection must be above the solder melting point to expedite efficient wetting. The solder must not be allowed to flow onto a surface that is cooler than the solder temperature since this will cause a cold or rosin joint. Solder, when applied to a properly cleaned, fluxed and heated surface will melt and flow without direct contact with the heat source. It will have a smooth, even surface, feathering out to a thin edge. An irregular, built-up appearance indicates improper solder application.

A good solder joint is characterized by a smooth surface, even distribution of solder to a feathered edge at the base metal, no porosity, good fillet between conductors, and good adherence to both parts. Charred or carbonized flux residue indicates excessive application of heat. Solder that obscures the contour of the wires, making visual inspection difficult, is due to excessive application of solder.

Resistance Soldering

Resistance soldering, shown in Fig. 10-2, is an effective method of applying heat to the metals of a solder connection. This process

213

passes current through the metal. The heat generated at the interface of the metal and electrode causes the solder to melt and flow. Since resistance soldering generates the heat directly in the metal area to be soldered, it offers the advantage of confining the heat to a selected area. This method is well adapted for soldering connectors.

One application of this method uses tweezer-type electrodes. When the metal is gripped between the electrodes, and electric circuit is completed through a low-voltage transformer and the metal between the electrodes is heated.

A second application of resistance soldering uses a carbon pencil electrode. When contact is made by the carbon pencil, the metal of the terminal is heated at the point of contact (where the resistance is at its maximum).

Preparing Conductors for Soldering

Insulation Stripping. To strip the insulation from a wire, a non-adjustable, factory set, cutting type stripper should be used. See Fig. 10-3. When using a tool with multiple stripping holes, the correct hole for the gage of the wire being stripped must be used. Tools equipped with single dies are recommended. For long production runs where a single wire size is used, the unused holes in the multiple conductor stripper can be masked off to prevent accidental use of an undersized hole which will result in nicks, scrapes, and cuts in the wire.

The calibration of all precision type cutting strippers should be checked periodically, and out-of-tolerance strippers should be removed from the production area.

Thermal type strippers, shown in Fig. 10-4, can be used on certain types of wire insulation which can be effectively stripped by this method. Care must be taken to insure that burned insulation residue does not interfere with the soldering operation. Adequate ventilation must be provided when using thermal strippers, because inhalation of the vapors from the breakdown of polymerized organic insulation can cause polymer fume fever.

Fig. 10-3. Proper cutting-type stripper.

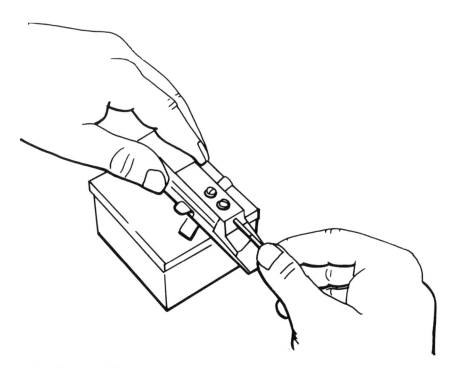

Fig. 10-4. Thermal stripper.

If the stripping operation has caused the wire strands to become separated or disarranged, the strands must be restored to their original lay before the ends are tinned. Stripped wire with nicked or cut strands is not acceptable since the stress concentration can cause failures during vibration. For this reason, the cutting type strippers shown in Fig. 10-5 are not recommended. They will invaribly cut, nick, or scrape the strands of wire.

Insulation Damage

Excessive pressure by the gripping jaws of hand-held strippers will crush the insulation at the wire end. Incorrect gripping blocks in a machine type stripper will also damage the insualtion. Wire with damaged insulation should not be used. However, a slight discoloration as a result of thermal stripping is acceptable.

Insulation Gap

The end of the insulation should be cut back far enough from the solder joint so that the insulation will not become embedded in the solder, but not so far that the exposed bare wire could cause

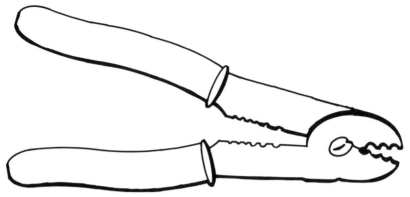

Fig. 10-5. Improper cutting-type stripper.

a short between two adjacent wires. A rule of thumb is that the insulation gap should be equal to approximately one wire diameter. See Fig. 10-6.

Cleaning Leads

To assure good wetting action between the conductors or leads to be soldered, all impurities such as grease, dirt, or oxide films must be removed. All surface contamination and corrosion formed on wire during processing, storage, or handling must be removed before the soldering operation. A typical cleaning tool is shown in Fig. 10-7. The wire should be tinned with the same alloy that will be used in the final soldering operation immediately after cleaning.

Stress Relief Allowance

An allowance to compensate for expansion and contraction dur-

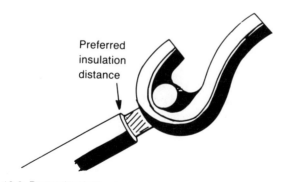

Preferred
insulation
distance

Fig. 10-6. Proper insulation gap.

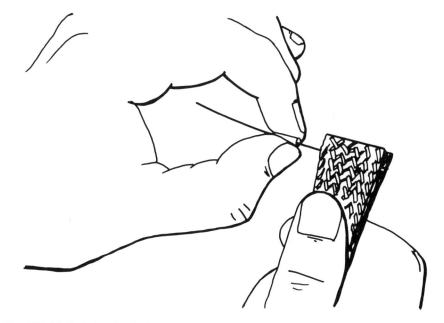

Fig. 10-7. Typical cleaning tool.

ing thermal cycling should be made in all parts. This also includes small jumper wires that could transmit tensile or compressive forces. Wires connected to devices having fixed terminals should have slack in the form of a gradual bend to allow flexing during vibration, as shown in Fig. 10-8. When multiple wires are routed from a cable trunk to equally spaced terminals, a uniform amount of slack should be provided to prevent a stress from occurring in the shortest wire. The cable trunk should be clamped for additional mechanical support.

Soldering

Tin melts at 450 °F and lead melts at 621 °F. The eutectic solder most commonly used in modern electronics melts at 361 °F. Solders other than eutectic will melt at higher temperatures. The manufacturing engineer must know and apply these temperatures to the equipment in use at the work stations. When heat is applied to solders other than the eutectic series, it becomes plastic, and then liquid. On the removal of the heat the process is reversed, the solder goes from liquid to plastic and finally to solid. If either member on the connection is moved during the plastic phase of the solder, the solder will become course grained, and the connection will

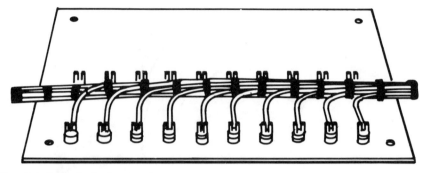

Fig. 10-8. Typical vibration bends.

be mechanicaly weak and unreliable. This type of connection, shown in Fig. 10-9, is called a fractured joint, and should be reflowed.

The length of time that the solder is kept molten, and the temperature at which it is maintained while a liquid, are critical since the molten solder absorbs gases. If an excessive temperature has been used or the solder has been kept molten for too long a period, the molten solder will oxidize, and the solder will appear granular and grey when cool. This will result in a weak and unreliable joint.

Solder and Flux

The core of wire solder should contain only a rosin or activated rosin flux. For general use, a solder composition of Sn60 or Sn63 (60 or 63 percent tin and 40 or 37 percent lead) should be used. Other compositions should be used only for special cases and only when specified by manufacturing engineering. Soldering paste, acid-type flux, or other corrosive or conductive fluxes should be avoided.

In some applications, such as removing excess solder by wick-

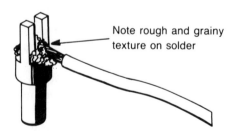

Note rough and grainy
texture on solder

Fig. 10-9. Fractured joint.

218

ing into a stranded wire or a shielded braid, liquid rosin flux may be used. To prevent any undesirable chemical reactions, the activating material in the liquid rosin flux must be compatible with the core flux of the wire solder used in the assembly process.

Flux Application

Flux should be applied to a surface before the solder melting temperature is reached. The rosin in the core solder melts before the solder and the application occurs automatically. If excessive temperatures are used, rosin flux will carbonize and will hinder the soldering operations to follow.

Tinning Stranded Wire

The tinning of stranded wire should extend only far enough to take full advantage of the depth of the terminal or cup. The ends of the stranded wire should be dipped in flux to the depth that the tinning is desired. The actual tinning is then accomplished by dipping the wire ends into a solder pot, as shown in Fig. 10-10, with a controlled temperature of 500 °F +/− 20 °F, or by using a soldering iron and wire cored solder, as shown in Fig. 10-11.

Should it become necessary to strip, tin, and solder wires within an assembly, care must be taken to avoid dripping or spraying solder or dropping insulation residue and other impurities.

Holding

The materials being soldered should be held motionless with respect to each other. Depending on the type of termination, the

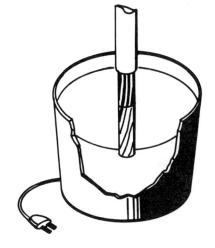

Fig. 10-10. Tinning pot.

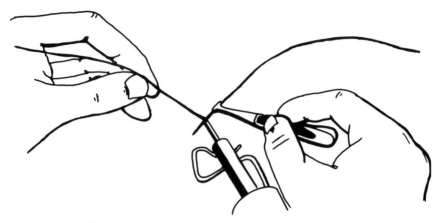

Fig. 10-11. Hand tinning.

tinned end of the wire should be formed into a hook or loop, and held firmly against the joining member during soldering, cooling and solidification.

Cleaning Solder Joints

Flux residue is usually tacky and tends to collect dirt and other foreign materials which can cause electrical leakage paths across insulation surfaces. To prevent this, the flux should be removed. After the solder has solidified, the flux residue should be dissolved by applying an approved solvent with a bristle brush or spray. The dissolved residue should be removed with industrial tissues or other absorbent materials. A clean corner of the tissue should be used each time to avoid transferring the dissolved flux back to the work-piece. Do not use large quantities of solvent or dip the workpiece into a solvent, because the dissolved solvent can enter spaces from which it cannot be removed.

Inspection

The quality of a soldered connection can be determined by visual inspection. It may be necessary to inspect the solder joints at various levels of production where further assembly will cover the joint. If a joint must be reworked, it should be completely disassembled, the excess solder removed, and the area thoroughly cleaned prior to remaking the connection. To remove a wire from cup terminals, as in plugs and connectors, the preferred method is the use of resistance type soldering irons. A standard type soldering iron may be used when necessary. In either method, the heat is transferred to the cup until the solder has melted. A light steady pull should easily remove the wire. The excess solder remaining in the cup can be removed by wicking into a stranded wire or by use of a vacuum type solder remover. In either case care must be taken to avoid prolonged heating of the terminal. A soldering iron with the tip well wetted with solder should be used for unsoldering turret, pierced, split or hook terminals. In very close quarters, it may be desirable to wick or vacuum most of the solder out before attempting to remove the wire from the terminal.

Terminal Connections

The design is responsible for insuring that the size and number of terminals are sufficient to accommodate the conductors in any assembly. The terminal cups and slots should never be modified to accept oversize conductors, nor should the conductors be modified to accommodate the terminals.

Hook Terminals

The stripped and tinned wire should be bent a minimum of 90° and held against the terminal during the soldering operation. The end of the wire should not extend more than one diameter beyond the hook. A bend of approximately 180° ("U" shape) is also permitted. See Figs. 10-6 and 10-12. No attempt should be made to squeeze the tinned wire against the hook with pliers.

Pierced Terminals

Wires to be soldered to pierced terminals should have a 90° minimum bend and should not extend more than a distance of one wire diameter beyond the terminal. A 180° bend is preferred.

Both the hook and pierced terminals should be mechanically protected by installing a flexible sleeving over the connection, as shown in Fig. 10-13. The sleeving should be cut to length and slid

Fig. 10-12. Hook terminal connection.

Fig. 10-13. Pierced terminal.

over the wire before making the solder connection, and slipped over the joint after it has been cleaned and inspected. In the final position, the sleeving should extend over the wire insulation by a minimum of one diameter of the wire insulation.

Solder Cups

When assembling wires to soldering cups, the connector should be firmly mounted with the cups facing the operator. The wires should be soldered in rows, progressing from the bottom to the top. The cups may be prefilled with solder before any of the wires are inserted. The cup should be heated by holding the soldering iron against the side of the cup until the solder is completely melted. Keep the heat on the terminal until all of the trapped solder flux comes to the surface. The tinned wire should be slowly inserted into the molten solder until the conductor is in contact with the back wall of the solder cup. A smooth fillet should be formed between the conductor and the inner wall of the cup. See Fig. 10-14. The solder should follow the contour of the solder cup and should not spill over, as shown in Fig. 10-15, or adhere to the outside of the cup. Wicking of solder up to the point of insulation termination is

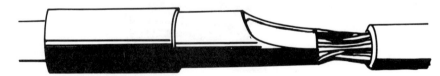

Fig. 10-14. Proper solder cup termination.

Fig. 10-15. Improper solder cup termination.

permitted. All of the outside strands of the wire should be discernible adjacent to the insulation.

Sleeving Cup Terminals

When a connector is to be potted, a protective sleeve over the wire and cup is not required. For all unpotted connectors the sleeving provides additional mechanical support.

Protection of Connectors

Connectors are an important and delicate part of every electronic assembly and probes should never be used for testing. A mating connector or test box should be used. Plastic or metal covers should be installed over all connectors and should not be removed except for inspection or engaging a mating connector. The covers should always be replaced when the connector is not in use.

Swage Cup Terminals

Bottom Entry. When a tinned conductor is inserted into a terminal from the bottom it should be stripped just far enough so that the wire insulation does not extend into the barrel. (1/32 inch minimum clearance is recommended).

Top Entry. Inserting a tinned wire into the top of the swage cup is the same as the insertion into a solder cup terminal, except that the wire should touch the bottom routed wire. See Fig. 10-16.

Bifurcated Terminals

The usual method of inserting conductors into bifurcated terminals is the bottom route or the side route. When it becomes necessary to insert from the top, care should be taken to insure that good solder fillets are made to both prongs of the terminal. When the tinned conductor is inserted from the bottom, as shown in Fig. 10-17, it should be stripped far enough to insure that the insulation does not extend into the barrel, (1/32 inch clearance is recommended).

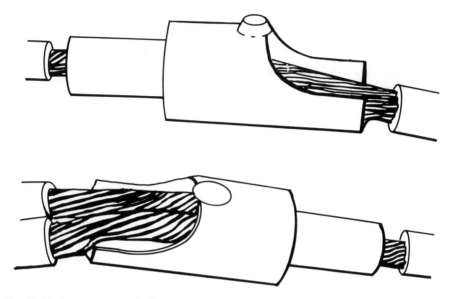

Fig. 10-16. Swage cup terminal.

For side entry into a bifurcated terminal, the tinned wire should be brought through the gap and bent flush against the post, as shown in Fig. 10-18. A second wire, when required, is bent flush in the opposite direction against the other post, as shown in Fig. 10-19. Additional wires alternate similarly. The gap may be filled, but under no circumstances should a wire extend beyond the top of the post. When wires must be routed to the top of a bifurcated terminal, the wire should fill the gap between the posts so that a good fillet is formed to each post. Where smaller wire gages are used, a filler wire may be used to fill the gap. See Fig. 10-20.

Turret Terminals

When terminating to a turret terminal the conductor should be

Fig. 10-17. Bifurcated terminal, bottom entry.

Fig. 10-18. Bifurcated terminal, side entry.

Fig. 10-19. Bifurcated terminal, side entry with two wires.

Fig. 10-20. Bifurcated terminal, top entry.

Fig. 10-21. Turret terminal.

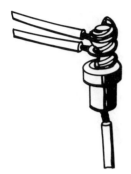

Fig. 10-22. Hollow post turret terminal.

stripped, tinned, and bent into a loop approximately 1/2 turn and slipped around the guide slot, snug against the shoulder, as shown in Fig. 10-21. Wires that are smaller than AWG 26 may be wrapped a full turn but should not overlap. When a hollow post terminal is used, the wire should be stripped to a length that will allow at least a 1/32 inch gap between the insulation and the terminal. See Fig. 10-22. Terminals should be stored in sealed plastic bags with a dessicant to eliminate the possibility of oxidizing during storage.

Chapter 11

Reference Designators

Reference designations are intended for uniquely identifying and locating discrete items on diagrams and in the hardware. A location numbering and coding method has been developed to permit rapid physical location of items in large complicated electronic equipment. The reference designations in this chapter are for use on equipment and related diagrams, drawings, and parts lists, in manuals or similar publications. The designer must remember that reference designations are intended to replace other identification numbers such as drawing, type, part or stock numbers. The following information describes the factors to be considered in the identification of parts, subassemblies, and assemblies, and the marking of electrical and electronic reference designations on equipment and related technical data. When reference designations are used, an explanation of the method employed must be furnished in the related technical data.

MARKING OF DIAGRAMS AND DATA

Systems, Sets, and Groups

When reference designations are used to identify systems, sets, or groups, an explanation of the method employed should be furnished as part of the accompanying technical data. See Fig. 11-1.

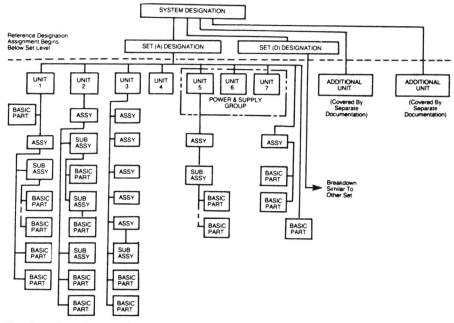

Fig. 11-1. Typical system subdivision.

Units of a Set

Each unit within a set should be assigned an identifying number, beginning with one (1) and running consecutively for all units of the set. This number becomes the reference designation of the unit. Where a set includes only one unit, the unit reference designation should be omitted. Units which are enclosed within the same cabinet, mounted in a common rack, or similarly joined with other units, subassemblies, etc., should be treated as subassemblies.

Units of a group that is not covered by separate documentation should be numbered as units of the set of which they form a part, without group identification. Units of a group that is covered by separate documentation should be designated as units of a set.

Units Not Part of a Set

Units of a system which are not part of a set should be assigned unit identifying numbers if covered by system technical data. However, when such units (e.g., existing designs, standard units, oscilloscopes, etc.) are covered by separate technical data, they should not be assigned unit identifying numbers.

Expansion of Method

In a multilevel unit, subassemblies of subassemblies should be identified as if they were parts of the subassemblies. The reference designation method can be expanded as necessary to permit identification of items subdivided for fabrication, stocking, or maintenance purposes. However, every effort should be made to keep designations as short as practicable. The reference designation should not contain more than the five levels shown in the example of Fig. 11-2 unless required by the number of plug-in levels. See Fig. 11-3.

Subassemblies and Parts Not Integral with Units

Subassemblies (such as interconnecting cables) and parts which are not incorporated within units, should be identified using sequential numbers in the same manner as those which are integral with units, except for omission of the unit identifying number. For example, the connectors at either end of cable assembly W15 are designated W15P1 and W15P2. (See Fig. 11-4.)

Partial Reference Designations

Partial or basic reference designations may be used in text relating to diagrams and units provided that the appropriate unit and subassemblies are evident. For these applications, the reference designation may be limited to a sufficient portion of the complete reference designation to identify the subassembly or part. For example, AR1C1, A1AR1, A2, etc., of Fig. 7. When parts compris-

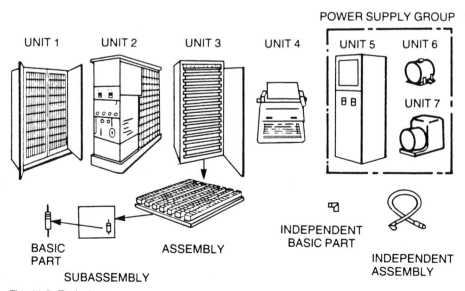

Fig. 11-2. Typical set.

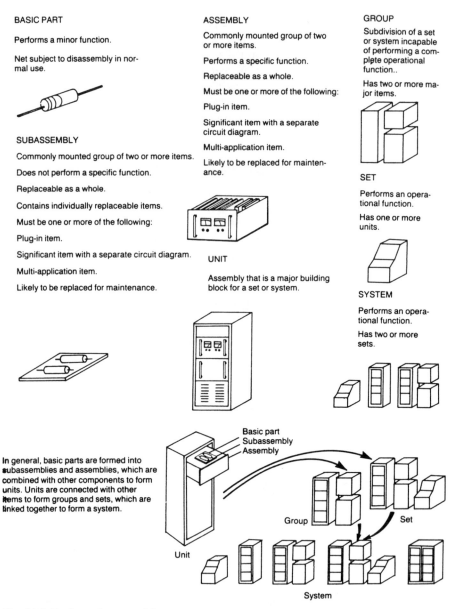

BASIC PART

Performs a minor function.

Net subject to disassembly in normal use.

SUBASSEMBLY

Commonly mounted group of two or more items.

Does not perform a specific function.

Replaceable as a whole.

Contains individually replaceable items.

Must be one or more of the following:

Plug-in item.

Significant item with a separate circuit diagram.

Multi-application item.

Likely to be replaced for maintenance.

ASSEMBLY

Commonly mounted group of two or more items.

Performs a specific function.

Replaceable as a whole.

Must be one or more of the following:

Plug-in item.

Significant item with a separate circuit diagram.

Multi-application item.

Likely to be replaced for maintenance.

UNIT

Assembly that is a major building block for a set or system.

GROUP

Subdivision of a set or system incapable of performing a complete operational function..

Has two or more major items.

SET

Performs an operational function.

Has one or more units.

SYSTEM

Performs an operational function.

Has two or more sets.

In general, basic parts are formed into subassemblies and assemblies, which are combined with other components to form units. Units are connected with other items to form groups and sets, which are linked together to form a system.

Fig. 11-3. Equipment nomenclature.

ing more than one unit or subassembly are scattered throughout a drawing, a sufficient portion of the complete reference designation shall be included to permit positive identification (e.g. A151 for switch of assembly 1, where the unit number is evident and has been omitted). On diagrams and units, either the complete desig-

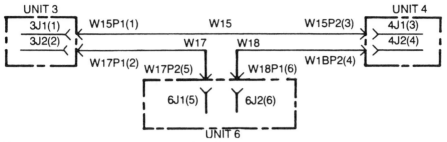

Fig. 11-4. Typical connector and interunit cable designations.

nation (with respect to the highest level illustrated) or partial designations may be used. Where partial reference designations are used, a note such as "REF DESIG PREFIX_____" (with appropriate reference designation prefix inserted) shall be provided. When more than one prefix is involved, a note having the intent of Note 1 of Fig. 11-5 shall be added to the drawing.

Intersubassembly and Interunit Cable Connections

Each cable should be identified on the appropriate schematic diagram by a unique reference designation. A cable assembly having multiple uses should be identified by a part number or nomenclature, and this should be shown on the schematic diagram near the reference designation. In a complex set having a large number of interassembly and interunit connections, proper interconnection of items should be expedited by assigning a unique identification to each mating pair of connectors in the set (provided that one or both are connected to a cable).

On diagrams and other technical data, this unique mating pair identification should be shown in parentheses following the basic reference designation for the connectors. The mating pair identification may (preferably) be in the form of sequential numbers, function designations (if suitable), or other methods mutually agreed upon. (See Fig. 11-6.)

Connectors

Connector reference designations should be assigned in accordance with the following principles:

- The movable (i.e., less fixed) connector of a mating pair should be designated "P" (see Fig. 11-6, connector P3 of assembly A7, and connector P1 of cable W2).
- The stationary (i.e., more fixed) connector of a mating pair should be designated "J" or "X".

231

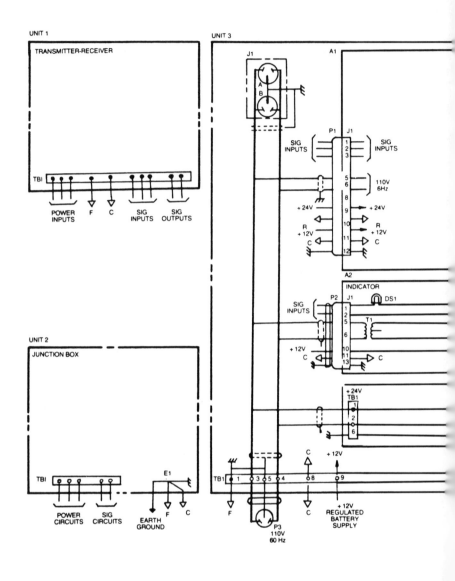

Fig. 11-5. Typical reference designations on schematic diagrams.

- A connector "P" of a flexible cable should mate with a fixed connector designated "J" rather than "X".
- When two cables are to be connected, each of the mating connectors should be designated "P".
- A connector used to mount an item, or affixed to the mount-

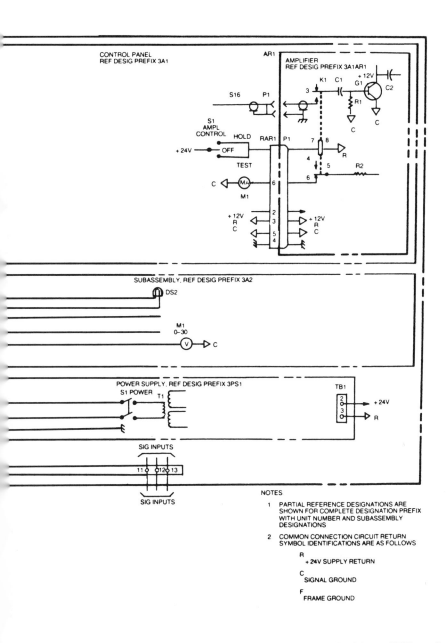

CONTROL PANEL
REF DESIG PREFIX 3A1

AR1

AMPLIFIER
REF DESIG PREFIX 3A1AR1

SUBASSEMBLY, REF DESIG PREFIX 3A2

DS2

M1
0–30

POWER SUPPLY, REF DESIG PREFIX 3PS1

S1 POWER

TB1

SIG INPUTS

11 12 13

SIG INPUTS

NOTES

1 PARTIAL REFERENCE DESIGNATIONS ARE
   SHOWN FOR COMPLETE DESIGNATION PREFIX
   WITH UNIT NUMBER AND SUBASSEMBLY
   DESIGNATIONS

2 COMMON CONNECTION CIRCUIT RETURN
   SYMBOL IDENTIFICATIONS ARE AS FOLLOWS

   R
    +24V SUPPLY RETURN

   C
    SIGNAL GROUND

   F
    FRAME GROUND

ing of an item, should be designated with an "X" prefix if its mating connector is directly affixed (i.e., not on flexible cable) to the mounted item. See Fig. 11-7. Should there be more than one directly affixed connector on the mounted item, the designation of each of the mating mounting con-

233

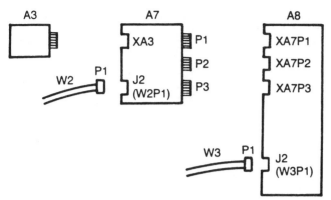

Fig. 11-6. Connector designations for plug-in items.

nectors should consist of the following in the order listed:

(1) The class code letter "X".
(2) The basic reference designation of the mounted item.
(3) The basic reference designation of its mating connector on the mounted item. If the mounted item has more than one integral connector and requires more than one mounting connector, the basic reference designation of the mounting connectors should include a letter suffix.

- If a cable has one end connector terminated and the other end permanently connected (i.e., soldered, etc.) to the circuit wiring, the connector and, if necessary, the wire should be assigned reference designations as individual parts of the circuit rather than as a separate subassembly.
- When more than one item of different class code plugs into one mounting connector, that connector should be designated "X", followed by a sequentially assigned number. For example, the single connector mounting AR1, R7, or Z3 (depending upon circuit instructions) should be designated X6 (provided that it is the sixth such application).
- Where there are alternate connections within a given item (for example, for different supply voltages, low impedance, or a patch board), the numerical portion of the basic reference designation for the mating "P" and "J" items should be in a nonduplicating numerical sequence. Preferably, the assignation of the same number to the P and J parts of any mating combination of alternate-connection connectors should be avoided. The connectors which should be mated for a given operating condition should be explained in the

supporting technical data or by functional designations on the equipment.

• If an adapter is located between other connecting devices, the adapter may be disregarded in assigning reference designations to the other connecting devices. However, the adapter should be assigned a reference designation (e.g., CP3).

Supplementary Information

When only one portion of a mating connector pair is shown on the schematic diagram, the reference designation for the mating connector or plug-in item should be indicated in parentheses adjacent to the connector shown. For example:

J1	J3
(P1)	(CP2)
	(W4P1)

If one connector has as its mate any one of several other connectors, or if the item has multiple uses, a suitable function designation may be shown in lieu of the reference designations of all of the potential mating connectors.

MARKING OF EQUIPMENT

Equipment should be permanently and legibly marked with the

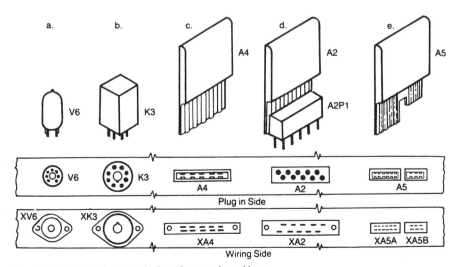

Fig. 11-7. Socket reference designations and markings.

reference designation for each subassembly and part except in the following instances:

- When space limitations preclude such marking. In this case, diagrams showing the location of parts or subassemblies should be placed on the subassembly or unit, respectively. These diagrams should be visible when the parts or assemblies are viewed. If the equipment is not completely marked, or appropriate diagrams are not placed on the unit, part location diagrams should be included in the maintenance data for the set.
- When the customer specifically requires that markings be omitted.
- Where it is customary in industry to omit markings on specific nonmilitary products, in which case, reference designation markings shall be optional.

Location of Markings

Reference designation markings should be located adjacent to each subassembly or part, and should be marked on the chassis, reverse side of the front panel, partitions, insulated mounting strips, etc. Reference designations should not be marked on parts and subassemblies which are subject to replacement if other means are feasible. This does not preclude markings for parts within such subassemblies. The reference designations should be marked in a location such that they locate the parts physically, yet remain readily visible for maintenance purposes without removal of the referenced part or other parts. The primary intent of this requirement is that removal of a part or subassembly should not result in the loss of the identification of its physical location.

Assemblies or parts which are not integral with units should be marked on the assembly or part unless they are multi-use items which should display only part numbers or nomenclature (see cables, as shown earlier in Fig. 11-6).

When equipment is designated for more than one type of mounting (e.g., rack and panel or transit case), consideration should be given to maximum visibility of reference designations under all mounting conditions.

Unit numbers should be marked on an external surface of the units in a prominent location to facilitate maintenance.

Cable Assemblies

Multiple-use cable assemblies or field-fabricated cables need not be marked with the reference designation "W" or mating connector designation prior to installation in the field. The marking of such cables and mating connector identifications should be determined by the permanency of the installation, the visibility of the cable run, and the actual need for reference designation identification. Cable assemblies having identical connectors at both ends should be marked only with their nomenclature or part number and, if single-use special-purpose cables, the assigned "W" designation. Mating connector identification should be marked on or adjacent to mating items.

Partial Reference Designations

Where partial reference designations are marked within a unit, a prominent note (e.g., "REF DESIG PREFIX_____," with the appropriate prefix inserted) should be placed on the unit. For those that are duplicated within a set or are used in more than one set, the unit number should be omitted from the note and a suitable space provided for insertion of the prefix by hand at the time of installation. Instructions should be provided to ensure that this space will be filled in prior to completion of installation.

Partial Designation

Reference designations marked on an identical assembly or on any subassembly thereof, should be partial designations as necessary to permit such subassemblies to be used in multiple applications.

Functional Designations

If functional designations which are not in the form of complete words or standard abbreviations are used as a result of the requirements of this subsection, these designations and their meanings should be listed on related drawings and diagrams, or in a separate document referenced on the related drawings and diagrams.

Identification Plates, Military Requirements

The most difficult phase in the definition of the requirements for identification plates is defining the applicable specifications. Since lead time is frequently required for military approval, the provisions of this subsection should be implemented as soon as possible after receipt of contract.

Precedence. The requirements for identification plates should be determined from the following documents in the order listed.

1) The contract on purchase order.
2) The product specification.
3) The general design specification.

General Design Specification. When the contract or purchase order does not specify identification plate requirements, the requirements of the general design specification, as shown in Table 11-1, should govern.

Cable Band Markers

Metal band markers or plastic zipper sleeving should be used for all external cable applications. Nylon band markers should not be used for cable band markings.

Serialization

Any product, assembly, or subassembly which falls within the following categories should be serialized.

1) All assemblies and subassemblies which are capable of connection by plugging into a receptacle.
2) All assemblies and subassemblies which are capable of and normally subjected to component level tests (except parts such as synchros, resolvers, etc.).

Serial Number Marking. When required, serial number marking should be related to the part number marking.

APPLICABLE DOCUMENTS

The military and industry specifications and standards listed below are applicable, for reference, to the material presented.

Military Specifications and Standards

MIL-E-16400   Electronic Equipment, Naval Ship and Shore

MIL-E-4158   Electronic Equipment, Ground, General Specification for

MIL-E-5400   Electronic Equipment, Airborne, General Specification for

MIL-E-8189   Electronic Equipment, Guided Missile

MIL-N-18307   Nomenclature and Identification for Electronic, Aeronautical, and Aeronautical Support Equipment Including

Table 11-1. Identification Plates Specified in General Design Specifications.

| Military Speci-fication or Description | General Design Specification | | Identification Plate Specification | Specification Paragraph |
	Title	Using Activities		
MIL-E-4158	Electronic Equipment Ground	AF	MIL-P-15024	3.6.2
MIL-E-5400	Electronic Equipment Airborne	Airborne	MIL-P-15024	3.1.16
MIL-E-8189	Electronic Equipment Guided Missile	AF, BAUER	MIL-P-15024	3.1.14
MIL-E-16400	Electronic Equipment Naval Ship and Shore	BuShips, BUWEPS	MIL-P-15024 MIL-N-18307	3.14.6.1 3.14.6.2
MIL-P-11268	Parts, Materials, and Processes Used in Electronic Equipment	ECOM	MIL-STD-130	
MIL-T-21200	Test Equipment for Use with Electronic and Fire Control Systems, General Specifications for	AF, BUAER	MIL-P-15024	3.1.16
Commercial or Factory Test Equipment	—	—	MIL-P-19834	—

	Ground Support Equipment
MIL-P-11268	Parts, Materials, and Processes Used in Electronic Equipment
MIL-P-15024	Plates, Tags, and Bands for Identification of Equipment
MIL-P-19384	Plates, Identification or Instruction, Metal Foil, Adhesive Backed, General Specification for
MIL-T-21200	Test Equipment for Use with Electronic and Fire Control Systems, General Specification for
MIL-STD-130	Identification Markings for U.S. Military Property
MIL-STD-17B-1,-2	Mechanical Symbols
MIL-STD-280	Definition of Item Levels, Item Exchangeability, Models, and Related Terms
MIL-STD-783	Legends for Use in Aircrew Stations and Airborne Equipment

Industry Specifications and Standards

ANSI Y32.16a-1970	Reference Designations for Electrical and Electronic Parts and Equipment.
ANSI Y32.2-1970	Graphic Symbols for Electrical and Electronic Diagrams
ANSI Y32.9-1972	Graphic Electrical Wiring Symbols for Architectural and Electrical Layout Drawing
ASA Y32.14-1962	Graphic Symbols for Logic Diagrams

Graphic Symbols

The graphic symbols used on mechanical, electromechanical, electrical, electronic (schematic) and logic diagrams should be those specified in the following documents:

1) ANSI Y32-9-1972, Graphic Electrical Wiring Symbols for Architectural and Electrical Layout Drawings
2) AMSI Y32.2-1970, Graphic Symbols for Electrical and Electronic Diagrams
3) MIL-STD-17B-1 and -17B-2, Mechanical Symbols

Table 11-2. Color Combinations Guide for Striped Plastic Insulation.

BASE COLORS	-0 Black	-1 Brown	-2 Red	-3 Orange	-4 Yellow	-5 Green	-6 Blue	-7 Purple	-8 Gray	-9 White
Black – 0	- - -	Poor Contrast	Poor Contrast	Looks Tan	Looks pale Green	Poor Contrast	Poor Contrast	Very poor contrast (invisible)	O.K.	O.K.
Brown – 1	O.K.	- - - - - -	Poor Contrast	Looks Tan	Looks Greenish Tan	O.K.	Poor Contrast	Poor Contrast	Poor Contrast	Looks Tan
Red – 2	O.K.	Too dark Looks almost blk.	- - - - - -	Poor Contrast off shade	Looks buff	O.K.	Too dark Looks Almost blk	O.K.	O.K.	O.K.
Orange – 3	O.K.	Too dark Looks Almost blk	Poor Contrast	- - - - - -	O.K.	Indistinct off shade	Too dark Looks Almost blk	O.K.	O.K.	O.K.
Yellow – 4	O.K.	Too dark Looks Almost blk	O.K.	O.K.	- - - - - -	O.K.	Looks Green	O.K.	O.K.	O.K.
Green – 5	O.K.	Poor Contrast Too dark	Looks Reddish brn	Looks Tan	Looks Pale Green	- - - - - -	Indistinct Too green	Poor Contrast Too dark	Looks Bluish	O.K.
Blue – 6	O.K.	Too dark Looks Almost blk	Too purple	Looks Tan	Looks Pale Green	O.K.	- - - - - -	O.K.	O.K.	O.K.
Purple – 7	O.K.	Poor Contrast	Poor Contrast Too brown	Looks Tan	Looks Pale Green	Poor Contrast	Poor Contrast	- - - - - -	O.K.	O.K.
Gray – 8	O.K.	O.K.	Too Brown	Looks Tan	Looks Pale Green	O.K.	O.K.	O.K.	- - - - - -	O.K.
White – 9	O.K.	O.K.	O.K.	O.K.	O.K.	O.K.	O.K.	O.K.	O.K.	- - - - - -

4) ASA Y32.14-19E2, Graphic Symbols for Logic Diagrams

CODING AND IDENTIFICATION OF CONDUCTORS

Identification by color coding each conductor not only facilitates the assembly, testing, and isolation of faults during manufacturing, but it also simplifies servicing the equipment in the field.

A single color code should be used throughout an entire system or series of equipment models to eliminate the requirement for service personnel to return to the coding charts continuously. Solid colors should be used whenever possible to simplify tracing leads. However, when numerous circuits are involved, multiple tracer colors are acceptable.

The colors selected should be readily distinguishable under incandescent lighting and should resist fading, color running, and discoloring due to heat. The color violet should be avoided since it has a tendency to be undistinguishable under certain lighting conditions. Refer to Table 11-2.

Identification Tags

Individual wires may be easily identified by the use of adhesive backed markers. Commercially available, pre-printed, self-sticking markers are a simple solution to identification of wires.

The markers may be permanently attached to the wires, or may be removed when no longer required for manufacturing. Permanent identification is preferred since it simplifies wire tracing when servicing equipment in the field. Permanent thermosetting tapes are available for marking wires and components, which are resistant to environmental conditions over the ranges specified for military equipment.

The identification of non-insulated wires can be accomplished by applying colored lacquer markings near each wire termination. No identification is required where the terminals are identified, such as on a printed circuit or terminal board, or if the wire length is less than 4 inches long and the placement permits obvious identification.

242

Chapter 12

Connections and Connectors

There are many ways to terminate wires for connection. This chapter will describe the most common methods.

LUGGING OF WIRE

Lugs are primarily used to terminate conductors where reliable connections and convenient repair or replacement are required. Many types, sizes, and configurations have been developed for industrial use. The most common types used in modern electronic assemblies are shown in Fig. 12-1.

The stripped end of the wire should be inserted into the lug until the insulation rests against the inner shoulder. Where no shoulder exists, make sure that the wire insulation is positioned so it will be held securely when it is crimped. There should be no evidence of bare wire between the lug barrel and the wire insulation.

The conductor should extend through the lug inspection hole from flush to a maximum of 1/8 inch, but must never interfere with the installation hardware. See Fig. 12-2.

Lugs should be installed on the terminal post in the order of their current carrying capacity. The largest current lug should always be on the bottom. See Fig. 12-3.

When two wires approach a terminal from the same side, the lugs should be installed back-to-back with the barrel of the bottom

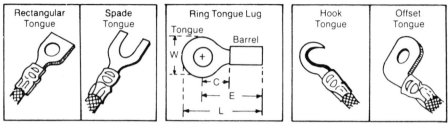

Fig. 12-1. Common lug types.

lug facing down. Single lug installations should always have the barrel facing up with the code marks showing. See Fig. 12-4.

Ground lugs should never be terminated to a component or part mounting hardware, nor should they be installed between a conductive and insulative material.

Where space does not allow for lugs, the wires may be stripped, tinned, and wound around a binding screw in the direction that will tighten as the screw is installed (usually clockwise).

SOLDERLESS CONNECTIONS FOR CABLES

Solderless connections depend on mechanical pressure rather than the fusion of metals. The advantages of solderless connections are high operating temperatures, ease of installation, good mechanical strength, and resistance to mechanical fatigue. However, solderless connections should not be used in government equipment unless they have been approved by the bureau or agenecy concerned. Solderless lugs and terminals are manufactured within close tolerances. The barrel design is critical and is dependent on the

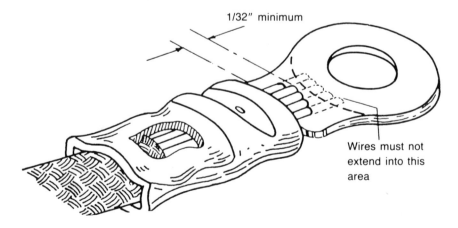

Fig. 12-2. Placement of wire in lug.

244

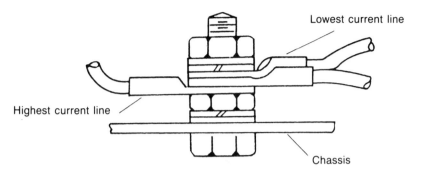

Fig. 12-3. The highest current line should always be lowest on the post.

wire and insulation size. Strict tolerances are held on the barrel length and the inside and outside diameters. The inside diameter of the barrel is considerably larger than the wire it is designed for, to provide for sufficient deformation when subjected to the installation pressure.

The size and type of crimping tool must conform to the manufactuer's recommendations or the installation will result in a weakened or defective joint. The condition of the crimping tool must be checked periodically by close examination of several completed connections to be sure that normal wear has not caused defective connections.

Care msut be taken when crimping a solderless lug or terminal to insure that the part being crimped has been fitted properly into the socket of the crimping tool, and that the stripped end of the wire is fully inserted into the barrel. If a terminal or wire is misaligned, a defective connection will result. **Caution:** The jaws of the crimping tool must be fully closed to achieve the proper crimp. When pressure is removed from the terminal the wires will

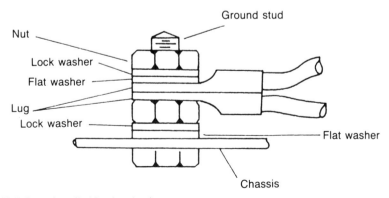

Fig. 12-4. Lugs installed back-to-back.

expand. The expansions are additive in stranded conductors with each strand contributing its own expansion. The total wire expansion will exceed the limits of the terminal causing the wires to exert pressure against the inner wall of the terminal.

Solderless terminals are designed specifically for either solid or stranded wire, and they are not interchangeable. Crimped solid wire will not expand as much as stranded wire.

Crimping of the barrel of a terminal supports the insulated wire connection by gripping the end of the wire insulation. Further support can be gained by the use of commercially available terminals manufactured with a vinyl sleeve over the barrel.

Installing Solderless Terminals on Cables

Care must be exercised in stripping the wires for assembly with solderless terminals to prevent cutting, nicking, scraping or otherwise damaging the wire. The stripped ends of the wire must be clear of all foreign materials to prevent insulation particles or frayed ends from becoming twisted among the wire strands. The number of short, untinned strands should not exceed the limits of Table 12-1.

After the stripping operation, the stripped ends must be thoroughly cleaned. Any contamination trapped inside the crimped joint will be cause for a defective connection that will occur after the system has been shipped to the field.

MECHANICAL CONNECTIONS

No electrical connection should ever depend on the solder joint for mechanical strength. Solder, even when it is solidified, is relatively soft, and when subjected to continuous tension will cold flow, causing an increase in electrical resistance. All electrical connections should be mechanically supported and secured before the solder joint is made. The wire should be wrapped around a terminal tightly to prevent movement during the solder cooling and setting. Refer to Chapter 10 for the proper methods of preparing and making solder joints.

Number of Strands	Allowable Clipped Strands	
7 to 15	1	
16 to 18	2	Table 12-1. Allowable
19 to 25	3	Number of Clipped Strands.
26 to 36	4	
37 to 40	5	
41 or more	6	

Fig. 12-5. Securing wire to a terminal lug.

STANDARD TERMINATIONS FOR WIRES

The methods used for terminating individual wires to terminals of various types is critical to the reliability not only of each
joint, but of the overall equipment being manufactured.

The following figures demonstrate some of the acceptable techniques used in both military and high reliability commercial
equipment.

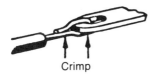

Crimp

Fig. 12-6. Securing wire to a terminal lug with limited space.

Minimum wrap
(for limited space only)

The wire is secured by inserting it through the hole in the lug
and wrapping it around the body of the lug. See Fig. 12-5.

Where space will not permit a standard wrap, or when heavy
wire is required, a reliable mechanical connection is made by inserting the wire through the lug, folding it 180° and crimping firmly.
See Fig. 12-6.

A secure wrap termination may be made by forming a loop and
wrapping one full turn around the shank. See Fig. 12-7.

Fig. 12-7. Connection to a hook
terminal.

247

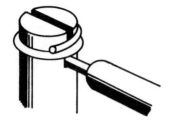

Fig. 12-8. Connection to a split terminal.

The split terminal is used on transformers and other heavy components. The wire is laid in the slot and wrapped around the terminal body. See Fig. 12-8.

Small lightweight lugs are used extensively for terminating conductors. Insulating sleeving should be used for mechanical support, and may also carry the lead identification marking. See Fig. 12-9.

Flat, perforated terminals are often used on variable resistors, switches, and sockets. See Fig. 12-10.

When stud or turret terminals are used for terminating wires to a printed circuit board, it is advisable to wrap component leads on the upper portion and wire on the lower portion. It is common to wrap the wire from the bottom of the terminal up, and the wrap should be made in a clockwise direction due to the tendency to attempt unwinding in a counterclockwise direction. See Fig. 12-11.

CONNECTORS

Right at the beginning, as the equipment is being designed, planning the interconnection and cabling requirements is difficult, but very important. As the equipment design progresses and is refined, the interconnection system should be developed at the same rate. The paramount consideration should always be the electrical requirements of the system.

- What are the current and voltage ratings?

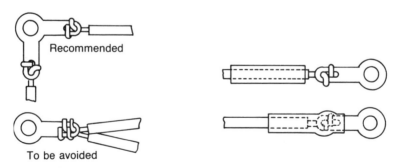

Fig. 12-9. Multiple lug connection and the use of insulating sleeves.

248

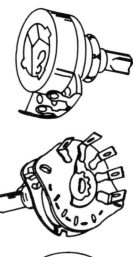

Fig. 12-10. Potentiometer, switch and socket with flat, perforated terminals.

- How many signal circuits?
- How many power circuits?
- What type and what number of conductors?
- Will shielded, coaxial, or rf conductors be required?
- What are the size and performance requirements of the wire?

Electrical isolation is the second consideration.

- Which signal and power circuits require isolation?
- Should individual circuits be combined in the cables?
- Can transient interference be determined?

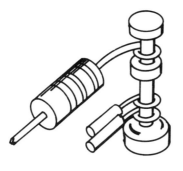

Fig. 12-11. Turret terminal with components attached.

- Can shielding be used to isolate the rf, pulse and power circuits?
- Are other types of cabling applicable? (ribbon cable, flexible cable, etc.).
- What are the potential space and geometry problems?

When the environment is studied some undesirable characteristics may be found. The connectors may be required to survive high or low temperatures, thermal shock, vibration, moisture, chemical or fuel exposure, radiation or any combination of these environments. In most electrical systems the wires are positioned close together eliminating the free circulation of air and interaction with each other to modify the heat rejection rate generated by the current passing through them. In these instances, consideration must be given to the cooling characteristics of the system, and to the possibility of derating the wires (lessening the current carrying capacity). The derating process must include the cooperation of the electrical design engineer.

Connections that are intended to be readily made or broken for maintenance or replacement of components are referred to as separable connections. This includes a large variety of connectors classified as rack and panel, external, and internal connectors.

The first consideration in the selection of a connector is the environmental application.

Secondly, the type, size and electrical requirements must be defined. The number of contacts, the size of the contacts (amperage rating), the style of contacts, shape of the plug (round or rectangular), the type of cable it is to be used on, and the available mounting space must all be considered. One of the major restricting elements of a connector is the number of circuits it must handle, where a large number of circuits are required, it may prove more satisfactory to use several connectors rather than a single very large connector. In selecting the size of the connector, it is always advisable to add 10% to the required number of pins as spares. To avoid accidental misconnecting of a unit, nearby connectors should not be identical. The size and spacing of the connector contacts is very important, and the controlling factor is the amperage the contact must carry. The voltage drop across the mating contacts and the contact resistance (which will probably increase with time) must also be carefully considered. Table 12-2 shows the average current carrying capacity of some connector contacts.

Connectors are classified by the method of coupling the connector halves. These include MS coupling threads, Acme coupling threads, reverse Acme threads, bayonet type, latchlock, quick-

Table 12-2. Maximum Current for Connector Contacts.	Contact Size Wire Gauge	Maximum Current (Amps)
	1/0	160 to 200
	2	115 to 120
	4	80 to 87
	6	60 to 65
	8	40 to 48
	10	30 to 35
	12	22 to 26
	14	15 to 20
	16	10 to 15
	18	8 to 11
	20	5 to 7

disconnect, and friction contact.

External Connectors

External connectors are used for the interconnection of cabling and electronic equipment, or for joining cables external to the equipment. These connectors have a strong outer shell, usually metal, which houses the dielectric or insulating material. The shells are designed for maximum protection of the electrical connections and normally provide some means of locking the two halves together.

MS Connectors. The interchangeability and operating characteristics of the MS series of electrical connectors are defined by the current military specifications. These government specifications are refined from time to time to incorporate new performance requirements as dictated by design advances and more stringent operating requirements. A list of approved suppliers of connectors approved under the MIL-C-5015 specification are listed in the qualified products list, QPL-5015, which is a publication of the Aeronautical Standards Group. Occasionally military approval may be granted by letter for certain connectors or groups of connectors for a specific application.

The MS type connectors are used on all equipment designed for use in severe military environmental operating conditions. The basic design of these connectors is covered in the military specification MIL-C-5051, and military standards, MS-3100 through MS-3108. The MIL-C-5051 series of connectors feature sturdy aluminum shells that lock together by a threaded coupling ring, with resilient or hard plastic inserts of various sizes and contact arrangements. Six standard styles of connector shells are available in this series.

- Wall receptacles—MS3100

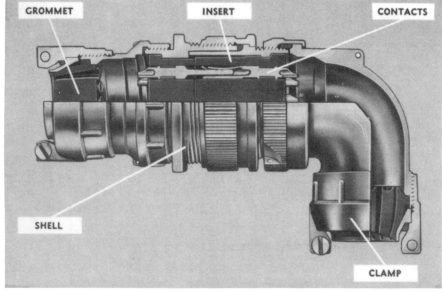

Fig. 12-12. MS-E connector.

- Cable receptacles—MS3101
- Box receptacles—MS3102
- Straight plug—MS3106
- Quick-disconnect—MS3107
- Angle plug—MS3108

The military specification MIL-C-5015 combined the performance requirements of moisture-proof and vibration-proof characteristics into a new concept of connector design designated as type "E", environmental resistant. The type "E" series is suitable for applications where heavy condensation, changes in temperature, and high vibratory conditions must be met. See Fig. 12-12.

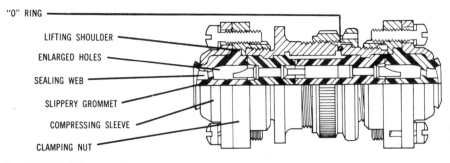

Fig. 12-13. MS-R connector.

For greater reliability, the latest version of MIL-C-5015 (issue D) has specified a new environmental resisting type, "R". Type "R" connectors are shorter and lighter, with the addition of an "O" ring at the main joint of the plugs. This provides a main-joint seal supplementary to the insert inter-facial seal, thus insuring a higher degree of reliability when connector halves from different sources are used. See Fig. 12-13.

The major disadvantage to these connectors is a lack of adaptability with the modern miniaturized electronic systems. However, there are still many applications where these rugged connectors will be used.

The type of military connectors to be used are specified by the part number call-out. The military part number specifies each requirement for a specific connector as shown:

General Description of MS Connectors

The military specification MIL-C-5015 provides designations

Table 12-3. Types of MS Connectors.

Designation	Description	Example of Identification
"A"	Solid Shell. General utility in aircraft, vehicles, stationary installations	MS3100A-20-27S
"B"	Split Shell. Same as "A" except shell is longitudinally split	MS3108B-20-27S
"C"	Pressurized. Intended for use through pressurized bulkheads. Air leakage limited to 1 cubic inch per hour at 30 pounds per square inch.	MS3102C-20-27S
"E"	Environmental resisting. Used where heavy condensation and rapid temperature and pressure changes are anticipated. Also for applications in high vibration environments.	MS3106E-20-27S
"K"	Fireproof. Used where flame exposure is anticipated.	MS3102K-20-27S
"R"	Environmental Resisting. Lightweight. Used when weight and size are restricted.	MS3106R-20-27S

253

Number of Contacts

*Insert Positions

Shell Size	Total	#16	#20	Service Rating	W	X	Y	Z
8	3	—	3		60°	210°	—	—
8	4	—	4		45°	—	—	—
10	6	—	6		90°	—	—	—
12	3	3	—	=	—	155°	180°	—
12	10	—	10		60°	155°	270°	295°
12	14	—	14	**		Non-Standard		
14	5	5	—	=	40°	92°	184°	273°
14	12	4	8		43°	90°	—	—
14	15	1	14	=	17°	110°	155°	234°
14	19	—	19		30°	165°	315°	—
16	8	8	—	=	54°	152°	180°	331°
16	26	—	26		60°	—	275°	338°
18	11	11	—	=	62°	119°	241°	340°
18	32	—	32		85°	138°	222°	265°
20	39	2	37		63°	144°	252°	333°
20	41	—	41		45°	126°	225°	—
22	55	—	55		30°	142°	226°	314°

Table 12-4. Shell Size, Number of Contacts and Insert Positions for MIL-C-26482.

for several different requirements as shown in Tables 12-3 ad 12-4, and Figs. 12-14 through 12-17.

RECTANGULAR CONNECTORS

Rectangular connectors suitable for external applications are so numerous in design characteristics that the description of any

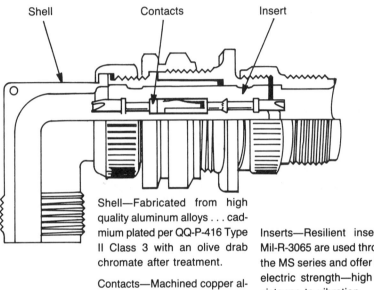

Shell   Contacts   Insert

Shell—Fabricated from high quality aluminum alloys . . . cadmium plated per QQ-P-416 Type II Class 3 with an olive drab chromate after treatment.

Contacts—Machined copper alloy pins and sockets with a silver plated finish. Sizes 16 and 12 sockets incorporate the closed entry design.

Inserts—Resilient inserts per Mil-R-3065 are used throughout the MS series and offer high dielectric strength—high arc resistance to vibration.

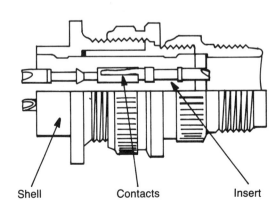

Shell   Contacts   Insert

Fig. 12-14. MS-A and MS-C connectors.

MS3100 A or C
Wall-mounting receptacle

MS3102 A or C
Box-mounting receptacle

MS3101A
Cable connecting plug

MS3106A
Straight plug

MS3108 E
90-degree plug

MS3119   Thru-bulkhead
receptacle

Fig. 12-15. Various MS connectors.

one distinct type would be difficult in this text. The outer shell of
these connectors are stamped sheet metal or die-cast aluminum.
The mating members of the rectangular connector series are locked
together by screws that are located at the ends, in the center, or
any other appropriate location. The dielectric inserts are available
in most plastics and meet a wide range of environmental service

MS3110   Wall-mounting receptacle

MS3112   Box-mounting receptacle

MS3114   Jam nut receptacle

MS3116   Straight plug

Fig. 12-16. Various MS connectors.

Backshell, straight without strain relief **MIL-C-83723**	Backshell, straight with strain relief **MIL-C-83723**	Backshell, 90° with strain relief **MIL-C-83723**
M83723-15N-8	M83723-15S-8	M83723-15A-8
M83723-15N-10	M83723-15S-10	M83723-15A-10
M83723-15N-12	M83723-15S-12	M83723-15A-12
M83723-15N-14	M83723-15S-14	M83723-15A-14
M83723-15N-16	M83723-15S-16	M83723-15A-16
M83723-15N-18	M83723-15S-18	M83723-15A-18
M83723-15N-20	M83723-15S-20	M83723-15A-20
M83723-15N-22	M83723-15S-22	M83723-15A-22
M83723-15N-24	M83723-15S-24	M83723-15A-24

Fig. 12-17. Various MS connectors.

257

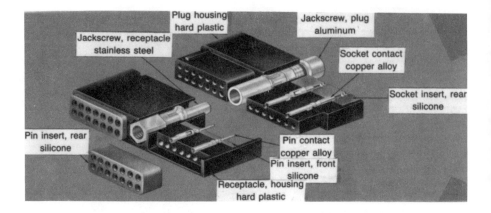

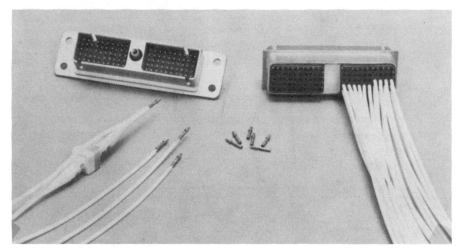

Fig. 12-18. Typical rectangular connectors.

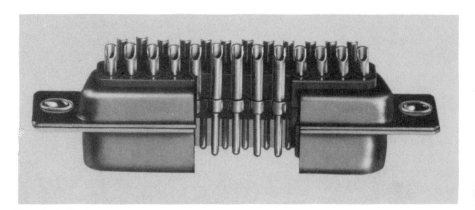

Fig. 12-19. Typical rectangular connectors.

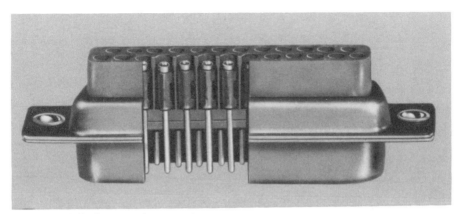

Fig. 12-20. Typical rectangular connectors.

conditions. The contacts are always the pin and socket type. These rectangular connectors do not meet the environmental limits of MS series described above. Figures 12-18 through 12-20 show some typical rectangular connectors.

Chapter 13

Generating an
Inhouse Cable Specification

The following outline is presented as a suggested method of generating a cable specification for custom designed cable assemblies. When documentation is required for the manufacture or purchasing of a cable assembly, the check-list in Fig. 13-1 will provide a specification to completely define the physical, environmental and electrical requirements of an inhouse designed cable assembly.

SPECIFYING CABLE CONSTRUCTIONS

There are many factors which must be included in cable construction specifications.

Insulated Conductors

Specify quantity and gauge of conductors. Allowance for 10% spares is common practice and for some contracts is mandatory.

Preferably call out a MIL specification for the wires. This ensures uniformity and that proper materials and processing are used in making and testing the basic wire.

The most popular wire specifications are:

For gauges 26 to 12: MIL-W-16878 (offers many insulations).

For gauges 10 to 4/0: MIL-W-5086 (Type II).

Note: It is common to specify military specification wires even on commercial grade equipment, since many wires made as mili-

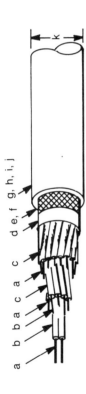

a b b a c a c   d e, f g, h, i, j

Fig. 13-1. Specifying cables.

(a) Number and gauge of conductors.
(b) Specification type of wire (military or commercial).
(c) Coding of conductors or subcables, striping or numbering, if any.
(d) Tape barrier, used as first mechanical protective layer. Can be of Vinyl, Mylar, Teslar, Polyethylene, or paper-fiberglass laminants.
(e) Type of electrical shielding or mechanical armor.
(f) % coverage required for electrical shielding.
(g) Type of outer jacket material.
(h) Color of outer jacket, sheath markings.
(i) Minimum and maximum wall thickness of outer jacket, if applicable.
(j) Necessary physical or environmental requirements, see below.
(k) Minimum and maximum overall diameter.

Physical Requirements

1. Length, tolerance; Diameter, tolerance.
2. Overall tensile strength, if applicable.
3. Weight limitations.
4. Minimum bend radius.

Environmental Requirements

1. Minimum and maximum operating temperatures.
2. Physical abuse: terrain, degree of movement of flexing, possible sudden impacts or pressures, etc.
3. Surrounding medium: water, oil, sunlight, ice, fuels, air, etc.

Electrical Requirements

1. Voltage rating of the conductor insulation.
2. Maximum current expected in the conductors.
3. Amount of electrical or magnetic shielding required.
4. Insulation resistance required.
5. Capacitance requirements.

261

tary specification items are essentially identical to UL or IPCEA types. Usually the essential difference is that the military types have tinned strands while UL types are not tinned.

For a MIL-spec reference as to preferred wire types for various applications and environments see MIL-C-27072.

Fillers

Fillers are used in lieu of a wire to fill space in a cable bundle so that it will have a round cross-section. This promotes uniform flexibility and avoids oval-shaped cables.

Failure to permit or require use of fillers in a cable often results in getting nonuniform cables from different sources making the same cable.

Although cotton or jute may be used as filler, they may be subject to rot and growth of fungus unless treated.

Preferable fillers are plastic rods of vinyl or polyethylene, usually of the same material as the wire insulation.

Sub-Cables (within the main cable)

Individually cabled groups of wires within the cable may be referred to as sub-cables.

The constructional details of sub-cables should be just as complete as the main cable in which they are used (i.e.: cabling, coding, shielding, jacketing, etc.).

Sub-cabling permits neat and simple formation of branch legs from the main cable and can be used to aid in identifying wire groups.

Jackets may be solid colors or striped, although striping is not recommended for diameters over .300″.

Cabling

Although short cables can be formed manually, precision machine cabling is always preferable.

Suggested wording: "Cabling shall be done on a planetary-type helical cabling machine in such a manner that no twist is introduced into the individual cable members."

The axial distance per turn is called the lay length. The lay length should be between 8 to 16 times the pitch diameter of the layer. (Pitch diameter is measured from center to center of diametrically opposed conductors.)

Although the rotation direction may be the same (unilay) for all layers, opposite directions of rotation for each layer in a cable is most common and is called contra-helical construction.

Over All Shielding

The most common and perhaps the most flexible shield is a woven braid, using tinned or bare copper strands. Strand sizes range from 30 to 38 AWG.

The effectiveness of the shield depends on how well it covers up the surface of the cable. A minimum coverage requirement of 85 to 90% of the cable surface is common.

Machinery limitations make coverages in excess of 96% impractical for a single layer of copper braid. Multiple layers may be used, although flexibility is reduced.

Braiding is a continuous operation; any desired length is possible.

For shields that must "push-back" easily or swell so that terminating rings may be used, the braid angle should be specified. We recommend angles of $25° \pm 6°$. (Not practical for diameters over .300″.)

For rodent protection of burial cables a .005″ thick tinned copper tape shield, spiral wrapped with nominal 25% overlap, is common usage.

Perhaps the simplest and most effective electrical shield is a "NAFOIL" Spiral tape shield wrapped over an uninsulated "drain" wire. (See section on "NAFOIL".) It is the lowest weight shield available, and fast to terminate.

Composite Shields

Various methods of shielding can be combined for optimum RFI protection.

Consult National Wire & Cable Engineering Department for recommendations.

SPECIFYING CABLE ASSEMBLIES

The following factors must be considered when specifying cable assemblies.

Bulk Cable

Provide exact specifications on the bulk cable desired.

Dimensioning

Overall dimensions and tolerances should be detailed. Leg or breakout dimensions are best measured from the exit face of the mold to the face of the connector.

The most convenient method of overall length measurement is from the rear of the hardware.

Connectors

The choice of connectors for a particular application requires consideration of both the cable requirements and the use to which the assembly will be put, as well as the environment which the connector must withstand. Common problems in the manufacture of cable assemblies occur when the designer assumes:

- the cable diameter will always be small enough to fit into the clamp at the rear of the connector.
- there is always adequate room to terminate all wires and shields within the normally supplied connector rear shells, or within the mold dimensions he provides.

The National Engineering Staff will readily provide technical information as to cable diameters, suggested rear hardware to mate the cable to the connectors, and mold dimensions. The designer should use this consulting service wherever possible.

Connector Rear Hardware

Whenever a large number of wires are to be terminated within a given connector or many shields are to be grouped and terminated at the connector, the use of backshell extension sleeves is recommended.

These shell extensions move the cable clamp back several inches. This permits adequate room to do all terminations without overcrowding. Further, the extensions are a convenient method to match the required cable clamp to the connector rear threads when an oversize cable clamp is required.

The backshell extension sleeve also makes potting convenient, since it can be completely filled with compound before the cable clamp is attached. The cable sheath is usually embedded into the potting so as to seal the cable. The most common potting compound is a poly-sulphide based material meeting MIL-S-8516.

Connector rear shells are available in hundreds of configurations to match special requirements. Sources of such items are:

Glenair, Inc., 1211 Air Way, Glendale 1, Calif.
    213—245-8587.
Sunbank Electronic Inc., 2511 N. Ontario, Burbank
    213—849-1191

Cable Clamps

To securely fasten the connector to the cable, and to minimize the entrance of moisture, several types of cable clamps are available.

The most popular are the type used on the MS series connector. With the use of backshell extension sleeves, these clamps may be mated to almost any type of connector.

This clamp type is specified as MS-3057 A or MS-3057 B. The B type employs a rubber compression grommet which constricts the cable radially as the clamp is threaded onto the connector.

The A type employs shallow u-shaped saddle bars which are tightened on the cable by two machine screws.

Although the B type seems to offer superior sealing on the cable to keep out dust and moisture, the A type can provide a tighter mechanical grip on the cable.

Connector Backshell Molding

In some cases, a cast mold is preferable to clamps at the rear of a connector. It is wise to specify that the maximum mold diameter be no greater than the coupling nut diameter (for round connectors). Often the cable source owns mold tooling for common connector types. Hence it may be wise to leave the exact mold dimensions to the vendor, unless there are special requirements which the design must meet.

Pre-potting of the connector rear prior to molding has been used where a hard (epoxy) compound is required to immobilize all terminations. The rubber mold is then cast over the epoxy onto the connector and cable.

A variation of this type of protection uses a perforated metal sleeve threaded onto the connector rear after all wires are terminated.

The mold is then poured, embedding the wires and perforated cylinder. The cylinder, being bonded to the compound and threaded to the connector, minimizes the strains which can be transmitted to the connector pins and solder joints, and resists crushing. Other types of mold-embedded strain-relief devices are also available.

Connector molding compounds usually are identical to those used for branch molds on bulk cable.

Cable Leg or Branch Molds

The transition of wires from the main cable body into branch legs may be protected by casting a synthetic rubber mold over the transition. This type of molding can be watertight and flexible. Almost any configuration may be obtained.

In most cases it is preferable to leave the exact mold dimensions to the vendor, although a note that the nominal mold wall thickness should not exceed 4 times the jacket wall thickness will help prevent excessively heavy molds. The mold should extend over the sheath not less than one cable diameter.

The molding compounds may be hot-cured neoprene, or may be room-temperature curing compounds. Neoprene is the preferable material if many shots will be made with the same tooling. Neoprene compounds should meet MIL-R-6855, Class 2, Grade 60. (Same as neoprene sheathing.)

Most common for small quantity production is the use of polyurethane compound, meeting MIL-S-8516. This low-temperature-curing material has the texture and appearance of neoprene. It is used extensively for connector and cable branch molds throughout the aerospace industry.

Electrical characteristics of polyurethane make it suitable for potting around connector pins without degrading the insulation resistance of the connector.

Use of polysulphide (potting) compounds for cable molds is not recommended, as they will cold flow readily and deform.

Common sources for the cable molding and potting compounds are:

Products Research, Inc., 2919 Empire Ave., Burbank
    213—849-3992
Coast Pro-Seal & Mfg. Co., 2235 Beverly Blvd., L.A. 57
    213—387-5141

Optional Leg or Branching Methods

Separation of wires from the main cable body may also be done by other methods:

- Laced cable legs (either straight or helically cabled). No outer sheath used.
- Sleeved cable legs. Leg has vinyl or neoprene tubing slipped on. (The vinyl may be expanded by momentary immersion on methyl ethyl ketone, or a commercial solvent called Zoluol (toluene). Neoprene can be slipped on by inflating with air pressure.

    Heat-shrinkable tubing is popular for leg jacketing. This is pre-expanded as received and shrinks up to 50% when heated to about 275 deg. F momentarily. Superior to vinyl sleeving.

- Shrinkable hollow molds. Manufactured from the same materials as heat-shrinkable tubing. May be slid over legs and shrunk in place. Suitable for one-shot assemblies. Should be bonded to cable with epoxy cement for proper seal. Shrinkable tubing and molds available through Rayclad Tubes, Inc., Redwood City, Calif. At this time, no military specifications have been written around these materials.

External Strain Relief

Where the cable may experience jerking, whipping or fixed pull the use of a "Kellems grip" may be desirable. These distribute the clamping pressure over a large area. Available with standard collars that are retained by conventional cable clamps. Length should be not less than 8 cable diameters. These will eliminate breakage of conductors at connector pins due to pull on cable. Seldom used with backshell molds due to sealing problems.

Internal Strain Reliefs

A steel strain member can be used as the central core of the cable so that the copper conductors bear little of the loads imposed on the cable. Although simple to include in the bulk cable, the method used to bring the strain member out of an assembly often poses such problems that a different approach is required.

The desired method of fastening the strain member to connectors should be accurately detailed. Although the strain member is normally plastic jacketed to avoid damage to conductors, it should have a neoprene cover if brought out of a mold so that adequate moisture sealing may be obtained.

Mechanical Performance

A cable assembly which is normally considered as being "flexible" may be expected to bend occasionally on a diameter equal to 6 cable diameter, or to stay in a fixed bend of that diameter. The cable will do this over its rated temperature range.

National is equipped to run proof tests of cold-bend capability on all cable types.

MIL-C-27072 lists a table of expected cable performance for various materials and temperatures.

Where special flexibility requirements exist contact National Engineering Department for design suggestions to permit the required characteristics.

Test Performance

Cable assemblies should normally pass high potential tests of 2 times the rated working voltage of the wire insulation.

Insulation resistance from any conductor to all else in an assembly should be no less than 100 megohms.

Identification

The desired identification should be specified. Common methods are:

- Stamped aluminum or cad-plated brass bands. Retained by crimping.
- Printed vinyl tubing or heat-shrinkable tubing.
- Hot-stamped impressions, ink filled (for neoprene only). Type should be Gothic not less than .12 inch in height.

Radio Frequency Interference

Special shielding techniques for reduction of RFI are available for cable assemblies.

In general, these consist of multiple layers of tight copper braid and tape wraps of aluminized mylar tape. Proper combination of these provide shielding equivalent to flexible armored conduit.

Special backshell extensions designed to adequately ground the shield are available from the previously mentioned sources.

Consult National's Technical Staff for application information of RFI Shielding.

CAPACITANCE OF SHIELDED WIRES AND CABLES

Capacitance exists from every metallic surface in a cable to all other metallic surfaces in and around cable.

An understanding of the relative amount of capacitance to be expected in a cable is helpful in specifying cable and designing terminal equipment for the cable to be used.

Although capacitance in a cable has negligible effect on dc or 60 cycle ac cable circuits used for power or control, it does affect higher frequency ac voltages.

Charge on Conductive Surfaces

Elementary electron theory states that the electron is the basic unit of negative electric charge; that a large charge is simply a large collection of electrons. The more electrons that are concentrated on a surface, the larger the electric charge on that surface. Positively charged surfaces may be regarded as having a deficiency of electrons. Charge is measured in coulombs. One coulomb consists of about 10^{17} electrons. Since they repel each other, a collection of electrons will distribute over a surface.

Current

We can force an exchange of charge (electrons) between two conductive surfaces if we connect any source of voltage, such as a battery, between them. Since electrons in motion constitute an electric current; current flows off one surface through the battery onto the other, until the repulsion of charges being forced onto the surfaces equals the forcing voltage. When the battery is removed, a voltage equal to that of the battery exists between the surfaces due to the stored charge. If the voltage source is ac, the charge exchange occurs each quarter cycle. The voltage source thus must handle this charging current in addition to any other current which may pass through circuitry connected to the two surfaces.

Capacitance

This behavior of charge on surfaces is termed capacitance. Capacitance may be defined as the ratio of voltage between two surfaces, divided by their difference in charge; and is measured in units called farads. Capacitors, or condensers, are sets of surfaces deliberately arranged to control the capacitance between them. Shielded wires and cables also have capacitance between the conductors and shields which should be considered in their design and application. Commonly used values of capacitance are microfarads (mfd) or (10^{-6} fd) and picofarads (pf) or (10^{-12} fd).

Dielectrics

The spacing or insulating material between two surfaces of a capacitor is called a dielectric. It may be vacuum, air, or one of many insulating materials. With the exception of gases, all insulating materials increase the capacitance between the surfaces. The term dielectric constant is used to show how large this effect is for various materials. If the space between two surfaces is filled with a material having a dielectric constant of 2, then the capacitance between the surfaces will be 2 times greater than it would be for an air or vacuum dielectric.

Wire Insulation

Not all dielectrics are suitable for use on wire and cable. The more commonly used insulations are listed in Table A. Most wire insulation choices are based on a compromise among cost, electrical performance, and the physical and chemical properties required for the application.

With the exception of Teflon® and some polyolefins, most wire insulations exhibit appreciable increases in their dielectric constant and insulation leakage with increasing temperature or frequency. This may make them undesirable for use where the capacitance, characteristic impedance or the leakage must be constant, such as in coaxial cable or instrumentation cables.

Geometry

The shape, diameter and spacing of the conductors and shields determine the capacity between them. Coaxial cables are a special-application version of a single shielded conductor and may be treated in the same way.

Coaxial Wires. The capacitance per foot between a single insulated wire and a shield around it is:

$$C = \frac{(7.36) \times (e)}{Lg_{10} \, (D/d)} \text{ mmfd per foot}$$

... where e is the dielectric constant of the insulation between wire and shield; and D/d is the diameter ratio of shield ID to conductor OD. See Fig. 13-2.

The only way in which the capacitance can be selected is by choice of insulation having a low dielectric constant, or by choosing a suitable value of D/d.

Shielded Pairs. Shielded pairs have three capacitances involved which combine to produce the effective wire to wire capacitance. Figure 13-3 illustrates these capacities. Since the wire-to-shield capacitances of each conductor are essentially in series, the effect of the two 40, mmfd capacitances is to produce an apparent 20 mmfd between the two wires in addition to the 5. mmfd which will exist whether the shield is present or not. Thus the effective capacitance is 20. + 5. = 25. mmfd./ft from wire to wire. (Ref. to Mil-C-17 C, Par. 4.6.7 for further detail.)

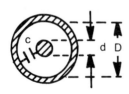

Fig. 13-2. Capacitance of coaxial conductors.

270

Fig. 13-3. Capacitance of shielded pairs.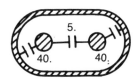

Multi-Conductor Cable Bundles

The capacitance from a wire to all else in a large cable bundle of identical wires may vary widely depending on insulation and geometry. In general, however, it will have values ranging from 40. to 65. mmfd/ft for PVC insulation (where C = 4.), and will vary from this for other materials. Conductors in the outer layer of a cable bundle which is overall-shielded will tend to have a higher capacitance than those closer to the bundle center. Typical variation for PVC* insulated wires will be a 15-20% rise in capacitance for conductors in the layer closest to the overall shield.

Inductance

When current flows in a wire it creates a magnetic field about the wire, which generates voltages along the same wire as the current changes. These opposing voltages act to limit the rate at which the current can change. This effect is termed inductance and is measured in units called henrys.

The self inductance of a round straight copper wire is on the order of .4 micro-henry/ft, and is relatively unaffected by diameter or length of wire. The self inductance of twisted pairs of wires is on the order of .08 micro-henry/ft; while the mutual inductance of a coaxial construction is .14 Lg10(D/d) micro-henrys/ft.

SIGNAL DELAY IN CABLES

Mechanical Delay

The electronic systems designer should consider possible problems which may arise due to cable delay.

For instance, in a multi-conductor cable of coax, the coax in the center of the bundle will be shorter than those in the outer layers by 4% to 6%, which mechanically will introduce delay in the signals traveling the long path.

Dielectric Delay

Although radio waves travel at the speed of light in free space or in air, this speed is much less when the wave is guided through coax or other shielded cables, where the electric field is contained in an insulator other than air.

Suppose that a radio-frequency sine-wave signal generator is connected to both an antenna and a 1000 foot length of coaxial cable, so that its signals will be launched simultaneously into both, and we go to the far end of the cable to see which arrives first.

When the generator is keyed on, the signal from the antenna arrives first, traveling at the speed of light in air, taking about one micro-second to make the trip.

Shortly thereafter, the same identical signal will arrive at the end of the coax cable, having taken longer to travel the same distance. It did not travel as fast, so its arrival at the end of the cable was "delayed" compared to the arrival of signal from the antenna. From this effect comes the term "Delay Line."

The velocity of a wave in a coax is usually expressed as a percentage of the velocity of light. For instance, a polyethylene insulation gives a "propagation velocity" of 65.9% of light velocity. This is sometimes expressed as a velocity factor of .659.

For straight round copper conductors, the velocity factor is the reciprocal of the square root of the effective dielectric constant (e) of the conductor insulation.

For cables where the dielectric is partially air and part plastic insulation, such as RG-62 coax, the effective dielectric constant (e) will be slightly less than that for the plastic alone, and the velocity will be correspondingly higher.

The dielectric constant, propagation velocity, and signal transit time for common insulations are listed in Table 13-1.

Characteristic Impedance

A transmission line such as a coaxial cable or shielded pair can be considered as a wave-guiding device in the broad sense. The relative amplitudes of the electric and magnetic fields due to a signal within the cable are determined by the capacitance and inductance per unit length of cable (assuming no reflections from the load.)

The characteristic impedance (Z) is the ratio of the two fields, or

$$Z = \frac{E}{H} = \sqrt{\frac{L}{C}}$$ where C and L are in farads and henrys.

Another equation for finding the value of Z is:

$$Z = \frac{101600}{(C)\ (\%V.P.)}$$

272

Table 13-1. Properties of Common Insulations.

Insulation	(e)	Prop. velocity: v c	Transit Time Micro-Sec/1000 Ft.
Air	—****	Nom 95.0%****	1.06****
Polyethylene	2.26	65.9%	1.54
Teflon® (TFE & FEP)	2.0	70.0%	1.45
Polypropylene	2.1	69.0%	1.47
Foam Polyethylene	1.55	80.0%	1.27
Polyvinyl-chloride	4.0***	50.0%	2.03
Nylon (#610)	3.0**	57.8%	1.76
Neoprene	5.0***	44.6%	2.28
Rubber (Buna S)	2.9***	58.7%	1.73
Rubber (Butyl)	2.35***	65.3%	1.56
Silicone Rubber (SE972)	3.16***	56.3%	1.80

* One micro-second is one millionth of a second.
** Susceptible to changes due to humidity. Absorbs moisture.
*** Dielectric constant varies widely with frequency. Many different values of dielectric constant may be obtained since the materials are a blend of filler and plasticizers with the base material, all of which have differing values of e.
**** Varies depending on the method used to support the center conductor of the cable. Inductance of shield and conductor limit upper value to about 96%.

where C is in pf/ft and V.P. is the propagation velocity expressed in percent.

The resistance of the conductors and shield attenuates the signal in a transmission line, but at radio frequencies has little effect in determining the characteristic impedance.

Pulse Cables

Cables designed for transmission of pulses for digital signals have carefully controlled surge impedances and capacitance. Generally they are 93 to 120 ohm constructions. A series of these for general use are shown in the instrument cable section.

Glossary

A

ABC—This is a BX armored bushing building wire rated at 600 volt PVC insulation.

ACA—An asbestos aircraft wire made to military specification ANJC-48A. 1000 volt was manufactured with cotton or glass braid overall. Cotton braid was rated at 90 °C, glass braid at 125 °C.

ACR—Designation for cable with corona resisting insulation.

ACSR—Aluminum conductor, steel reinforced. Aluminum wires stranded around a steel core. Usually used for high voltage cross-country transmission lines.

ACT—An armored cable made with plastic insulation on the conductors.

ACV—A designation for varnish cambric insulation and Polyvinyl Chloride, with overall interlocked armor, rated at 5 kV.

AFC—Multiple conductors of AF, twisted together, no jacket, 300 volt, 150 °C.

AFPD—Multiple conductors of AF wire twisted together with overall cotton or asbestos braid, 300 volt, 150 °C.

AFPO—Two parallel laid AF conductors with overall braid, 300 volt, 150 °C.

AGS—Special nickel conductor wire with silicone impregnated asbestos insulation and overall glass braid, 300 volt, 200 °C.

AIEE—Formerly American Institute of Electrical Engineers. Now called Institute of Electrical and Electronics Engineers (IEEE).

AN—For example AN-6 signifies a wire size of No. 6 AWG. Literally "aircraft number."

ANC-68—This military specification covers 2 and 3 conductors, 18 AWG through 6 AWG flexible portable type power cord.

ANC-161—Military specification covering low tension, single aluminum conductor, insulated cable for aircraft use.

ANC-168—Military specification covering shielded wire with a 75% coverage tinned copper shield. Identified by a bare copper tracer braided in the shield.

ANJC-48A—Military specification covering low tension, single copper conductor, insulated cable for aircraft use.

annealed wire—Wire which has been softened by heating and gradually cooling. Also called soft drawn wire.

ANSI—American National Standards Institute. A federation of trade, technical and professional organizations, government agencies and consumer groups. Coordinates standards development and publishes standards. Operates a voluntary certification program.

artos stripper—A machine that will automatically measure to a predetermined length, cut, strip, count and tie wire in bundles.

ASA—American Standards Association—See ANSI.

ASESA—Armed Services Electro Standards Agency.

ASG—Aeronautical Standards Group.

ASTM—American Society for Testing Materials. An organization that tests materials and attempts to set standards on various materials for industry.

AVA—Asbestos, varnished cambric and asbestos braided wire.

AVB—Asbestos, varnished cambric and cotton braided wire.

AVL—Asbestos, varnished cambric and lead.

B

beaded coax—A coaxial cable in which the dielectric consists of beads made of various materials.

belt (belted type cable)—Refers to number of layers of insulation on a conductor or number of layers of jacket on a cable.

blasting wire—Wire used for detonating explosives. It is usually a very inexpensively constructed wire.

bondable wire—An insulated wire whose surface has been especially treated to make it possible to adhere to other material such as potting compounds. The term usually refers to extruded Teflon® insulated wires. The etching process roughens the surface of the insulation permitting an interlocking effect with potting compounds.

bonded construction—A type of insulation construction in which the glass braid and nylon jacket are bonded together as in certain wire sizes of MIL-W-5086 Type II.

braided wire—Woven bare or tinned copper wire used as shielding for wires and cables and as ground wire for batteries or heavy industrial equipment. There are many different types of construction.

breakout—A breakout is a joint where a conductor or conductors break out from a multi-conductor cable to complete circuits at various points along the main cable. The rest of the conductors continue on within the jacket. The breakout may itself be jacketed and the joint sealed. Actually, the joint itself is the breakout.

B & S gauge—Brown and Sharpe wire gauge used for describing different sizes of copper conductors. It is the same as American Wire Gauge.

bunch strand—A conductor in which all individual wires are twisted in the same direction without regard for geometrical arrangement.

butt braider—A machine used for braiding or shielding cable or wire. It may be 8, 16, 24, 32, 48, 64 carriers. These braiders are manufactured by New England Butt Company and operate on the maypole type principal.

BX—A very common type of armored building wire in various configurations, rated at 600 volt.

C

caged armor—The armor wires within a polyethylene jacket. Often used in submarine cables.

CCIR—International Radio Consultative Committee. An international committee which reports to the International Telecommunications Union.

ceroc magnet wire—Copper wire coated with ceramic for high temperature use. Manufactured by Sprague Electric Company.

CF—The designation for cotton fixture wire. It is cotton insulated, impregnated with moisture resisting, flame retarding compound. It is used in lighting fixtures up to 90 °C.

CF glass—Means continuous filament glass yarn which is used in braiding, in making glass fabric and glass thread.

CFPO—Parallel CF wires with overall braid, 300 volt, 90 °C.

CFT—The abbreviation for 100 feet.

chromax—Chromax is the trade name of Driver Harris Company for a resistance wire. It is an alloy of 35% nickel, 20% chromium and the balance iron. It was developed as a cheaper substitute for nichrome resistance wire.

chromel-alumel—The alloys used in making Chromel Alumel thermocouple wires. Chromel is an alloy of nickel and chrome plus nine other elements. Alumel is an alloy containing nickel manganese, aluminum, silicon and nine other elements. Chromel is non-magnetic; alumel is highly magnetic. Chromel is the positive wire; alumel is the negative. Chromel and Alumel are registered trademarks of the Hoskins Mfg. Co.

coaxial cable—A transmission line in which one conductor completely surrounds the other, the two being coaxial and separated by a continuous solid dielectric or by dielectric spacers. Such a line has no external field and is not susceptible to external fields from other sources.

cold bend—Generally refers to a test to determine cable or wire characteristics at low temperatures. The test specimen and a specified mandrel are cooled in a low temperature box to the specified temperature. The wire specimen is then wound around the mandrel after which it is examined for cracks or other defects caused by bending at low temperatures.

cold test—Tests performed on cables to check their performance at a specified low temperature as outlined in various specifications.

Comet C—Comet C is the trade name of resistance wire manufactured by the Driver Harris Company. It is an alloy of 30% nickel, 4.5% chromium, and the balance iron. It is used from low to medium temperatures.

concentric lay inductor—A single conductor composed of a central core surrounded by one or more helically laid wires. Each of these succeeding layers is applied with an opposite direction of twist. The number of wires laid up the center wire is six, and each succeeding layer consists of six additional wires so that the number of wires in the strands are 7, 19, 37, 61, etc.

concentric strand—A strand that consists of a central wire or core surrounded by one or more layers of spirally laid wires. Each layer after the first has six more strands than the preceding layer and is applied in a direction opposite to that of the layer under it.

conductance—The measure of ability to conduct electricity.

constantan—An alloy of 55% copper and 45% nickel used in thermocouples with copper in the temperature range—169 °C to 386 °C. Temperature coefficient of electrical resistivity, 0.0002/ °C.

continuous duty—In some portable cords there are two standard number of strands of a given wire size. The one with the greater number (most flexible) is called continuous duty and the other is called stationary duty.

continuous vulcanization—The process of extruding on a wire, under high pressure, a uniform seamless, close-fitting tube of a rubber of rubber-like compound. The covered wire then continues into a vulcanizing chamber, where, under high pressure and temperature control, the insulation or jacket is vulcanized, continuously rather than in sections.

copolene—Copolene is a dielectric material used in manufacturing coaxial cable. Developed as a substitute for polystyrene, it is composed of polystyrene and polyisobutylene. Since it has undesirable characteristics it has been replaced by polyethylene.

copper constantan—Copper and constantan are two alloys used in making thermocouple wires. The copper is the positive wire and the constantan is the negative wire.

Copperweld® —Copperweld® is the trade mark of copper covered steel wire manufactured by Copperweld Steel Company. It is made by an exclusive molten welding process whereby a thick copper covering is inseparably welded to a steel core. Copperweld® thus performs as one metal. Hot rolling, cold drawing, pounding or temperature changes cannot affect it.

corona—Ionization of air surrounding a conductor caused by the influence of high voltage.

cross-linked polyethylene—A recently developed dielectric material used for insulating and jacketing.

cross-sectional area of a conductor—Cross-sectional area of a conductor is the sum of cross-sectional areas of all the individual wires comprising the strand.

cross talk—The faint conversation that can be heard in the background of your own conversation when using paired telephone cable. A phenomenon usually due to induction.

CSA—Canadian Standards Association. This is the Canadian counterpart of the Underwriters Laboratories (UL) in the U.S.

CV—The abbreviation for continuous vulcanization. A process for applying and curing rubber and rubber-like material on a mass production basis.

CX—Christmas tree wire, two conductors 18 AWG, rubber insulated, twisted, 300 volt.

CXT—Christmas tree wire, two conductors twisted, 18 AWG, plastic insulated, 300 volt.

D

DCC wire—Double cotton covered magnet wire.

decibel—A unit used to express ratios of sound or signal power, defined in such a way that n, the number of decibels, is given by

$$n = 10 \log_{10} P_2/P_1$$

where P_1 and P_2 are the power levels. Since decibels represent a ratio, it is necessary to establish a reference level in order to indicate an absolute level. For sound, the reference level is a pressure of 0.0002 microbar.

delay line—A conductor that is made of a specific material in a specific size and length that will permit the delay of an electrical impulse for a pre-determined specific length of time. The delay is measured in microseconds or nanoseconds.

design voltage—Voltage at which a cable is designed for maximum work.

DHOF—Two conductor, heat, oil and flame resistant, Navy type small boat cable covered by MIL-C-915.

dielectric—Any insulating material that is a non conductor of electricity.

dielectric constant—The factor by which the electric field strength in a vacuum exceeds that in the dielectric for the same distribution of charge.

dielectric loss—Energy dissipated as heat when the dielectric is placed in a varying electric field.

dielectric strength—The maximum potential gradient (volts per mil) a dielectric will stand without breaking down.

duplex—Two conductors twisted together, usually with no outer covering. This word has a double meaning and it is possible to have parallel wires and jacketed parallel wires, and still refer to them as duplex.

E

E-CTFE—Copolymer—polyethylene—chlorotrifluoro ethylene a high temperature fluoropolymer of high dielectric strength (HALAR®).

EIA—Electronics Industries Association. Formerly known as RETMA (Radio-Electronics-Television Manufacturers Association).

electro-tinned—Wire tinned with pure tin using an electrolytic process.

environment—Surroundings into which wire or cable is to be placed.

EPDM—Ethylene—propylenediene monomer rubber.

EPR—Ethylene—propylene copolymer rubber.

ETFE—Copolymer of ethylene and tetra fluoroethylene. A high temperature insulation of high dielectric strength.

extrusion—A method of applying insulation to a conductor or jacketing to a cable. The process is continuous and utilizes rubber, neoprene or a variety of plastic compounds.

F

farad—A unit of capacitance. Usually expressed in microfarads (μF) one millionth of a farad; or picofarads (pF) one millionth of a microfarad.

fatigue resistance—Resistance to metal crystalization that occurs when the conductors or wires break from flexing.

F.E.P. (fluorinated ethylene propylene)—Was formerly called X-100 or FEP-100. This "Teflon"® FEP flurocarbon resin is a registered trademark of the duPont de Nemours Co.

ferrite—A compound of bivalent iron and caron used in computer memory cores, transformers, etc.

FF—There are two types, commercial and military. Commercial type is UL approved fixture wire. Construction: stranded copper conductor, rubber insulation, cotton braid. **Military Type FF MIL-W-16878D**—Voltage 1000. Temp. 200 °C. Sizes 24 AWG to 4/0 AWG. Construction: stranded T/C conductor, silicone-rubber insulation with or without an outer glass braid.

FHOF—This type of shipboard cable is covered by MIL-C-915A. It is a 4-conductor, heat and oil resistant flexible cable. 600 volt, 16 AWG to 250 MCM. Construction: Rubber insulation, impervious sheath overall.

figure 8 cable—An aerial cable in which the conductors and steel supporting strand are jacketed together in such manner that a cross section of the cable approximates the figure "eight."

flexoprene—Standard Wire & Cable Co. for neoprene jacketed portable cord and cable.

FR-1—Vertical flame test for wire and cable. A standard established by Underwriters Laboratories. Now designated as VW-1.

fused spiral tape—This refers to a type of Teflon® insulated hookup wire. The conductor is run through a taping head so that each successive wrap overlaps the previous wrap. The spiral wrapped conductor is then passed through a sintering oven where the overlaps are fused together. The wire is then sized and polished.

FX—Christmas tree wire, single conductor, rubber insulated and braid, 125 volt, 60 °C.

FXT—Christmas tree wire, single conductor, plastic insulation, 125 volt, 60 °C.

G

G. cable—Is a type W or power cable with ground wires. The total CM area of the ground wires is approximately one-half to three-quarters of the CM area of one of the conductors. For immediate delivery call Standard Wire & Cable.

gas pressure compensated—A saturated paper insulated cable containing tubes for the transmission of gas pressure along a cable, and with external gas feed to the tubes.

glass braid—Used to provide thermal and/or mechanical protection to the underlying insulation of certain types of conductors.

glyptal—Synthetic resin used as an insulating varnish. Resistant to heat, oil and other agents.

GRS (Government Rubber Synthetic)—This is a government standard for Buna-S Rubber for jacketing and insulating compounds for military wires and cables.

GTO—Gas tube, sign and oil burner ignition cable. Stranded T.C. conductor, Polyethylene Insulation, PVC jacket overall. Manufactured in 14 AWG for 10kV and 15kV service.

H

H film—High temperature Polyimide "Kapton"® film, a trademarked product of DuPont de Nemours.

Halar® —Registered trademark of the Allied Chemical Co. Polyethylene—chlorotrifluoroethylene or E-CTFE copolymer. A high temperature insulation.

hard drawn—Refers to the temper of conductors that are drawn without annealing or that may work harden in the drawing process.

heat and pressure cure—Uncured rubber or rubber-like compound that is usually cooked in a mold under high pressure at a given temperature. The pressure, temperature and time required for curing depends upon the type of compound used.

helical stripe—A continuous spiral stripe applied to the insulation of a conductor for purposes of circuit identification.

henry—The measure of inductance, defined as the inductance of a circuit in which a counter electromotive force of one volt is generated when the current is changing at the rate of one ampere per second. (H)

hertz.(Hz)—A term replacing cycles-per-second as an indication of frequency.

HF—Heavy Formvar Magnet Wire. Soft BC wire with baked synthetic insulation overall.

high tension—Same as Hi Voltage.

hi-pot—A test designed to determine the highest potential that can be applied to a conductor without breaking through the insulation.

hot tin dip—A process of passing bare wire through a bath of molten tin to provide a coating.

HPD—Heater cord, rubber and asbestos insulated with overall braid.

HPN—Heater cord, neoprene, parallel, two conductor.

280

HSJ—Rubber jacketed heater cord. 300 volt 18 and 16 AWG 2 and 3 conductor, B.C. cond., rubber insulation, asbestos cotton braid rubber jacket overall.

HSJO—Same as HSJ except with neoprene jacket.

HW—Type designation for heavy wall, 2500 volt electronic hookup wire to MIL-W-76.

hypalon—A synthetic product of the DuPont de Nemours Co. Resistant to oxidation by ozone, sun, weather, heat and chemicals.

I

IEEE—Institute of Electrical and Electronic Engineers. Formerly American Institute of Electrical Engineers (AIEE).

impulse strength—The voltage breakdown of insulation under voltage surges on the order of microseconds in duration.

I.M.S.A.—International Municipal Signal Association, specifications for fire alarm cable.

insulation resistance—The resistance offered by an insulating material to the flow of current resulting from an impressed D.C. voltage.

intercalated tapes—Two or more tapes, generally of different composition, applied simultaneously in such a manner that a portion of each tape overlays a portion of the other tape.

IPCEA—Insulated Power Cable Engineers Association. An association of power cable engineers from many different companies. Their object is to establish standards in the insulated power cable industry.

IRE—Former Institute of Radio Engineers. (See IEEE)

iron constantan—A combination of metals used in thermocouples, thermocouple wires and thermocouple lead wires. The iron wire is positive, the constantan the negative wire.

irradiated polyolefin—A dielectric compound which has been exposed to electron beam radiation.

J

JAN-C-17A—Joint Army-Navy specifications covering coaxial cables used for high frequency applications in radio, television, radar.

JAN-C-76A—Joint Army-Navy specification covering radio hook-up wire. Types: SRIR, SRHV, WL and SRRF. Superseded by MIL-W-76.

J-box, or junction box—A box for joining different runs of raceway or cable, plus space for connecting and branching the enclosed conductors.

joule—The unit of energy or work. The international joule is equal to the work required to maintain a current of one ampere for one second in a resistance of one ohm.

jute-filler—Rope-like strands of material used in cables for filling in the interstices to form a rounded shape.

K

Kapton® —Trademark of the DuPont de Nemours Co. for polyimide resin.

kelf—Polymonochlorotrifluoroethylene MIL-W-12340. High temperature insulation—55 °C. to 135 °C. used on hook-up wire and for tubing where temperatures are beyond the range of PVC, and where resistance to solvents the range of PVC, and where resistance to solvents is needed.

kovar—An alloy of iron, nickel and cobalt.

Kynar® —VF$_2$ Vinylidene fluoride resin manufactured by the Pennwalt Corporation. A crystalline, high molecular weight polymer of VF$_2$ having high dielectric strength as well as abrasion resistant characteristics.

L

leaching and non-leaching—In a leaching wire the plasticizer will migrate or leave the vinyl compound when exposed to the heat of baking. The wire so treated becomes brittle and hard. A non-leaching wire will retain its plasticizer under extreme temperature conditions and remain flexible after baking. Non-leaching wire is desirable for use as motor lead wire.

lead-cured—A cable that is cured or vulcanized in a metallic lead mold.

litz wire—Short for litzendraht wire. A construction of fine individually insulated strands specially woven or braided together to reduce skin effect and thus lower resistance to high frequency currents.

LW—Nomenclature for light wall, 300 volt duty, electronic hookup wires to MIL-W-76.

M

marker tape—A tape laid parallel to the conductors under the sheath in a cable, imprinted with the manufacturer's name and the specification to which the cable is made.

marker thread—A colored thread laid parallel and adjacent to the strand in an insulated conductor which identifies the manufacturer and sometimes the specification to which the wire is made.

MCM—One thousand circular mils. e.g. 500 MCM = 500,000 circular mils.

MCOP—Multiple conductor (16 AWG) oil resistant, portable synthetic insulation cable. Cabled with fillers, binder, impervious sheath overall. Covered by MIL-C-915.

melamine—A thermosetting resin chemically known as Melamin formaldehyde. Has excellent resistance to acids and alkalines and good resistance to water and solvents. Has high strength, high insulation resistances as referred to plastics.

MHD—MMedium hard drawn copper wire.

MHFF—Multiple conductor (16 AWG) heat and flame resistant, flexible synthetic resin and felted asbestos insulation, rayon braid, cabled with fillers, binder, impervious sheath overall. Covered by MIL-C-915A.

MI—Nomenclature for mineral insulated cable, made with one or more conductors using mineral for insulation and overall solid metal tube sheath.

migrating or migration—The movement of the non-resinous plasticizer in vinyl which takes place at elevated or lowered temperatures. The

282

migrating plasticizer from the jacket will contaminate the polyethylene core of a coaxial cable and thus change its electrical characteristics.

ML—Type A. AVC Mine locomotive cable covered by Table ML 600 volt UL approved. AVC cables will not carry flame or support combustion. Type B. Motor Lead type wire used as lead wire to electric motors. Stranded copper conductor PVC, rubber or rubber and braid insulation.

M.S.H.A.—Mining Safety and Health Administration.

MT—Machine tool wire used for internal wiring of appliances or tools. Solid or stranded conductor. Thermoplastic insulations.

MTW—Machine tool wire, plastic insulated, 600 volt, varies 90 °C. to 105 °C.

MW—1000 volt plastic insulated wire covered by MIL-W-76.

N

N.E.C.—National Electrical Code. Recommendations of the National Fire Protection Association, revised every three years. City or State regulations may differ from Code regulations and take precedence over National Electrical Code rules, which of themselves have no legal status.

NEMA—National Electrical Manufacturers Association. It is known in industry for its standardization of electrical motors and gear reducers and for wire and cable specifications.

NICHROME—Driver Harris Company's trade name for an alloy of 60% nickel, 16% chromium and the balance steel. Used extensively in wire wound resistors and heating elements.

NMC—Naval Material Command. Central Navy agency for the development, procurement, maintenance, supply, disposal, distribution and storage of material. Includes the following Systems Commands: the Naval Ships Systems Command (NAVSHIPS), the Naval Ordnance Systems Command (NAVORD), the Naval Air Systems Command (NAVAIR), the Naval Electronics Systems Command (NAVELEX), the Naval Facilities Engineering Command, (NAVFAC) and the Naval Supply Systems Command (NAVSUP).

non-contaminating—Refers to a type of PVC jacketing material whose plasticizer will not migrate into the dielectric of a coaxial cable and thus avoids contaminating and destroying the dielectric.

non-migrating—Same as non-contaminating.

O

OEM—Original Equipment Manufacturer.

ohm—The practical unit of electrical resistance.

oil filled cable—Paper insulated, lead sheathed cable, into which high grade mineral oil is forced under pressure, saturating the insulation. Main object is to prevent moisture and gases from entering. Also easier to detect flaws due to leakage, as the oil is kept under constant pressure at all times.

oil filled pipe cable—Basically the same as oil filled cable, but inside of rigid pipe, instead of lead sheath. Is sometimes a standard oil filled cable inserted into rigid pipe, under pressure. Both units being oil filled.(Usually for much higher voltage. Kept under constant pressure at all times.)

Okocord—Trade name for portable power cables made by Okonite Company.

Okoprene—Trade name for neoprene covered wire and cable made by Okonite.

outgassing—The dissipation of gas from a dielectric evidencing decomposition.

oxygen bomb test—To determine aging effect, heat, tensile strength and elongation of wire (wire is placed in a bomb, at 70 °C., under 300 PSI using pure oxygen gas for a period of 48 to 96 hours.)

P

P—Reinforced portable cord. Stranded copper conductor. It has a separator, rubber insulation, cotton braid, twisted conductor. It has a rubber jacket cotton braid overall. It is used in dry places on drop cord and portable lines.

pan cured—Method of vulcanizing. Coils of unvulcanized insulated wire are coiled in pans and vulcanized under pressure with live steam.

PBM-109—Trailing mine cable with an outer sheath of flame-resistant neoprene. Cable conforms to requirements of Penna. Bureau of Mines, and Federal Bureau of Mines.

PCTFE—Polychlorotrifluoroethylene. One of the fluoropolymers which have high dielectric strength used at temperatures to 250 °C.

petrol wire—Wire insulated to withstand immersion in gas and oil. Usually thermoplastic (with or without nylon jacket).

PFA—Perfluoroalkoxy resin. High temperature compound in the fluorcarbon family of dielectrics. Used at temperatures to 250 °C.

pipe type cable—Pressure cable. Pressure medium is a loose rigid metal pipe.

plain enamel—Type of magnet wire. Wire is dip coated with a varnish and then baked.

PLSJ—Cord, light duty, all rubber, parallel, two conductor, 300 volt.

PLT—Same as PLSJ except plastic.

PNR—Control cable using Polyethylene and Nylon on the conductors and PVC jacket.

PO—Rayon parallel lamp cord with a stranded copper conductor, separator, rubber insulation, cotton braid, rayon braid overall. Used in dry places, on small appliances.

PO—Lamp cord insulated with rubber and braid, parallel laid and overall cotton braid.

polyamide—Same as Nylon.

polychloroprene—Chemical name for Neoprene. Used for jacketing wire and cable that will be subject to rough usage, moisture, oil, greases, solvents, and/or chemicals. May also be used as a low voltage insulating material.

polyethylene—A family of insulating materials derived from the polymerization of ethylene gas. They are basically pure hydrocarbon resins, often with small amounts of other additives to impart needed properties. All members of the polyethylene family are excellent dielectrics. Electrically they are far superior to any other extrudable dielectric in use today. Outstanding electrical properties include high insulation resistance, high dielectric strength, low dielectric constant, low dielectric loss at all frequencies, excellent resistance to cold flow, and good abrasion resistance. One or more members of the polyethylene family also have the following properties: resistance to sunlight, weather chemicals, flame. Polyethylene is being widely used for insulation on telephone, signal and control cables, high-frequency electronic cables, high- and low-voltage power cables, line wire, neutral supported secondary and service drop cables. They are suitable for direct earth burial. Temperature ratings vary with type and application, from 75 °C. up.

polyimide—A relatively high temperature plastic which was developed for use as a dielectric or jacketing material.

polyolefins—A family of plastics including cross-linked polyethylene and various ethylene copolymers.

polypropylene—A thermoplastic with good electrical characteristics, high tensile strength, and resistance to heat.

polysulfone—A polymer highly resistant to mineral acid, alkali and salt solutions. Good dielectric properties up to 350 °F.

polyurethene—Enamel that has excellent moisture resistance, easily soldered, also has excellent winding properties, as a magnet wire insulation.

polyvinylchloride—A family of insulating compounds whose basic ingredient is either polyvinyl chloride or its copolymer with vinyl acetate, in combination with appropriate plasticizers, stabilizers, fillers and pigments. Like many other plastic materials, these insulations can be compounded to provide a wide variety of properties for various applications. Among the properties obtainable are: resistance to moisture, cold heat, flame, oils, solvents, chemicals, ozone. Electrical properties are adequate for low-voltage power applications. Temperature ratings up to 105 °C. are recognized by UL for certain applications. These insulations are widely used for types T and TW building wires, series street lighting cable, machine tool wiring, hook-up and appliance wiring, overhead line wire, control and signal cables, and many others. Known as PVC or Vinyl.

POSJ—Rubber parallel lamp cord. Stranded copper conductor, cotton separator, rubber insulation. Mid-Rip (Ripcord) used on small appliances not subject to hard usage. Also known as Type SP.

pressure cable—Oil impregnated, paper insulated conductors. Lead or steel pipe outer covering, in which positive pressure is maintained constantly. Has higher dielectric strength, greater insulation, stability, increased current-carrying capacity. Saves space.

prototype—Original design or first operating model.

PSH—Three conductor cable. Each conductor cable. Each conductor has type PS shielding over the insulation and contains ground wires. The insulation is extra heavy. Recommended for intermediate voltage where extra safety factor is needed.

PS tape—Non-metallic shielding, very flexible. Remains in positive contact with insulation. Prevents formation of air gaps between conductor and insulation.

pulse cable—Type of coaxial cable with or without a magnetic core. Usually multi-shielded. Operates at very high voltage.

PTFE—Polytetrafluoroethylene. One of the fluorocarbon compounds having high dielectric strength for use to 260 °C.

PVC-105 °C.—Specially compounded high temperature Vinyl.

PWP—Moistureproof reinforced portable cord. Stranded copper conductor, separator, rubber insulation, cotton braid, twisted conductors, rubber drop cords. The jacket is cotton braid overall and has a moistureproof finish. Used in damp places on drop cords, portable lines. Now known as Type PW.

Q

QPL—Qualified Products List issued by U.S. Government Agency.

R

ram extruder—Wire-making machinery for extruding Teflon® insulation over conductor. A predetermined amount of cylindrical shaped molded Teflon® powder is placed in a cylinder chamber. A ram is pushed through the cylinder by a jack screw. This forces the Teflon® through an orifice or tip through which the conductor is moving and forms a homogeneous tube of insulation around the conductor. The unsintered insulated wire is then passed through a curing oven to complete the process. The limitation of a ram extruder is the size of the slug of performed Teflon® powder. Since it is of constant size, when the slug is extruded it is the end of the run. It cannot be continuously fed. As the conductor diameter increases, the maximum length of the wire decreases.

resin—A solid or semi-solid organic substance, originally of plant origin but largely synthesized now. It may be clear, yellowish or brown, ranging from transparent to translucent; typically a non-conductor of electricity and soluble in organic solvents but not in water. Consequently, resins are widely used in insulating, potting and encapsulating. Resins are broadly classified as thermoplastic or thermosetting according to whether they soften or harden with the application of heat.

RETMA—Radio-Electronics-Television Manufacturers Association (changed to EIA-Electronics Industries Association).

RETMA color code—A system of color markings for purposes of identification devised by the Radio-Electronics-Television Manufacturers Association (See EIA).

RF—Tinned copper conductors, rubber insulation, cotton braid saturated with moisture resisting flame-retarding compound, smoothly finished in white, black, red, green, blue and yellow for identification. The lubricated surface finish of the wire permits easy pulling through conduits.

RF connector—Connector used for connecting or terminating coaxial cable.

RG—Radio Frequency (Government). Prefix for coaxial cables.

RG 17/U—A coaxial cable having specific characteristics and construction. The prefix RG means "radio frequency government." The number 17 is the numerical assignment and U means for universal use.

RHO—(written P, p) The seventeenth letter of the Greek alphabet, used symbolically to represent various coefficients, principally resistivity or specific resistance.

RHRW—Tinned copper conductors, rubber insulation, saturated braid, flame and moisture resistant finish for moist locations.

RHW—75 °C. rubber insulated. Heat and moisture resistant insulation with an outer cover of moisture resistant, flame retardant with a non-metallic covering. Generally used in wet locations.

ribbon cable—A flat cable with individually insulated conductors processed together in a parallel position. Conductors may be all one color, or each individual conductor of a different color.

ridge-marker—One or more ridges running laterally along the outer surface of plastic wire for purposes of identification.

rigid wave guide—A type of coaxial cable. A metal form using air as a dielectric.

RL—600 volt tinned copper conductors solid or stranded, rubber insulation, rubber filled tape (cotton braid on small sizes only) with a lead sheath. Used in creameries, laundry, wherever moist conditions exist.

RLJFJ—(Indicating Rubber-Lead-Jute-Flat-Armor-Jute). Metallic parkway cables designed for direct earth installation without additional protection, except at points of extreme mechanical hazard. These cables provide an economical, dependable underground system, are well protected from mechanical injury and easy to install. Extensively used for underground street lighting circuits, railroad yard lighting, railroad signal systems, airport power and lighting circuits, and in industrial plants and mines.

rod mill—In general, a factory in which copper rod is drawn down usually to 14 AWG. This is then sold to other wire mills for drawing to smaller sizes.

rolling mill—Processing plant where copper bars or ingots are rolled into copper rod.

romex—Trade name for non-metallic sheathed cable (N) Romex uf multi-conductor non-metallic sheathed cable.

rr—An all-rubber, non-metallic underground cable suitable for direct burial in the earth or in conduit. It has heat and moisture resistant insulation and an outer neoprene jacket.

S

S—600 volt senior service rubber insulated portable cord. 18 AWG-2 conductor through 6 AWG-4 conductor.

SA—Nomenclature for silicone rubber insulation with asbestos or glass braid overall for use up to 125 ° C.

sector strand—A group of wires laid in triangular shape with rounded corners, for use as one conductor of a three conductor cable with 120° angle between faces, and with 90° angle for a 4 conductor cable.

segmental conductor—In single conductor cables 1,000,000 C.M. or more, the conductors are divided into three or four segments insulated from each other by paper tapes to reduce current resistance in ac circuits.

selenium cure—Process used in curing neoprene and rubber jacketed wires and cables. The process makes a dense, tough, durable jacket.

semi-conducting jacket—A jacket having a sufficiently low resistance so that its outer surface can be kept at substantially ground potential by a grounded conductor in contact with it at frequent intervals.

serving of a cable—A serve is a separator applied directly over the conductor. The serve may consist of one or a combination of materials such as paper, cotton, silk, nylon, rayon. These materials may be applied spirally or laterally.

SF—Fixture wire, silicone rubber insulated. Can be solid or stranded.

SFF—Same as SF but in flexible grade standing.

SH-A—Portable power cable, commonly known as shovel cable, neoprene jacket, usually three or four conductors individually shielded. Cable rated 5kV.

SH-B—Similar to SH-A except shield over all conductors.

SH-C—Similar to SH-B except with grounds.

SH-D—Similar to SH-A except with grounds.

SHFS—Nomenclature for 600 volt switchboard wire to MIL-C-915, insulated with Vinyl and felted asbestos, overall flameproof cotton braid.

SHOF—Navy type shipboard cable, single conductor, heat and oil resistant, flexible.

shunt wire—A conductor joining two parts of an electric circuit to divert part of the current.

silicone impregnated—The complete saturation of insulating tapes or braids, with a silicone varnish compound. The process may be performed under a vacuum. The compound serves as a heat and flame retardant as well as a binder.

sintered—Usually refers to curing of Teflon® .

SJ—300 volt junior service rubber insulated UL approved portable cord, rubber jacket. 18 AWG-2 conductor through 16 AWG-4 conductor.

SJO—300 volt junior service rubber insulated UL approved portable cord, neoprene jacket.

SJT—300 volt junior service vinyl insulated UL approved portable cord, vinyl jacket.

SJTO—300 volt. Same as SJO except all thermoplastic construction.

skeleton braid—Widely separated braid of fiber, copper or steel, may be used to hold core together, for reinforcing jacket or for shielding.

skin effect—In an alternating current system, a phenomenon that occurs at increased frequencies causing an increase in resisting of the conductor leaving the outer skin to carry most of the current. The phenomenon increases in intensity the higher the frequency.

SO—600 volt senior service neoprene jacket UL approved portable cord. 18 AWG-2 cond., through 10 AWG-4 cord.

solderable nylon litz—Litz wire made up of Solderese strands with a nylon serve overall.

spark test—Test given to wire or cable to determine if there are defects in the insulation.

specific inductive capacity (SK)—Dielectric constant of insulating material.

spiral shield—A metallic shield of fine stranded wires applied spirally rather than braided.

SP-1—Lamp cord, parallel, all rubber, two conductor, 300 volt.

SP-2—Similar to SP-1 except heavier insulation.

SP-3—Similar to SP-1 except heavier insulation, also may have a ground.

SP shield—Silver plated shield.

SPT-1—Same as SP-1 except in plastic.

SPT-2—Same as SP-2 except in plastic.

SPT-3—Same as SP-3 except in plastic.

SR—Silicone rubber insulated cable, 600 volt.

SR-AW—Silicone rubber insulated, overall glass braid, with nickel plated copper conductor, flexible stranding, 600 volt.

SRHV—2500 volt insulated hookup wire, JAN-C-76.

SRRF—1000 volt radio frequency wire, polyethylene, glass braid, JAN-C-76.

ST—Same as SJT, except 600 volt.

Stancote—Standard Wire & Cable Co. trade name for plastic insulated wire.

standing wave ratio—In a transmission line, waveguide or analogous system, a figure of merit used to express the efficiency of the system in transmitting power, specifically taking into account the mismatch between source, line and load. The standing wave ratio S is given by

$$S = V_{max}/V_{min} = I_{max}/I_{min}$$

In an ideally matched system $S = 1$, indicating the presence of a pure traveling wave and no reflected power. As the proportion of power reflected increases S approaches infinity, which value would indicate a pure standing wave.

Stanflex—Standard Wire & Cable Co. trade name for rubber jacketed portable cords and cables.

stanflex twin—A duplex laid parallel cable used for trailer and truck electric brakes. May have a waxed braid or PVC jacket. Also, used in drive-in theatres to hook up speakers.

STO—600 volt—same as SO except all thermoplastic construction.

stranded conductor—A conductor made with a specified number of strands. Rope lay strand, for example, is a conductor made of multiple groups of strands (filaments). A 7 × 19 rope lay strand has 19 wires laid into a group and then 7 such groups cabled laid into a conductor.

strip insulations—Strip process insulation consists of one or more longitudinal strips of unvulcanized thermosetting material folded around a conductor and vulcanized after application.

SV—Vacuum cleaner cord 18/2, 300 volt, light duty rubber portable.

SVO—Same as SV except with neoprene jacket.

SVT—Same as SV except non-marking plastic jacket.

sweep test—A test given to check attenuation by oscilloscope, as in coaxial cable.

swept coax—Coaxial cable which has been checked out by sweep test, and certified by the manufacturer.

T

TA—The UL designation for switchboard wire insulated with thermoplastic and felted asbestos.

TAGT—Stranded nickel-clad copper conductor insulated with fused Teflon® tape, felted asbestos and Teflon® impregnated glass braid. 600 volt, 250 °C rating.

T.C.—Tinned copper.

Teflon® —Trademark of the DuPont de Nemours Co. for Polytetrafluoroethylene.

Teflon® impregnated—Refers to the saturation of a heat resistant fibrous glass braid with Teflon® suspensoid. After saturation, the Teflon® is cured.

tefzel® —Registered trademark of the DuPont de Nemours Co. This is modified ETFE a copolymer of ethylene and tetrafluoroethylene. Used as a dielectric to 150 °C.

tellurium cure—A curing process similar to selenium cure, except a different element is used.

TEW—Nomenclature for appliance wire by Canadian Standards Association (CSA), plastic insulated, solid or stranded conductor, 600 volt.

textile braid—Any braid made from threads of cotton, silk, or synthetic fibers.

TF—The UL designation for fixture wire, solid soft copper conductor, insulated with Thermoplastic lead wire.

TFE—(Polytetrafluoroethylene).—A fluorocarbon resin.

TFF—Same as TF, except stranded copper conductor.

TG—Teflon® tape with-overall glass braid, stranded nickel clad copper conductor.

thermal resistance—The resistance of a substance to conductivity of heat.

thermal shock—The resulting characteristic when a material is subjected to rapid and wide range changes in temperature in an effort to discover its ability to withstand heat and cold.

thermocouple—A union of dissimilar metals in which a voltage is generated due to difference in temperature at the junctions. The voltage is usually in micro or milli volts.

thermocouple wire—Wire drawn from special metals or alloys and calibrated to established specifications (U.S. Bureau of Standards, or Instruments Society of American Standards).

THHN—Building wire, plastic insulated, 90 °C, 600 volt, nylon jacketed.

THOF—U.S. Navy designation meaning triple conductor, heat, oil and flame resistant, portable flexible cable. MIL-C-915.

THW—Building wire, plastic insulated, heat, flame and moisture resistant, 75 °C.

THWN—Same as THW with overall nylon jacket.

tinsel cord—Extra flexible cord made with tinsel conductors to give the ultimate in flexibility. Used mostly in the communications field on headsets, handsets, and anywhere that repeated flexing is necessary.

tinsel wire—A low voltage, stranded wire in which each strand is very thin copper ribbon spirally wrapped around a textile yarn. Insulation is generally a textile braid. Intended usage is for severe flexing.

TPA—A 125 volt, 400 °F wire. It is constructed with a stranded tinned conductor, glass braid, or tape, impregnated felted asbestos, and asbestos braid.

tracer stripe—When color coding is accomplished by more than one stripe on the same wire. The first stripe (or widest) is called the base stripe, the others (usually narrower stripes) are called tracer stripes.

transistor—An electron device made by attaching three or more leads to a small wafer of semiconductor material. The three terminals are called the emitter, base and collector. They perform functions somewhat similar to the cathode, grid and plate of a vacuum tube, respectively.

transite—Johns-Manville trade name for Asbestos-Cement. It is made in pipe and fitting form, for use in the building industry, as electrical conduit.

triaxial—Refers to a three conductor cable with one conductor in the center, a second circular conductor concentric with the first and third circular conductor insulated from and concentric with the first and second, usually with insulation, and a braid or impervious sheath overall.

triplex—A group of three insulated conductors twisted and/or sheathed or held together mechanically. Usually color-coded or ridge-marked.

TRPA—A 125 volt, 650 °F wire. It is constructed with a stranded nickel clad conductor, glass braid, or tape, impregnated felted asbestos, and asbestos braid.

TTOP—U.S. Navy designation meaning twisted pair telephone, oil resistant, portable, synthetic insulation, binder, jacketed with an impervious sheath. A dash number following the designation letter indicates the number of pairs. MIL-C-915.

TTRS—U.S. Navy designation meaning twisted pair, telephone, radio, shielded, synthetic insulation, each pair shielded, binder, jacketed with impervious sheath. A dash number following the letter designation indicates the number of pairs. MIL-C-915.

TTRSA—U.S. Navy designation meaning twisted pair, telephone, radio, each pair shielded, armored. A dash number following the letter designation indicates the number of pairs. MIL-C-915.

TW—The UL designation for thermoplastic insulated wire for use in conduit and underground and wet locations. It is a common building wire having a bare soft copper conductor, which may be either solid or stranded.

TWX—Abbreviation for "teletypewriter exchange." It is a direct wire communication system.

U

UF—Single or multi-conductor, with or without ground, used for direct burial underground feeders and branch circuits between buildings, yard lights, flood lights, and smaller installations.

UG—The two letter designation that precedes the number on connectors for coaxial cable. It means Universal Government.

UL—Underwriters Laboratories Inc., chartered as a non-profit organization. Maintains and operates laboratories for the examination and testing of devices, systems and materials relative to life, fire and casualty, hazards and crime prevention. Founded in 1894, the enterprise is sponsored by the National Board of Fire Underwriters. It is operated for service, not for profit.

UL approved—A product that has been tested and approved to Underwriters Laboratories standards.

unilay conductor—A central core surrounded by one or more concentric layers of helically wound strands in a fixed geometrical arrangement with the direction of lay the same for each layer (and the central core).

unsintered—Means uncured. This word is usually used to differentiate between cured and uncured Teflon® tape.

URC—Nomenclature for weatherproof wire.

USASI—United States of American Standards Institute superseded ASA and in turn was superseded by ANSI.

USE—Neoprene jacketed underground service entrance cable, made in various configurations.

V

VCB—Varnished cambric with flame and moisture resistant cotton braided jacket.

VCL—Lead jacketed cable, using varnished cambric insulation on conductors.

voltage breakdown—Test to determine maximum voltage of insulated wire before electrical current leakage through insulation.

VSWR—Voltage/standing/wave/ratio. The ratio of the voltage maximum to voltage minimum which exists in a transmission line. Caused when there is reflection of incident wave, due to a discontinuity or improper match to the transmission line. See standing wave ratio.

VW-I—See FR-1.

W

waveguide—Hollow rectangular or round pipe used as a transmission line for the propagation of microwaves.

wire gauge AWG—The American Wire Gauge, originally called Brown & Sharpe Gauge. A system of numerical wire sizes starting with the lowest numbers for the largest sizes. (See "Wire Data Chart" on page 119) Gauge sizes are each 20.6% apart based on cross-sectional area.

X

X-100—See FEP.

XHHW—Cross-linked polyethylene insulated, rated at 90 °C in dry locations, and 75 °C in wet locations.

Index